MODERN MATHEMATICS

MONOGRAPHS

ON TOPICS OF

MODERN MATHEMATICS

RELEVANT TO THE ELEMENTARY FIELD

EDITED BY

J. W. A. YOUNG

WITH A NEW INTRODUCTION BY
MORRIS KLINE, PROFESSOR OF MATHEMATICS,
NEW YORK UNIVERSITY

DOVER PUBLICATIONS, INC.

This new Dover edition, printed in 1955, is an unabridged republication of the first edition with a new introduction by Professor Morris Kline. Published by special arrangement with Longmans, Green and Co.

Printed in the United States of America.

EDITOR'S PREFACE

THE purpose of this collection of monographs may be indicated by the following citation from the letter that was sent to those who were requested to act as authors.

"Among the various publications on mathematics that are being made, it would seem that there is room for a serious effort to bring within reach of secondary teachers (in service or in training), college students, and others at a like stage of mathematical advancement, a scientific treatment of some of the regions of advanced mathematics that have points of contact with the elementary field. Undoubtedly one of the most crying needs of our secondary instruction in mathematics to-day, is that the scientific attainments of the teachers be enlarged and their mathematical horizon widened; and I believe that there is a large body of earnest teachers and students that are eager to extend their mathematical knowledge if the path can be made plain and feasible for them."

"A volume of monographs dealing with selected topics of higher mathematics might well be a useful contribution to the meeting of this need. Such monographs would aim to bring the reader into touch with some characteristic results and viewpoints of the topics considered, and to point out their bearing on elementary mathematics. They would therefore contain:

(1) A considerable body of results proved in full, so that the reader can materially extend his mathematical acquisitions by the reading of the monograph alone.

(2) Statement without proof of some leading methods and results, so as to give a bird's-eye view of the subject.

(3) A small number of references indicating what the reader may profitably take up after he has mastered the contents of the monograph."

Both the plan itself, and the invitation to act as author, were most cordially received; work on the monographs was promptly begun, has been carried through substantially as planned, and the results are presented herewith.

The manuscripts have, whenever feasible, been read carefully by at least one collaborator other than myself, and in consequence various questions and suggestions have been submitted to the authors and acted upon by them. Each author, however, retains sole responsibility for his monograph as it now appears. No attempt has been made to secure uniformity in style of treatment; each monograph is an independent unit, that can be read without reference to the others.

The amount of technical mathematical knowledge that is presupposed on the part of the reader varies with the different subjects. A large part of the book presupposes only knowledge of elementary geometry and algebra, together with a certain measure of mathematical maturity. On the other hand, there is much that will repay careful and detailed study by advanced students. So far as the subject-matter permits, the less difficult topics are taken up first in each monograph.

J. W. A. YOUNG.

INTRODUCTION

The reasons given by the editor for organizing and publishing in 1911 the present survey of topics in advanced mathematics are all the more cogent for reprinting this volume in 1954. The mathematical student body is now much vaster, and mathematics itself is a more vital activity. In addition, the subject matter of mathematics has increased so rapidly during the twentieth century that no one can master all of it. Even the professional mathematician must be content with glimpses at ideas outside the domain of his own specialization. Hence, any book which provides insight into many branches of mathematics now serves several purposes.

Developments in mathematics during the twentieth century have comprised not only the creation of new branches and the extension of old ones but also the formulation of new approaches to previously established branches. For example, there are now a half a dozen major approaches to as elementary a subject as Euclidean geometry, each of which would certainly bewilder Euclid himself. It is therefore most advisable that the reader be oriented to the approaches used in these monographs. The purpose of the following remarks is to assist the reader in this task. Though the authors of the monographs recommended additional reading material, a number of valuable books have since appeared. Some of these are suggested herewith.

The first monograph presents Euclidean geometry from the familiar axiomatic, deductive point of view. Since a reader of this book has no doubt studied Euclid's presentation, or some minor modification of it often made in high school texts for pedagogical reasons, why should it be necessary to go over the subject again? The answer, as the mathematicians themselves first appreciated during the late nineteenth century, is that Euclid's presentation is faulty. The creation of non-Euclidean geometries (see the third monograph) during the nineteenth century awakened mathematicians to the fact that Euclid's axioms could not be accepted as sound intuitions or self-evident truths about space. They re-examined, therefore, the entire logical structure of Euclid with the primary purpose of studying the role of the axioms in his development of geometry. The results of this critical re-examination were rather astonishing. It was found that Euclid had used definitions he had no right to use because they involved non-mathematical concepts and that Euclid had unconsciously employed intuitive arguments in the course of his proofs. Several now classical reconstructions of Euclidean geometry were therefore undertaken. The essentials of one of these will be found in the first monograph by Veblen. Another will be found in David Hilbert's *Grundlagen der Geometrie*, seventh edition (Teubner, Leipzig, 1930). From a study of Veblen's monograph, the reader may proceed to the full development of Euclidean geometry on a thoroughly rigorous basis in Henry G. Forder's *The Foundations of Euclidean Geometry*, (Cambridge Univ. Press, Cambridge, 1927). The reader of these works may doubt at the beginning that he is indeed studying the best known branch of mathematics but after plodding through unfamiliar ground, he will begin to recognize some landmarks.

The second monograph, "Modern Pure Geometry", has two objectives. First, it demonstrates that new results can be obtained by purely geometric or synthetic methods as opposed to the algebraic methods of Descartes and Fermat. In this respect the monograph continues a line of thought active in the nineteenth century when pure geometers who had been seemingly crowded out of existence by the very successful and powerful methods of coordinate geometry reasserted themselves and sought to show that they could beat Descartes at the game of geometry. The material amply demonstrates that the struggle to rehabilitate pure geometry was successful. It is, however, also true that the concepts and theorems of this monograph can be treated very elegantly by algebraic methods. A thorough presentation will be found in William C. Graustein's *Introduction to Higher Geometry* (The Macmillan Co., N.Y., 1933).

The concepts and theorems of the second monograph are presented as extensions of Euclidean geometry. Indeed the presentation endeavors to show that the new concepts, chiefly projection and section, not only lead to new theorems but relate older, isolated results of Euclidean geometry. It would be more proper to say to-day that the monograph is an introduction to projective geometry. This subject did indeed arise in the seventeenth century and was pursued for quite some time in the nineteenth century as an extension of Euclidean geometry. However, within the last 75 years, mathematicians have seen clearly that projective geometry is not only an independent branch of mathematics but that it should logically precede Euclidean geometry. As a consequence of recent work in the subject, it is now possible to approach projective geometry directly by starting with axioms appropriate to the subject. These axioms are distinguished from those pertaining to Euclidean geometry in that they make no assertions involving length, size of angles, congruence, or similarity; in short, the axioms of projective geometry involve no metric concepts. Moreover, it is possible to derive the concepts and theorems of Euclidean geometry and of the several basic non-Euclidean geometries (see the remarks below and the third monograph) without introducing further axioms. Thus, the original relationship of Euclidean and projective geometry has now been inverted. An excellent introduction to this newer approach to projective geometry, and thereby to Euclidean and non-Euclidean geometry, is John W. Young's *Projective Geometry* (The Open Court Pub. Co., Chicago, 1930). The approach sketched in this book is carried out in detail in Oswald Veblen and John W. Young: *Projective Geometry*, 2 vols. (Ginn and Co., N.Y., 1910 and 1918). This last reference is a classic of mathematics.

The third monograph, "Non-Euclidean Geometry", presents the most revolutionary development in all of mathematics. In the early part of the nineteenth century Gauss, Lobachevsky, and Bolyai realized that there can be geometries different from Euclid's, and they constructed such a geometry. Their approach to this new geometry was the same as Euclid's; that is, they started with axioms and deduced theorems by the methods of pure or synthetic geometry. However, in place of Euclid's parallel axiom, these men adopted an axiom which permits more than one parallel to a given line through a given point. Hence the resulting geometry, now called hyperbolic non-Euclidean geometry, contains many theorems in sharp conflict with the theorems in Euclid. About the middle of the century, Bernhard Riemann created another non-Euclidean geometry, now called spherical or double elliptic geometry, by the methods of differential geometry which depend upon the calculus. Actually, Riemann showed how to construct many different non-Euclidean geometries but, with the exception of double elliptic geometry, these new geometries differ so much from Euclidean geometry that they are now called Riemannian geometries.

It has already been noted in connection with the second monograph that Euclidean and the basic non-Euclidean geometries can be derived as special cases of projective geometry. By pursuing this connection, Felix Klein discovered a third basic non-Euclidean geometry, now called single elliptic geometry. Woods, in the third monograph, calls both the double and single elliptic non-Euclidean geometries, Riemannian geometry, and indeed does not distinguish the two geometries. Though his terminology is logically justified in the sense that hyperbolic non-Euclidean geometry and both elliptic non-Euclidean geometries can be derived from Riemann's differential geometric approach, it is no longer used.

After reading Wood's monograph the reader will find helpful the historical survey by R. Bonola: *Non-Euclidean Geometry*, translated by H. S. Carslaw (Dover Publications, N.Y., 1954). In this survey, the axiomatic approach of Euclid, the differential geometric approach of Riemann, and Klein's approach through projective geometry are presented. A full treatment of the direct axiomatic approach will be found in Harold E. Wolfe: *Introduction to Non-Euclidean Geometry* (The Dryden Press, N.Y., 1945).

In the structure of mathematics, algebra and geometry appear on the whole as two independent branches, each possessing its own origin, development, and applications. Though, as in the instance of coordinate geometry, these two branches were united to their mutual advantage, they never did lose their separate identities and independent usefulness. Yet their histories are disparate in one essential respect. Whereas geometry received its logical formulation from Euclid, the logical foundations of the real and complex number systems, whose properties are exploited in algebra, was not supplied until the late nineteenth century. The historical reasons for this remarkable neglect of the foundations of algebra, which contrasts sharply with the intensive and fruitful activity in the subject proper, are too complex to be related here. The fact is that from pre-Greek times until the late nineteenth century, algebra and the various branches of analysis, which stem logically from algebra, continued to be essentially ingenious but also rather ingenuous complexes of manipulatory schemes with some rhyme, perhaps, but with very little reason. After Weierstrauss, Dedekind, and Cantor showed how to define irrational numbers and to derive their properties, it finally became possible for mathematicians to supply the proper logical bases for the real and complex number systems. Huntington's monograph indicates how these systems may be built up axiomatically. His axioms suffice to derive all the theorems of algebra and analysis. An alternative approach to the complex number system, which is very much in vogue to-day and which must be distinguished from Huntington's, is to start with axioms for the positive whole numbers, more properly, the unsigned natural numbers, and to deduce the existence and properties of the entire complex number system from the system of axioms for the natural numbers. The latter procedure is admittedly much more lengthy but has the advantage of requiring fewer axioms. This approach may be found in Edmund Landáu: *Foundations of Analysis* (Chelsea Pub. Co., N.Y., 1951). Still another approach to the number systems of algebra is due to Bertrand Russell and Alfred North Whitehead, who derive all the properties of the real and complex number systems from logic itself, the thesis of these men being that mathematics is but a child of logic. An exposition of the ideas employed in this approach will be found in Russell's *Introduction to Mathematical Philosophy* (George Allen and Unwin, Ltd., London, 1919).

The monographs on "The Algebraic Equation", "The Function Concept and the Fundamental Notions of the Calculus", and "The Theory of Numbers" require no introduction. The reference to Cajori in the first monograph will be most useful for further study of that subject, and the reader who has progressed beyond the fundamentals of the calculus will profit most from Richard Courant's *Differential and Integral Calculus*, 2 vols. (Interscience Pubs., N.Y., 1937). The fascinating study of the numerous and remarkable properties of the integers may be pursued after completing the third of the above mentioned monographs in H. Davenport: *The Higher Arithmetic* (Hutchinson's University Library, N.Y., 1952) and in G. H. Hardy and E. M. Wright: *An Introduction to the Theory of Numbers* (Oxford Univ. Press, N.Y., 1945).

One of the most satisfying accomplishments of nineteenth century mathematics was the solution of the twenty-five hundred year old problems of squaring the circle, doubling the cube, and trisecting the angle. It was finally proved that these constructions cannot be performed with straight edge and compass. The combined powers of algebra and geometry prevailed over the difficulties which had frustrated the mathematicians, and the successful method is described in the eighth monograph. Final disposition of the problem of squaring the circle is not made, however, until it is proved that π cannot be the root of an algebraic equation with rational coefficients. A much improved proof of this last fact, which incorporates the best features of earlier proofs, is presented by David Eugene Smith in the final monograph.

The method employed by the late nineteenth century mathematicians to settle these age-old construction problems has been systematized and reclothed in the framework of modern abstract algebra. This more sophisticated formulation will be found in Louis Weisner: *Introduction to the Theory of Equations* (The Macmillan Co., N.Y., 1938). Variations on the classical construction problems will be found in Hilda P. Hudson: *Ruler and Compass* (Chelsea Pub. Co., N.Y., 1953).

The reader who masters the contents of these monographs will have obtained a fine introduction to modern developments in algebra and geometry and to the interrelationships of these two fields. Regardless of his ultimate goals in mathematics, he can be assured that the material herein provided will fill many hours with rewarding reading.

New York, 1954 MORRIS KLINE

CONTENTS

* A fuller Table of Contents precedes the Monograph itself.

* A fuller Table of Contents precedes the Monograph itself.

I

THE FOUNDATIONS OF GEOMETRY

By Oswald Veblen

CONTENTS

I

THE FOUNDATIONS OF GEOMETRY*

By Oswald Veblen

I. INTRODUCTION

In connection with the foundations of geometry there arise many questions of psychology, logic and epistemology. Into these the present paper does not enter. Instead we propose to write out the preliminary pages of a geometry such as *Euclid* might be imagined to write to-day. The resulting treatment of geometry as a whole will not be very different from that actually written by *Euclid*. We shall, however, go into detail only with those parts of the subject in which the modern exposition is essentially different from the ancient.

That there are such differences is not because *Euclid's* logical

* This essay is based mainly on two articles in the Transactions of the American Mathematical Society. The first one is by the present writer (Vol. V [1904], pp. 343–84) and the second by *Dr. R. L. Moore* (Vol. IX [1908], pp. 487–512). I have modified my assumptions in accordance with a suggestion of *Dr. Moore's* and have also changed the form of his assumptions in some respects. The literature is too large to cite in detail. We shall be content to mention the names of the following European contributors to the subject: *Pasch, Veronese, Peano, Pieri, Schur, Hilbert, Dehn;* and the following works in the English language:

Hilbert (tr. by *Townsend*), Foundations of Geometry, Chicago.

E. H. Moore, On the Projective Axioms of Geometry. Trans. Am. Math. Soc., Vol. III (1902), pp. 142–58.

Halsted, Rational Geometry, New York.

Whitehead, The Axioms of Descriptive Geometry, Cambridge, 1907.

Coolidge, Non-Euclidean Geometry, Oxford, 1909.

Schweitzer, A Theory of Geometrical Relations, American Journal of Mathematics Vol. XXXI (1909), pp. 365–410.

methods and purposes were different from those of the modern mathematical students of foundations. *Euclid* overlooked certain assumptions that entered tacitly into his arguments, but this was by mistake. His purpose was the same as that of the moderns, to prove every proposition which he could prove, and to prove it with a minimum of assumptions. This required him often to prove statements that were intuitively evident. Thus an axiom might be a self-evident truth, but certainly all self-evident truths were not axioms according to the usage of *Euclid*.

In geometry a great many technical terms are defined, and each is defined in terms of other terms. Hence at the beginning of a book on geometry at least one term must be undefined; otherwise the book would have no beginning. We shall leave undefined the term **point**. This implies that the reader is free to carry in his mind any image of a point which he can reconcile with what is said about it. We may try to impart a notion of our image of a point by saying it has no length, breadth, or thickness, or by like phrases, but these are no part of our book on geometry; they have nothing to do with the logical steps by which the theorems are derived.

If the propositions of geometry are arranged in logical order so that each proposition after a start has been made shall follow by deduction from its predecessors, it is clear that the first propositions of all cannot be deduced, because there are no previous propositions to deduce them from. There must therefore be *assumptions*. These may be stated so plausibly that no one doubts their truth,* but whether they are true or not cannot affect the correctness of the reasoning based upon them, nor the fact that they are assumptions. We shall not enter into the metaphysical question as to whether these assumptions are self-evident truths, axioms, common notions, experimental data or what not, but shall try to keep within the

---

* The writer is inclined to believe that the truth of a statement can be determined only by testing all its consequences, so that the real test of the validity of the hypotheses of geometry is in the validity of the theorems.

realm of mathematics by using the non-committal word assumptions.

In addition to the word *point,* we shall take as undefined a *relation* among points which we indicate by saying "the points *ABC* are in the order {*ABC*}." This relation may mean anything the reader desires, provided it is consistent with the following statements.

These assumptions were all used implicitly in the older geometries, as well as in most text-books of to-day, but have not been formulated explicitly as part of the foundations of geometry until very recent times.

II. THE ASSUMPTIONS OF ORDER

Assumption I. *If points A, B, C are in the order {ABC} they are distinct.*

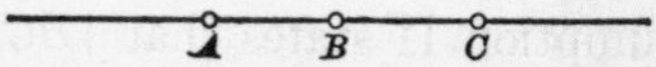

FIG. 1.

Assumption II. *If points A, B, C are in the order {ABC} they are not in the order {BCA}.*

Definitions. If *A* and *B* are distinct points the **line** *AB* consists of *A* and *B* and all points, *X*, in one of the orders {*ABX*}, {*AXB*}, {*XAB*}. The points *X* in the order {*AXB*}

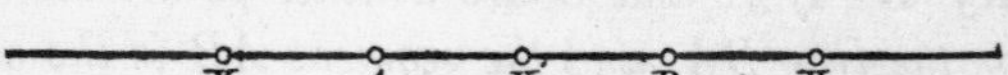

FIG. 2.

constitute the **linear segment** *AB*, and are said to be **between** *A* and *B*. *A* and *B* are called the **ends** of the segment. The segment, together with its ends, constitutes a **linear interval.**

Assumption III. *If points C and D* ($C \neq D$)* *are in the line AB, then A is in the line CD.*

Assumption IV. *If A and B are two distinct points, there exists a point C such that A, B, and C are in the order* {*ABC*}.

---

* The notation $A \neq B$ indicates that *A* and *B* are symbols for different objects.

Assumption V. *If three distinct points, A, B, and C do not lie on the same line and D and E are two points in the orders $\{BCD\}$ and $\{CEA\}$, then a point F exists in the order $\{AFB\}$ and such that D, E and F lie on the same line.*

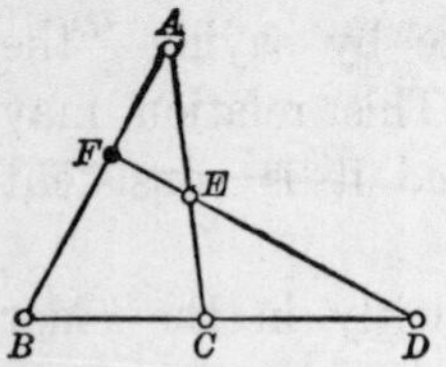

FIG. 3.

Assumption VI. *There exist three distinct points, A, B, C, not in any of the orders $\{ABC\}$, $\{BCA\}$, $\{CAB\}$.*

Theorem 1. *If points A, B, C are in the order $\{ABC\}$ they are in the order $\{CBA\}$, and not in any of the orders $\{CAB\}$, $\{BAC\}$, $\{ACB\}$, $\{BCA\}$.*

Proof. From the definition of a line, A is on the line BC. By Assumption I, C and A are distinct. Hence by Assumption III, B is on the line CA. This means, since B is distinct from C and A, that there is one of the orders $\{CAB\}$, $\{CBA\}$, $\{BCA\}$. But Assumption II states that $\{BCA\}$ is impossible, and if we had $\{CAB\}$ it would follow by Assumption II that we did not have $\{ABC\}$. Hence $\{ABC\}$ implies $\{CBA\}$ and excludes $\{BCA\}$ and $\{CAB\}$.

By what we have just proved, if we had $\{BAC\}$, we should also have $\{CAB\}$. Hence $\{BAC\}$is eliminated. Since $\{ACB\}$ would imply $\{BCA\}$, $\{ACB\}$ is also excluded.

Corollary 1. *If A and B are distinct points the line AB is the same as the line BA, and the segment AB is the same as the segment BA.*

Corollary 2. *If points A, B, C are in the order $\{ABC\}$ then they are all on the lines AB, BC, CA.**

Theorem 2.† *For every two distinct points there is one and only one line containing them.*

Proof. Let A and B be two distinct points. By Theorem 1, Corollary 1, the lines AB and BA are identical. Let C be any point on the line AB distinct from A and let X be any point of the line AB distinct from C and A. Since C is

---

* The lines AB, BC, CA are proved identical in Theorem 2.

† Cf. Euclid, Postulates 1, 2.

on AB it follows by Assumption III that A is on the line CX, and hence that we have one of the orders ACX, CAX, CXA. Whichever of these three cases holds it follows by Theorem 1 and the definition of a line that X is on AC. Hence all points of the line AB are on the line AC.

Let Y be any point of AC distinct from B and A. Since C is on AB, by Assumption III and Corollary 2 of Theorem 1, B is on AC. Since B and Y are on AC it follows by Assumption III that A is on BY. Hence $\{ABY\}$ or $\{BAY\}$ or $\{BYA\}$. Hence by Theorem 1, Y is on AB.

Thus we have shown that the lines AB and AC are identical. If D is any point of AB different from C, it follows that the line CD is identical with the line CA and hence with the line AB. In other words any line containing C and D is identical with the line CD.

Corollary. *Two distinct lines cannot have more than one point in common.*

Proof. If there were two common points, the line determined by them would be identical with each of the given lines.

Theorem 3. *If DE is any line there exists a point F not on this line.*

Proof. If every point were on the line DE then this line would contain the three points A, B, C mentioned in Assumption VI. By Theorem 2, the line AB would be identical with DE. Hence the line AB would contain C, contrary to Assumption VI.

Theorem 4. *If A and B are any two points there is a point F in the order AFB.*

Proof. By Theorem 3, there is a point E not on the line AB (Fig. 3). By Assumption IV there is a point C in the order $\{AEC\}$. The point C cannot be on the line AB, for if so this line would also contain E, by Theorem 2. By Assumption IV, there is a point D in the order $\{BCD\}$. Hence by Assumption V there is a point F in the order $\{AFB\}$.

We have now the information that a line AB must always contain at least five points, namely A and B, and at least one point X_1 between A and B (Theorem 4), and at least one X_2

and one X_3 in each of the orders $\{ABX_2\}$ and $\{X_3AB\}$ (Assumption IV and Theorem 1). The points X_1, X_2, and X_3 are distinct by Theorem 1.

The theorems proved above are all intuitively obvious provided the reader of these lines has in mind the same set of images as the writer. It is necessary to prove them, however, in order to show that our list of assumptions is actually a characterization of the points and lines which we image to ourselves. An obvious fact in the figure (Fig. 3), described by Assumption V, is that the points D, E, F are not only collinear as stated in that assumption, but are in the order $\{DEF\}$. This we shall now prove as a theorem. The reader will observe that most of the other assumptions are used in the argument.

Theorem 5. *The points D, E, F of Assumption V are in the order $\{DEF\}$.*

Proof. Since D, E, F are on the same line, it follows by Theorem 2 that F is on the line DE. Hence they are in one of the orders $\{DEF\}$, $\{DFE\}$, $\{FDE\}$.

Suppose they were in the order $\{DFE\}$. The points E, C, D are not on the same line, because if they were, Theorem 2 would require A, B, C to be on this line. Hence by Assumption V (Fig. 4) the orders $\{CEA\}$ and $\{EFD\}$ would imply that there

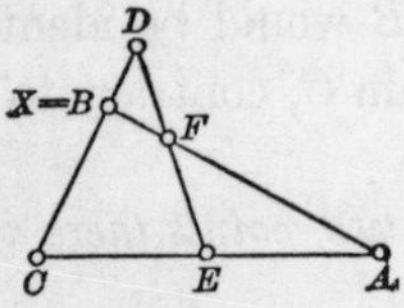

Fig. 4.

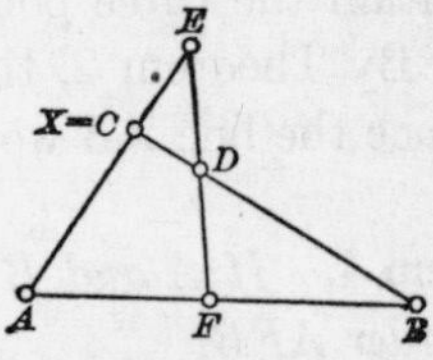

Fig. 5.

is a point X in the order $\{DXC\}$ and on the line AF. But B is common to the lines AF and DC. Hence, by the Corollary of Theorem 2, $X=B$. Hence we would have the order $\{DBC\}$ as well as $\{BCD\}$, contrary to Theorem 1.

Suppose the points were in the order $\{FDE\}$. As before, the points E, F, A are not on the same line. Hence by Assumption V the orders $\{AFB\}$ and $\{FDE\}$ imply the existence of a point X on the line BD and in the order $\{EXA\}$.

But the lines BD and EA, have C in common. Hence there would be the order $\{ECA\}$ as well as $\{CEA\}$, contrary to Theorem 1.

We need also to prove the following theorem, which is intuitively quite as obvious as Assumption V. We shall use the word **collinear** of a set of points to indicate that they are all on the same line.

Theorem 6. *If A, B, C are non-collinear points and A' is between B and C, B' between C and A, and C' between A and B, then A', B', C' are non-collinear.*

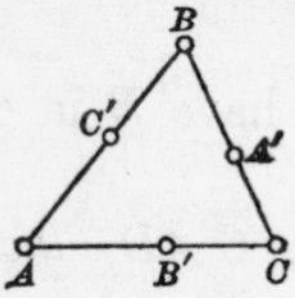

FIG. 6.

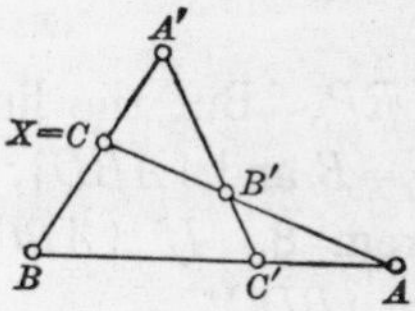

FIG. 7.

Proof. If A', B', C' were collinear we should have one of the orders $\{A'B'C'\}$, $\{B'A'C'\}$, $\{A'C'B'\}$. Consider the possibility of $\{A'B'C'\}$. The points A', C', B cannot be collinear, because their line would, by Theorem 2, also have to contain A and C. Now by Assumption V, the orders $\{BC'A\}$ and $\{C'B'A'\}$ imply the existence of a point X in the order $\{BXA'\}$ and on the line AB'. But C is common to the lines $A'B$ and AB'. Hence $X=C$ and we should have both $\{BCA'\}$ and $\{BA'C\}$.

The proof that $\{B'A'C'\}$ and $\{A'C'B'\}$ are impossible is similar.

III. ORDER ON A LINE

Theorem 7. *If $\{ABC\}$ and $\{BCD\}$, then $\{ABD\}$.*

Proof. By Theorem 3, and Assumption IV, there exist points P and O not on the line AB, and in the order BPO. By Assumption V, and Theorem 5, the orders $\{CBA\}$ and $\{BPO\}$ imply the existence of a point Q in the orders $\{OQC\}$ and $\{APQ\}$. Similarly the orders $\{BCD\}$ and $\{CQO\}$ imply the existence of a point R in the orders $\{ORB\}$ and $\{DQR\}$.

The points A, Q, D are not collinear, for, if so, P would be on AD. Hence, by Assumption V, the orders $\{DQR\}$ and $\{QPA\}$ imply the existence of a point X in the order $\{AXD\}$ and on

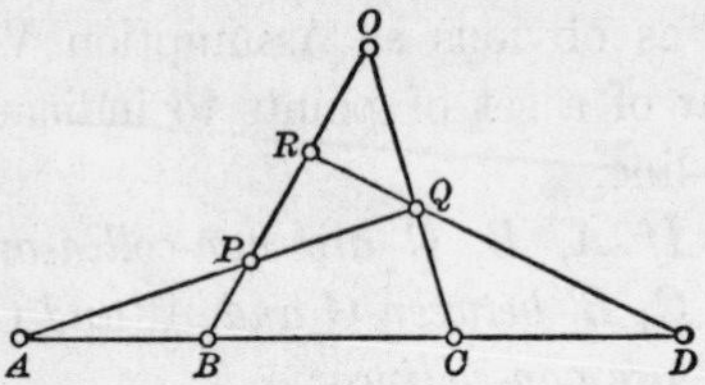

FIG. 8.

the line RP. But the lines RP and AD have B in common Hence $X=B$ and $\{ABD\}$.

Theorem 8. *If* $\{ABC\}$ *and* $\{ABD\}$, $C \neq D$, *then either* $\{BCD\}$ *or* $\{BDC\}$.

Proof. In view of Theorem 2, it is necessary only to show that $\{CBD\}$ is impossible. By Theorem 3 and Assumption IV, there exist points O and P not on the line BC and in the order $\{OCP\}$. The orders $\{OCP\}$ and $\{CBD\}$ would then imply the existence of a point Q in the orders (Fig. 9) $\{DQO\}$

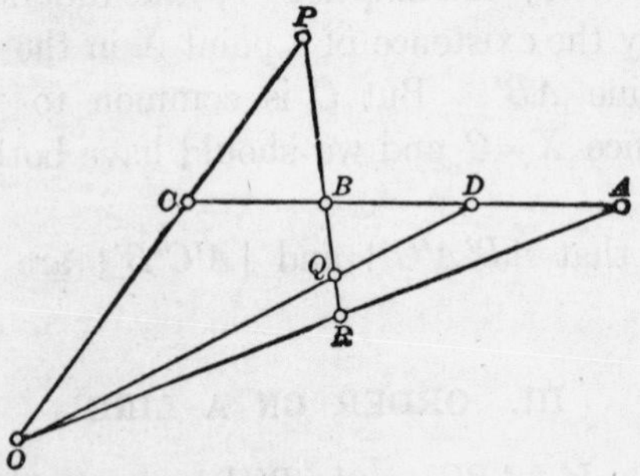

FIG. 9.

and $\{PBQ\}$. Now A, being on the line BC, is not on the line CP. Hence the orders $\{OCP\}$ and $\{CBA\}$ imply the existence of a point R in the orders $\{ARO\}$ and $\{PBR\}$. Thus we would have three non-collinear points, O, A, D, and three points B, Q, R, B between A and D, Q between D and O, R between

O and A, and B, Q, R would all be on the line BP, contrary to Theorem 6.

The following are corollaries of Theorems 7 and 8.

Corollary 1. *If* $\{ABC\}$ and $\{ABD\}$, $C \neq D$, *then either* $\{ACD\}$ or $\{ADC\}$.

Proof. By Theorem 8, we have either $\{BCD\}$ or $\{BDC\}$. If $\{BCD\}$, then $\{DCB\}$ and $\{CBA\}$ lead by Theorem 7 to $\{DCA\}$. If $\{BDC\}$ then $\{CDB\}$ and $\{DBA\}$ imply $\{CDA\}$

Corollary 2. *If* $\{ABD\}$ and $\{ACD\}$, $B \neq C$, then either $\{ABC\}$ or $\{ACB\}$.

Proof. $\{BAC\}$ with $\{ACD\}$ would by Theorem 7 imply $\{BAD\}$, whereas our hypothesis is $\{ABD\}$.

Corollary 3. *If* $\{ABC\}$ *and* $\{ACD\}$ *then* $\{BCD\}$.

Proof. By Theorem 7 $\{CDB\}$ would imply with $\{ACD\}$ the order $\{ACB\}$, contrary to hypothesis. $\{CBD\}$ with $\{CBA\}$ would by Corollary 1 imply either $\{CDA\}$ or $\{CAD\}$, contrary to hypothesis.

Corollary 4. *If* $\{ABC\}$ *and* $\{ACD\}$ *then* $\{ABD\}$.

Proof. By Corollary 3 we have $\{BCD\}$, which combined with $\{ABC\}$ leads by Theorem 7 to $\{ABD\}$.

These propositions are all preliminary to the following theorem.

Theorem 9. *If A is any point of a line AB, the points of the line exclusive of A are in two sets such that A is between any point of the first set and any point of the second set, and is not between any two points of the same set.*

Proof. Let $[X]$ be the set* of all points in the order $\{XAB\}$ and let $[Y]$ be the set including B and all points in the orders $\{AYB\}$ and $\{ABY\}$. By definition, the line comprises no other points than A and $[X]$ and $[Y]$.

A is between any X and any Y. For we have $\{XAB\}$ and either $\{AYB\}$ or $\{ABY\}$. In the first case Corollary 3 gives the conclusion $\{YAX\}$ and in the second case Theorem 7 yields the same result.

---

* We let $[X]$ denote a class of objects, the individuals of which are denoted by X, X_1, X_2, X'', etc.

A is not between two X's, because $\{X_1AB\}$ and $\{X_2AB\}$ lead by Theorem 8 either to $\{AX_1X_2\}$ or $\{AX_2X_1\}$.

A is not between two Y's, for the possible cases are: (*a*) $\{AY_1B\}$ and $\{AY_2B\}$, which by Corollary 2 gives $\{AY_1Y_2\}$ or $\{AY_2Y_1\}$; (*b*) $\{AY_1B\}$ and $\{ABY_2\}$ which, by Corollary 4 gives $\{AY_1Y_2\}$; (*c*) $\{ABY_1\}$ and $\{ABY_2\}$, which by Corollary 1 gives $\{AY_1Y_2\}$ or $\{AY_2Y_1\}$.

Definition. The two sets of points in Theorem 9 are called **half-lines** or **rays**; A is called the **origin** or the **end** of either half-line. If AB is any segment the ray of the line AB whose end is B and which does not contain A is called the **prolongation of the segment** AB **beyond** B.

A ray whose end is A and which contains B is designated as the **ray** AB.

Corollary 1. *If B is a point of a ray whose end is A the points of the ray exclusive of B are in two sets, the segment AB and a ray whose end is B.*

Proof. The ray is by definition composed of B and the points X in the order $\{AXB\}$ and the points Y in the order $\{ABY\}$.

Corollary 2. *If C is a point of a segment AB, then the points of the segment, exclusive of C, are in one or the other, but not both, of the segments AC and BC.*

Proof. A and B are respectively in the two rays α and β, whose common end is C. The ray α contains by definition all points $\{X\}$ in the order $\{CXA\}$ and β contains similarly all points $\{X'\}$ in the order $\{CX'B\}$. Hence the segments CA and CB have no points in common.

The other points $\{Y\}$ of the ray α are in the order $\{CAY\}$. Since we have $\{BCA\}$ it follows by Theorem 7 that the points Y are also in the order $\{BAY\}$ and hence not on the segment AB. The ray β also contains points $\{Y'\}$ in the order $\{CBY\}$. These must also be in the order $\{ABY\}$ and hence not on the segment AB. Hence every point on the segment AB, except C, is on one of the segments AC and CB.

Definition. A set of n ($n > 3$) points $A_1, A_2, \ldots A_n$ are in the order $\{A_1A_2 \ldots A_n\}$ if and only if $\{A_iA_jA_k\}$ wherever

$i<j<k$ $(i, j, k=1, 2, \ldots, n)$. Two points A_1, A_2 are always in the orders $\{A_1A_2\}$ and $\{A_2A_1\}$.

Theorem 10. *To any set of n distinct points* $(n \geqq 2)$ *on a line can be assigned the notation so that they are in the order* $\{A_1A_2 \ldots A_n\}$. *The other points of the line fall into* $n+1$ *sets, no two of which have a point in common. These sets are the segments* A_1, A_2, $A_2A_3, \ldots A_{n-1}A_n$ *and the rays which are the prolongations of the segment* A_1A_n *beyond* A_1 *and* A_n.

Proof. We prove the theorem first for the case $n=2$. The first statement of the theorem is in this case part of the definition. Let A_1 be an arbitrary one of the two points, and let η_1 and η_2 be the two rays which it determines according to Theorem 9, η_2 being the one which contains A_2. The ray η_2 is by Corollary 1 of Theorem 9 composed of the segment A_1A_2, the point A_2, and another ray η_2' with A_2 as its end.

This proves the theorem for $n=2$. We establish it for the general case by proving that if it is true for $n=k$ then it is true for $n=k+1$. Consider k points in the order $\{A_1A_2 \ldots A_k\}$. A point A_{k+1} may fall in the ray whose end is A_1 or in one of the segments $A_1A_2, A_2A_3, \ldots, A_{k-1}A_k$, or in the ray whose end is A_k.

If it falls in one of the two rays it separates this into a segment and a ray by Corollary 1 of Theorem 9. If it falls in a segment it separates this into two segments by Corollary 2 of the same theorem. So in either case we have increased the number of segments by one and left the number of rays unaltered.

Call the end of one of the rays A_1'. Let A_2' be the other end of the segment, one of whose ends is A_1'. Let A_3' be the other end of the other segment whose end is A_2'. By a finite number of steps the points $A_1, \ldots, A_k, A_{k+1}$ are exhausted and the notation has been assigned to them in such a way that A_1' and A'_{k+1} are ends of rays and the segments are $A_1'A_2', \ldots, A'_kA'_{k+1}$. Since none of the points $A_3', \ldots A_{k+1}$ are on the segment $A_1'A_2'$ of the ray whose end is A_1, we have the order relations $A_1'A_2'A_j'(2<j<k+2)$. Similar considerations show that all the order relations exist which are implied by the symbol $(A_1'A_2'A_3' \ldots A'_{k+1})$.

Theorem 11. *On any segment AB and on either of its prolongations there is an infinitude of points.*

Proof. By Theorem 4 there is a point X_1 on the segment AB. By the same theorem there is a point X_2 on the segment AX_1. By Theorem 8, Corollary 4, X_2 is on AB. In like manner we obtain points $X_3, X_4, \ldots$ on AB. By Assumption I and Corollary 2 of Theorem 9, these points are all distinct.

By Assumption IV there is a point Y_1 on the prolongation of AB beyond B, a point Y_2 on the prolongation of AY_1 beyond Y_2, and so on. By Theorem 7 all these points are on the prolongation of AB beyond B.

IV. THE TRIANGLE AND THE PLANE

Definition. Three non-collinear points A, B, C, together with the segments AB, BC and CA, are called a triangle ABC. The points A, B, C are called the **vertices,** and the segments AB, BC, CA are called the **sides of the triangle.**

We shall now prove a theorem which must be carefully distinguished from Assumption V.

Theorem 12. *If A, B, C are three non-collinear points and D and F exist in the orders $\{BCD\}$ and $\{AFB\}$ then E exists in the orders $\{AEC\}$ and $\{DEF\}$.*

Proof. By Assumption IV there exists a point, O (Fig. 10), in the order $\{ABO\}$ which is therefore by Theorem 8, Corollaries 3 and 4, also in the orders $\{AFO\}$, $\{FBO\}$. Since we also have $\{BCD\}$ it follows by Assumption V and Theorem 5, that there exists a point P in the orders $\{OCP\}$ and $\{FPD\}$. By the same argument there follows from the orders $\{AFO\}$ and $\{FPD\}$ the existence of a point Q in the orders $\{OPQ\}$ and $\{DQA\}$. The orders $\{OPQ\}$ and $\{OCP\}$ imply by Theorem 8, Corollary 3, the order $\{CPQ\}$. Since A, C, Q, are not collinear (Theorem 2), the orders $\{AQD\}$ and $\{QPC\}$ imply (Assumption V) the existence of a point E on the line DF and in the order $\{CEA\}$. By Assumption V and Theorem 2, the line DE meets the segment AB in F only, and hence by Theorem 5 we have the order $\{DEF\}$.

ABC is identical with the plane ABP, and this is identical with PAO, and this with $C'AO$, and this with $C'AB$.

Now if $A'B'C'$ are three non-collinear points of the plane ABC, at least one of them, say C', is not on the line AB. Hence by the argument above ABC is identical with ABC'. A' and B' are not both on the line AC'. Let B' be the one which is not, and we have that ABC' is identical with $AB'C'$. Since A' is not on the line $B'C'$ the same argument shows that $AB'C'$ is identical with $A'B'C'$. Hence ABC is identical with $A'B'C'$.

Theorem 16.* *A line having two points in common with a plane lies wholly in the plane.*

Proof. Let the two points be taken as A and B in defining the plane, ABC. The plane contains the line AB.

Corollary. *If two planes have two points in common they have a line in common.*

Theorem 17. *A line of a plane which contains one and only one point of a side of a triangle whose vertices are in the plane contains one other point of the triangle.*

Proof. Let the triangle be ABC and let a line l meet the segment AB in a point O. By Theorem 14, since any other point of l is in the plane ABC the line l meets the triangle in a point different from O.

V. REGIONS IN A PLANE

In this section we shall be dealing entirely with the points of a single plane.

Definition. The set of $n-1$ intervals $A_1A_2, A_2A_3, \ldots, A_{n-2}A_{n-1}, A_{n-1}A_n$ determined by n points $A_1, A_2, \ldots, A_n$ is called the **broken line** $A_1A_2A_3 \ldots A_n$. A_1 and A_n are called its **ends,** and it is said to **join** A_1 and A_n. A single interval is a special case of a broken line.

A **region** is a set of points such that (1) any two points of the set can be joined by a broken line consisting entirely of points of the set, and (2) any point of the set is on at least two non-collinear segments consisting entirely of points of the set.

* Cf. Euclid, Definition, I, 7.

The last clause excludes the possibility of a single segment being a region. A region is said to be **convex** if the interval joining any two points of it is composed entirely of points of the region.

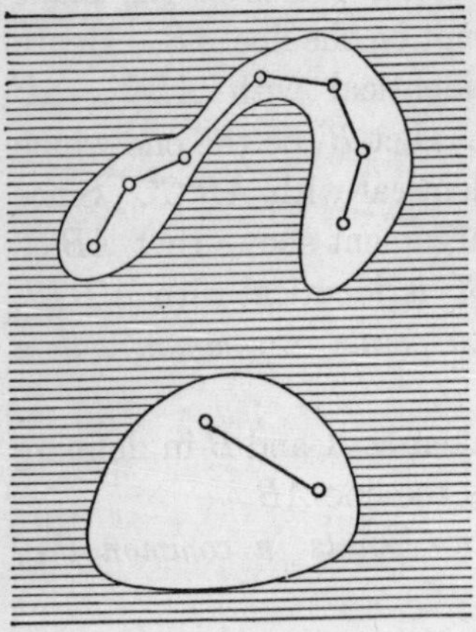

FIG. 23.

It is evident that the set of all points in a plane is an example of a convex region. Further cases are developed by the theorems below.

Theorem 18. *If l is any line passing through a point of a convex region* **R** *in a plane then the points of* **R** *not on l constitute two convex regions* $\mathbf{R}_1$ *and* $\mathbf{R}_2$ *such that any segment joining a point of* $\mathbf{R}_1$ *to a point of* $\mathbf{R}_2$ *contains a point of l.*

Proof. Let O be a point of **R** on l. By the definition of a convex region there is a segment intersecting l in O and consisting entirely of points of **R**. Let A_1 and A_2 be two points of this segment in the order $\{A_1OA_2\}$.

Consider the set $\mathbf{R}_1$ of points of **R** which are joined to A_1 by intervals containing no point of l. If X', X'' are two such points, the segment $X'X''$ can contain no point of l since, if it did, one of the intervals $X''A_1$ and A_1X' would contain a point of l (Theorem 17). Moreover, all points X of the segment $X'X''$ are in $\mathbf{R}_1$ because if l should meet the segment A_1X it would have, by Theorem 17, to meet A_1X'. Hence the set $\mathbf{R}_1$ is a convex region.

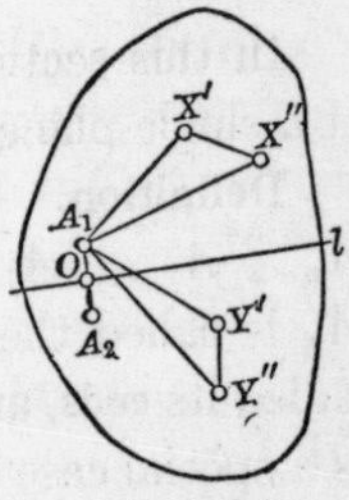

FIG. 24.

Consider also the set $\mathbf{R}_2$ of points of **R** such that the segments joining them to A_1 each contain points of l. A_2 is evidently a point of $\mathbf{R}_2$. If Y' and Y'' are two points of $\mathbf{R}_2$ the segment $Y'Y''$ can contain no point of l, because in that case the line l would meet three sides of the triangle $A_1Y'Y''$, contrary to Theorem 6. Again, if Y is any point of the segment $Y'Y''$, the segment A_1Y contains a point of l by Theorem 17, because the segment A_1Y' does and the interval $Y'Y$ does not. Hence $\mathbf{R}_2$ is a convex region.

Clearly all points of $\mathbf{R}$ are in $\mathbf{R}_1$, on l, or in $\mathbf{R}_2$. Any segment joining a point X of $\mathbf{R}_1$ to a point Y of $\mathbf{R}_2$ meets l. This follows by Theorem 17, because the segment A_1Y does and the interval A_1X does not contain a point of l.

Since the set of all points in a plane is a convex region, we have at once the following

Corollary. Definition. *The points of a plane ABC not on the line AB constitute two convex regions such that any segment joining a point of one region to a point of the other region contains a point of AB. These two regions are called the two* **sides** *of the line. Either of them is called a* **half plane.**

Definition. A set of points $[X]$ is said to **separate** two other sets of points $[Y]$, $[Z]$ if and only if every broken line joining a point Y to a point Z contains a point X. A set $[X]$ is said to **decompose** a region $\mathbf{R}$ into regions $\mathbf{R}_1, \ldots, \mathbf{R}_n$ if the points in $[X]$ and $\mathbf{R}_1, \ldots, \mathbf{R}_n$ comprise all points of $\mathbf{R}$ and each pair of regions $\mathbf{R}_1, \ldots, \mathbf{R}_n$ is separated by $[X]$ together with the points of the plane not in $\mathbf{R}$.

Theorem 19. *A line containing a point of a convex region decomposes it into two convex regions.*

Proof. This follows from Theorem 18, as soon as we prove that a broken line joining a point of $\mathbf{R}_1$ to a point of $\mathbf{R}_2$ meets l. Let $A_1 A_2 A_3 \ldots A_n$ be a broken line not meeting l. Then A_1 and A_2 are on the same side of l by Theorem 18. In like manner A_3 is on the same side as A_1 and A_2. By repeating this argument we find that A_n is on the same side as A_1. Hence a broken line joining points on opposite sides meets l.

Definition. A point and two distinct rays having it as their common origin are called an **angle.** The origin is called the **vertex** and the rays are called the **sides** of the angle. If the rays are collinear the angle (which is identical with the line) is called a **straight angle** or a **flat angle.**

An angle is denoted by the symbol $\measuredangle ab$, if a and b denote the sides. The symbol $\measuredangle ABC$ denotes the angle whose sides are the rays BA and BC.

Theorem 20. Definition. *An angle $\measuredangle ABC$ not a straight angle decomposes the plane in which it lies into two regions, one of which is convex. The convex region is called the* **interior** *of the angle and the other region the* **exterior** *of the angle. Any ray with B as origin containing a point of the interior meets the segment AC and consists entirely of interior points.*

Proof. Let D be a point in the order $\{DBA\}$. Let $[I]$ be the set of all points of the plane such that the segment DI contains a point of the ray BC. Let $[O]$ be the set of all points such that the interval DO does not contain B or a point of the ray BC. Since all points of the plane ABC are on rays having D as origin, every point of the plane is in $[I]$ or $[O]$ or on $\measuredangle ABC$.

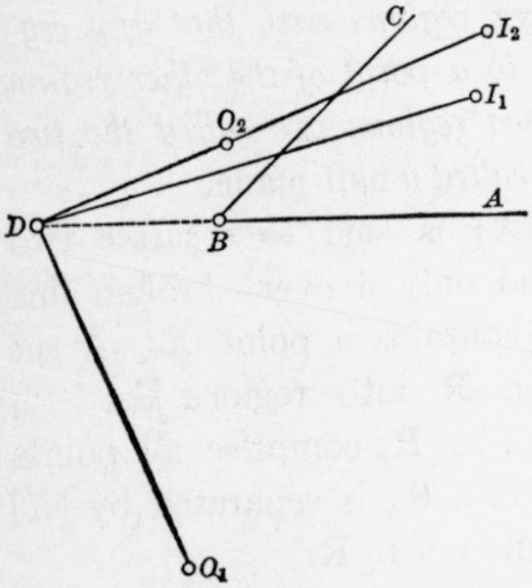

FIG. 25.

Two points, O_1, O_2, are joined by the broken line O_1DO_2, which by definition contains no point of $\measuredangle ABC$. Two points, I_1, I_2, are by definition on the same side of BA with C and on the opposite side of BC from D. Hence the segment I_1I_2 does not meet $\measuredangle ABC$. Moreover if IP is any interval not meeting $\measuredangle ABC$, and I is in $[I]$, then P is on the same side of AB with I and also on the same side of BC with I. The line BC meets the side DI of the triangle DIP and does not meet the interval IP. Hence it must meet the segment DP in a point Q. Since the segment DP is on the same side of the line AB with C, Q is on the ray BC. Hence P is a point of $[I]$. Now if $IP_1P_2P_3 \ldots P_n$ is a broken line not meeting $\measuredangle ABC$, the argument just made shows first that P_1 is in $[I]$, then that P_2 is in $[I]$ and so on. Hence every broken line joining a point of $[I]$ to a point of $[O]$ meets $\measuredangle ABC$.

The rays which have B as origin and are on the opposite

side of the line AB from C are all composed of O points and cannot meet the segment AC. The ray BD is composed of O points and does not meet the segment AC. The other rays whose origin is B, aside from BA and BC, meet one of the segments DC and CA. Those meeting the segment DC evidently are composed entirely of O points and those meeting the segment CA of I points. Hence the set of points $[I]$ is composed of the points on the rays whose origin is B and which meet the segment AC.

Theorem 21. Definition. *A triangle decomposes its plane into two regions one of which is convex and is called the* **interior.** *The other region is not convex and is called the* **exterior.** *A ray whose origin is an interior point meets the triangle in one and only one point, and the interior consists of all points having this property.*

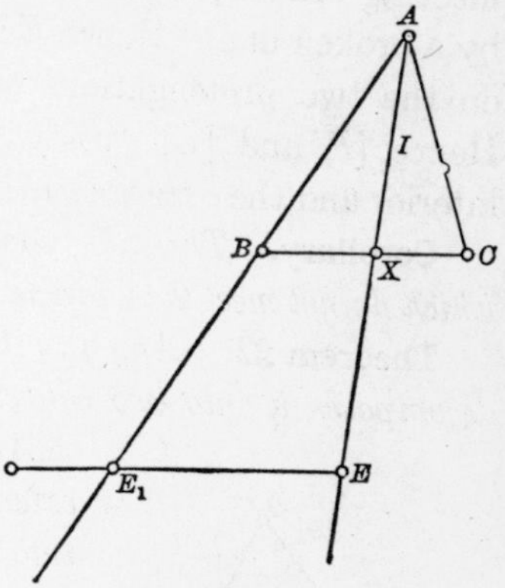

FIG. 26.

Proof. Let the triangle be ABC and let $[I]$ be the set of all points on the segments $[AX]$ where $[X]$ is the segment BC. By Theorem 17, any line through I except the line IX meets the triangles AXB and AXC each in one point. But as B and C are on opposite sides of the line AX these points are one in each of the rays into which I decomposes the line. Hence every ray through I meets the triangle ABC once and only once.

A segment I_1I_2 cannot contain a point of the triangle for then the ray I_1I_2 would contain at least two points of the triangle, one on the segment I_1I_2 and one on its prolongation beyond I_2. Hence $[I]$ is a convex region.

A segment one of whose end points is I must be composed entirely of I-points if it does not contain a point of the triangle; for if P is any point of the segment, the single point of the triangle on the ray IP is by hypothesis on the prolongation of IP beyond P. From this it follows as in Theorem 19 that a broken line joining a point I to a point not in $[I]$ contains at least one point of the triangle.

A point E not in $[I]$ or on the triangle ABC must either be exterior to $\measuredangle BAC$ or on the prolongation of a segment AX beyond X. One of the latter points E is joined to a point E_1 of the prolongation of AB beyond B by an interval which does not meet the triangle ABC because its ends are on the opposite side of BC from A. The prolongation of EE_1 beyond E_1 is composed of points in the exterior of $\measuredangle BAC$. Since any two points exterior to $\measuredangle BAC$ are connected by a broken line not meeting $\measuredangle BAC$, it follows that any two points E are connected by a broken line. Hence E is a region. Since it contains points on the two prolongations of a segment AX it is not convex. Hence $[I]$ and $[E]$ satisfy the definitions respectively of the interior and the exterior of the triangle.

Corollary. *Through each exterior point there pass lines which do not meet the triangle.*

Theorem 22. *Any ray BD in the interior region of $\measuredangle ABC$ decomposes it into two convex regions, the interiors of the angles $\measuredangle ABD$, $\measuredangle DBC$. Any ray BD in the exterior region of $\measuredangle ABC$ decomposes it into two regions at least one of which is convex. One of these is the interior or the exterior of $\measuredangle ABD$ and the other the interior or the exterior of $\measuredangle DBC$.*

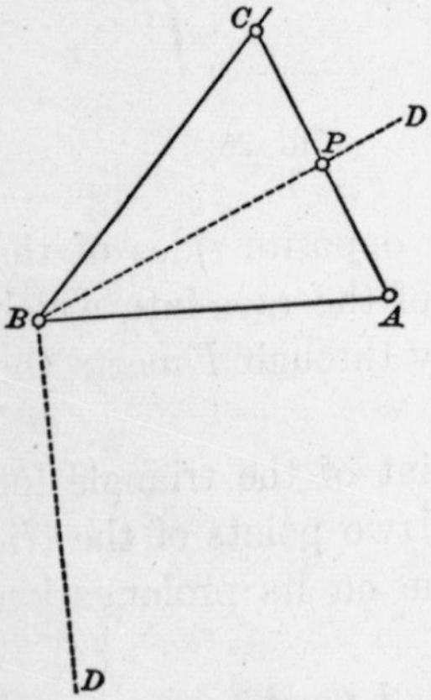

Fig. 27.

Proof. To prove the first part of the theorem we observe that the ray BD meets the segment AC in a point P. Hence the points X on the rays joining B to the segment AP are on the opposite side of the line BD from the points $[Y]$ on the rays joining B to the segment PC. But the sets $[X]$ and $[Y]$ are the angles $\measuredangle ABD$ and $\measuredangle DBC$ respectively.

The proof of the second part is analogous to that just made. The details are left as an exercise for the reader.

Definition. If R is a region and there exists a set of points $[B]$ not points of **R** such that every broken line joining a point of **R** to a point not in **R** contains a point B_1, then $[B]$ is called the **boundary** of R.

For example, a line is the boundary of each of the half-planes it determines; an angle is the boundary of its interior and also of its exterior.

Definition. Two rays a, b, are **separated** by an angle $\measuredangle hk$ if the four rays a, b, h, k have a common origin and one of a and b is interior while the other is exterior to $\measuredangle hk$. A set of rays having a common origin are said to be **in the order** $\{a_1a_2a_3a_4a_5 \ldots a_n\}$ if no two of the rays are separated by any of the angles $\measuredangle a_1a_2$, $\measuredangle a_2a_3$, $\ldots$, $\measuredangle a_{n-1}a_n$, $\measuredangle a_na_1$.

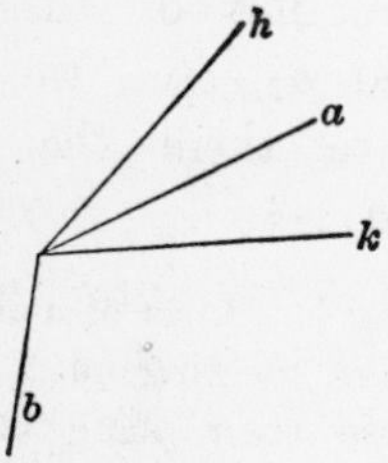

FIG. 28.

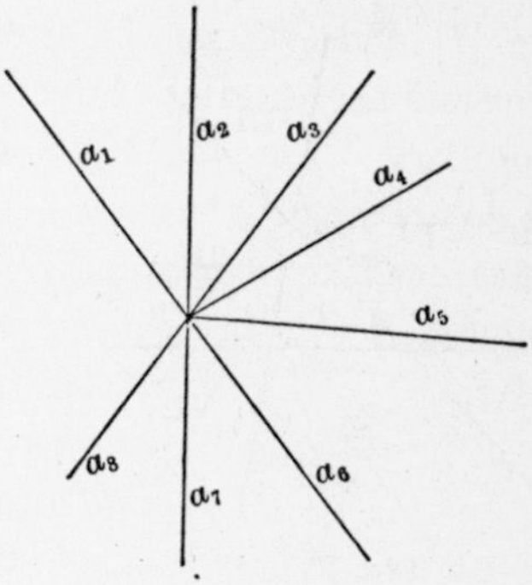

FIG. 29.

Corollary 1. *A set of rays in the order* $\{a_1a_2 \ldots a_{n-1}a_n\}$ *are also in the orders* $\{a_2a_3 \ldots a_na_1\}$ *and* $\{a_na_{n-1} \ldots a_2a_1\}$.

Corollary 2. *Any two rays, a, b, having a common origin are in the orders $\{ab\}$ and $\{ba\}$. Any three rays, a, b, c, having a common origin are in the orders $\{abc\}$, $\{bca\}$, $\{cab\}$, $\{acb\}$, $\{bac\}$, $\{cba\}$.*

Theorem 23. *To any finite number $n>2$ of rays having a common origin may be assigned notation so that they are in the order $\{a_1a_2a_3 \ldots a_n\}$. They decompose the plane into n regions of which at most one is not convex.*

Proof. The theorem is obvious for $n=2$. Hence we can

prove it in general by showing that its truth for $n=k$ implies its truth for $n=k+1$.

To k of the given $k+1$ rays let us assign notation so that they are in the order $b_1b_2 \dots b_k$. They decompose the plane into k regions $\mathbf{R}_1, \mathbf{R}_2, \dots, \mathbf{R}_k$, whose boundaries are $\measuredangle b_1b_2$, $\measuredangle b_2b_3, \dots, \measuredangle b_kb_1$. The other ray, b, lies in one of the k regions determined by $b_1b_2 \dots b_k$. By Theorem 22 it separates this region, $\mathbf{R}_i$, into two regions $\mathbf{R}_i'\mathbf{R}_i''$ of which one at least is convex if $\mathbf{R}_i$ is not convex and both of which are convex if $\mathbf{R}_i$ is convex. Hence the $k+1$ rays decompose the plane into $k+1$ regions $\mathbf{R}_1, \mathbf{R}_2 \dots \mathbf{R}_i'\mathbf{R}_i'' \dots \mathbf{R}_k$ of which at most one is not convex.

Suppose that the boundary of $\mathbf{R}_i$ is $\measuredangle b_ib_{i+1}$. Then the boundaries of the two regions into which $\mathbf{R}_i$ is decomposed are $\measuredangle b_ib$ and $\measuredangle bb_{i+1}$. Hence the $k+1$ rays are in the order $\{b_1, b_2 \dots b_ibb_{i+1} \dots b_k\}$. By calling the first of these a_1, the second a_2, etc., we have assigned to them the order $\{a_1a_2 \dots a_{k+1}\}$.

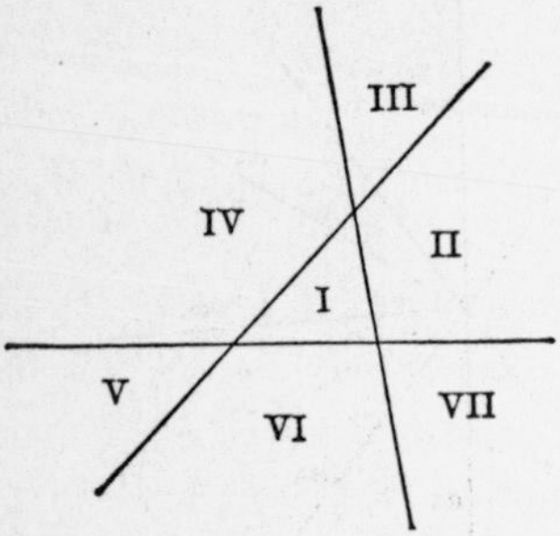

Fig. 30.

Exercise 1. A set of n distinct coplanar lines meeting in a point O decompose their plane into $2n$ convex regions.

Exercise 2. Three lines AB, BC, CA not meeting in a point decompose their plane into seven convex regions, one of which is the interior of the triangle ABC.

Exercise 3. A set of n lines in a plane each pair of which intersect, but no three of which pass through the same point, decompose their plane into $\frac{n(n+1)}{2}+1$ convex regions.

VI. CONGRUENCE OF POINT PAIRS

We now introduce a new undefined term to express a relation between point pairs. The relation is called **congruence.** Denoting pairs of distinct points by (A, B), (C, D), etc., we write (A, B) *is congruent to* (C, D). Since this phrase is undefined the reader may attach to it any meaning consistent with the assumptions below. It is intended, however, to express the common notion implied by saying that the distance from A to B as measured by a tape-line is the same as the distance from C to D.

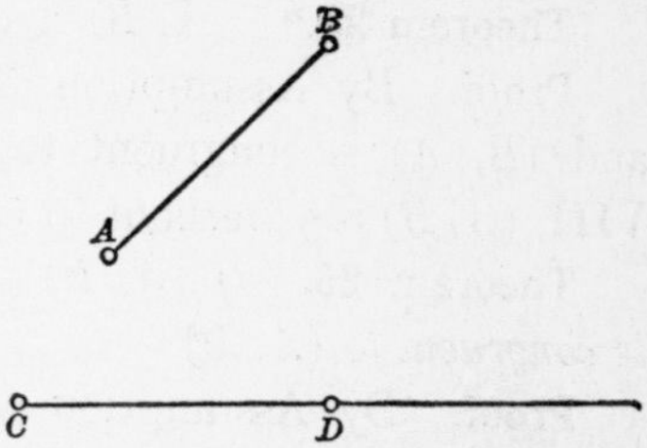

FIG. 31.

Assumption VII.* *If $A \neq B$ then on any ray whose origin is C there exists one and only one† point D such that (A, B) is congruent to (C, D).*

Assumption VIII.‡ *If (A, B) is congruent to (C, D) and (C, D) is congruent to (E, F) then (A, B) is congruent to (E, F).*

Assumption IX.§ *If (A, B) is congruent to (A', B') and (B, C) is congruent to (B', C') and $\{ABC\}$ and $\{A'B'C'\}$ then (A, C) is congruent to (A', C').*

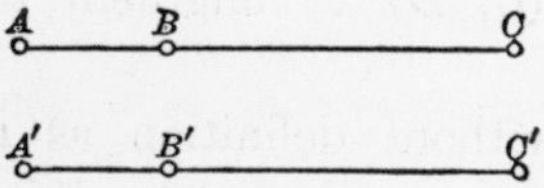

FIG. 32.

Assumption X. *(A, B) is congruent to (B, A).*

Theorem 24. *If $\{ABC\}$, and C' is a point on a ray $A'B'$ such that (A, B) is congruent to $(A'B')$* and *(A, C) is congruent to $(A'C')$ then $\{A'B'C'\}$.*

Proof. By Assumption VII there is a point C'' on the ray $B'C'$ such that BC is congruent to $B'C''$. The point C'' is in

* Cf. Euclid, Postulate 3.

† Evidently there are two statements here, (1) the existence and (2) the uniqueness of D.

‡ Cf. Euclid, Common Notion 1.

§ Cf. Euclid, Common Notion 2.

the order $A'B'C''$. But by Assumption IX, AC is congruent to AC''. Hence by Assumption VII, $C''=C'$. Hence $\{AB'C'\}$.

By combining this theorem with Assumption IX we have the following

Corollary. *If (A, B) and (A, C) are congruent respectively to (A',B') and (A',C'), and if C is on the ray AB and C' on the ray $A'B'$, then (if $B \neq C$) (B, C) is congruent to $(B,' C')$.*

Theorem 25.* *(A, B) is congruent to (A, B).*

Proof. By Assumption X, (A, B) is congruent to (B, A) and (B, A) is congruent to (A, B). Hence by Assumption VIII, (A, B) is congruent to (A, B).

Theorem 26. *If (A, B) is congruent to (C, D) then (C, D) is congruent to (A, B).*

Proof. By Assumption VII there exists on the ray AB a point B' such that (C, D) is congruent to (A, B'). Hence by Assumption VIII (A, B) is congruent to (A, B'). Hence by Theorem 25 and Assumption VII $B'=B$.

Corollary.† *If (A, B) is congruent to (C, D) and also to (E, F) then (C, D) is congruent to (E, F).*

Proof. Since (A, B) is congruent to (C, D), (C, D) is congruent to (A, B). Since also (A, B) is congruent to (E, F) it follows by Assumption VIII that (C, D) is congruent to (E, F).

The word congruent was taken without definition as a relation between point-pairs. We now proceed to extend its significance by means of a definition.

Definition. A set of points $[X]$ is **congruent** to a set of points $[Y]$ if (1) every point X corresponds to one point Y in such a way that whenever (X_1, X_2) corresponds to (Y_1, Y_2), (X_1, X_2) is congruent to (Y_1, Y_2) and (2) every point Y is the correspondent of one point X.

This definition corresponds precisely to the intuitive conception of *superposition.* If two plane figures are represented by drawings on sheets of paper it is perfectly clear that a test for their congruence is to lay one on top of the other. The

* Cf. Euclid, Common Notion 4. † Cf. Euclid, Common Notion 1.

superposition with which we have to do in geometry is, however, a kind of intellectual matching of two figures together. The attention is transferred from one to the other and we try to see whether corresponding pairs of points are congruent. It would be perfectly feasible to substitute the word superposable for congruent in the definition above.

Theorem 27.* *Any figure is congruent to itself. If a figure is congruent to a second figure the second figure is congruent to the first. Two figures congruent to the same figure are congruent to each other.*

Theorem 28. *Any point is congruent to any other point, any line to any other line, any ray to any other ray, any straight angle to any other straight angle.*

Proof. That any point, A, is congruent to any point, B, is obvious from the wording of the definition.

Let AB and LM be any two rays. Let each point Y of the ray LM correspond to that point X of the ray AB which is such that (A, X) is congruent to (L, Y). Thus every X has a Y corresponding to it. Moreover, if Y_1 and Y_2 correspond to X_1 and X_2 we have (L, Y_1) and (L, Y_2) congruent respectively to (A, X_1) and (A, X_2) and hence by the corollary of Theorem 24 (X_1, X_2) is congruent to (Y_1, Y_2). Hence the ray LM is congruent to the ray AB.

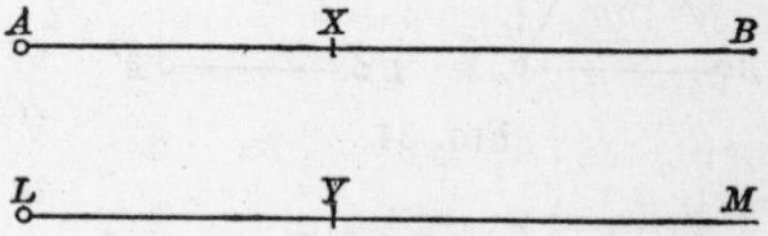

FIG. 33.

By applying like reasoning to the rays AB' and LM', which are the prolongations beyond A and L of the segments BA and LM respectively, we have that the straight angle BAB' is congruent to the straight angle MLM'. Hence the two lines AB and LM are also congruent.

Theorem 29. *If (A, B) is congruent to (C, D) then the segment AB is congruent to the segment CD and the interval AB is congruent to the interval CD.*

* Cf. Euclid Common Notions 1 and 4. By the word, figure, we mean any set of points.

Proof. Let A correspond to C and B to D and any point X of the segment AB correspond to that point Y of the ray CD such that (A, X) is congruent to (C, Y). By Theorem 24, Y is on the segment CD and by the corollary of the same theorem, (D, Y) is congruent to (B, X). By the corollary of Theorem 24, if X_1X_2 correspond to Y_1Y_2 then (X_1, X_2) is congruent to (Y_1, Y_2).

VII. CONGRUENCE OF ANGLES

In order to deal with the congruence of angles and other figures in a plane, we must introduce an additional assumption.

Assumption XI. *If A, B, C are three non-collinear points and D is a point in the order $\{BCD\}$, and if $A'B'C'$ are three non-collinear points and D' is a point in the order $\{B'C'D'\}$ such that the point pairs (A, B), (B, C), (C, A), (B, D) are respectively congruent to (A', B'), (B', C'), (C', A'), (B', D'), then (A, D) is congruent to (A', D').*

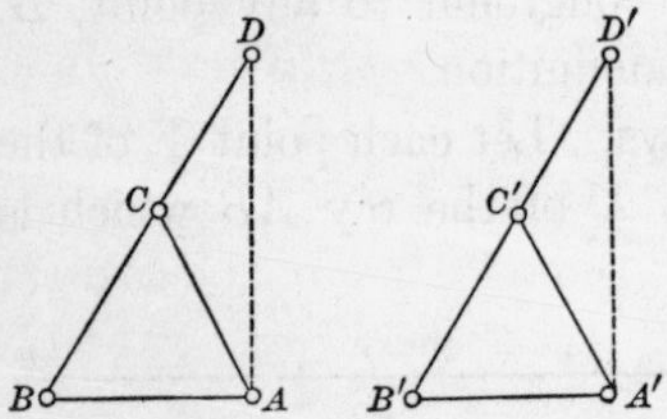

FIG. 34.

Theorem 30.* *Two angles $\measuredangle BAC$ and $\measuredangle MON$ are congruent in such a way that A corresponds to O if there are two points P and Q on the rays OM and ON such that the point pairs (A, B), (A, C) and (B, C) are respectively congruent to (O, P), (O, Q) and (P, Q).*

Proof. If the points P and Q exist as stated let A correspond to O, B to P and C to Q. The ray AC is congruent to the ray OQ and the ray AB to the ray OP. Hence to prove the angles congruent we need to show that if X_1 is any point of the ray AC and X_2 any point of the ray AB and Y_1 and Y_2 are the corresponding points of the rays ON and OM respectively, then (X_1, X_2) is congruent to (Y_1, Y_2).

Let B' and P' be points on the prolongations of BA and PO beyond A and O respectively such that (A, B') is congruent to

* Cf. Euclid, I, 8.

(O, P'). Since (A, C), (C, B), (B, A), (B, B') are congruent respectively to (O, Q), (Q, P), (P, O), (P, P'), it follows by Assumption XI that $(B'C)$ is congruent to (P', Q). Now if X_2 and Y_2 are points of the rays AB and OP respectively such that (A, X_2) is congruent to (O, Y_2), it follows, since (A, C), (C, B'), (B', A), (B', X_2) are respectively congruent to (O, Q), (Q, P'), (P', O), (P', Y_2), that (C, X_2) is congruent to (Q, Y_2). In similar fashion we can prove that if X_1 and Y_1 are points of the rays AC and OQ respectively such that (A, X_1) is congruent to (O, Y_1), then (X_1, X_2) is congruent to (Y_1, Y_2).

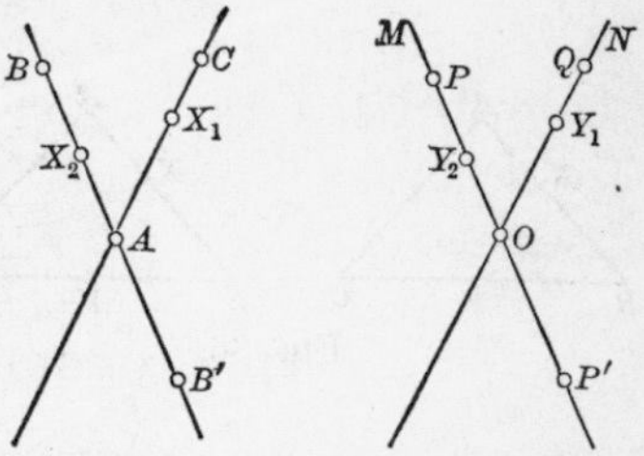

Fig. 35.

Definition. If B' is on the prolongation of the segment BA beyond A, the angle $\measuredangle B'AC$ is said to be a **supplement** of $\measuredangle BAC$. If C' is a point on the prolongation of the segment CA beyond A, the angles $\measuredangle CAB$ and $\measuredangle C'AB'$ are said to be **vertical**.

Corollary 1. *Supplements of congruent angles are congruent.*

Corollary 2.* *Vertical angles are congruent.*

Definition. In a triangle ABC, the sides AB and BC are said to **include** $\measuredangle ABC$. The side AC and angle $\measuredangle ABC$ are said to be **opposite** each to the other. The sides AB and BC are said to be **adjacent** to each other and to $\measuredangle ABC$.

Theorem 31.† *If the sides of one triangle are congruent respectively to the sides of another triangle, the triangles are congruent.*

Proof. Let the two triangles be ABC and $A'B'C'$ and let the segments AB, BC, CA be congruent respectively to the segments $A'B'$, $B'C'$, $C'A'$. This determines a correspondence between the two triangles in which by Theorem 30 the angles at A, B, and C correspond to congruent angles at $A'B'C'$. But since $\measuredangle ABC$ is congruent to $\measuredangle A'B'C'$ it follows by

---

* Cf. Euclid, I, 15.

† Cf. Euclid, I, 8.

definition that if X and Y are any two points of the segments BA and BC respectively, and X' and Y' the corresponding points of the segments $B'A'$ and $B'C'$ respectively, then (X, Y) is congruent to (X', Y'). Applying the same argument to the angles $\measuredangle ACB$ and $\measuredangle A'C'B'$ and the angles $\measuredangle BAC$ and $\measuredangle B'A'C'$ we have that the two triangles are congruent.

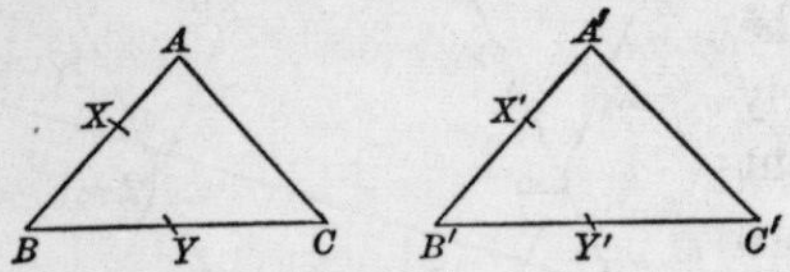

FIG. 36.

The following theorems are proved similarly and are left as an exercise for the reader.

Theorem 32.* *If two sides and the included angle of one triangle are congruent to two sides and the included angle of another triangle the two triangles are congruent.*

Theorem 33.† *If two sides of a triangle are congruent, the angles opposite them are congruent.*

VIII. INTERSECTIONS OF CIRCLES

Definition. If O and X_0 are two points of a plane α, then the set of points $[X]$ of α such that (O, X) is congruent to (O, X_0) is called a **circle.** O is called its **centre** and any one of the intervals OX is called a **radius.** The two radii on any line through O constitute a **diameter.** The points, except the points $[X]$, on radii of the circle are said to be **interior** to the circle. The points of α not on radii are said to be **exterior to** the circle.

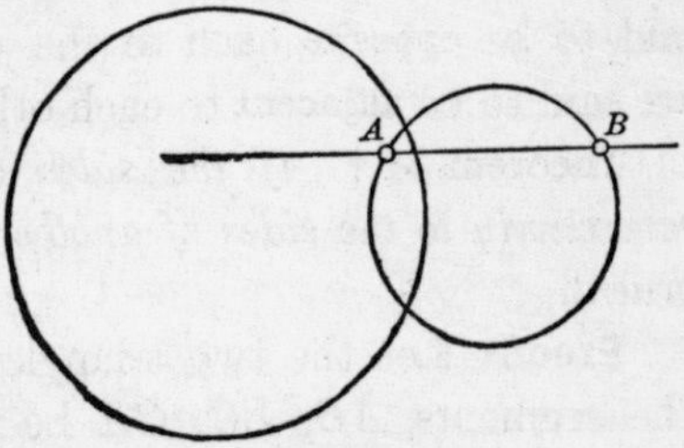

FIG. 37.

It can be proved that the interior and exterior points constitute two regions into which the plane α is decomposed by

* Cf. Euclid, I, 4.

† Cf. Euclid, I, 5.

the circle. Another assumption, however, is necessary before this can be done.

Assumption XII. *A circle passing through a point, A, interior and a point, B, exterior to another circle in the same plane has in common with the other circle at least one point on each side of the line AB.*

Definition. A triangle is said to be **isosceles** if two of its sides are congruent and to be **equilateral** if all three are congruent.

Theorem 34.* *If AB is any segment there exists in any half plane of which the line AB is the boundary an equilateral triangle of which AB is a side.*

Proof. Let S and T be the two circles in the given plane of which A and B are centres respectively and the interval AB is the radius. If B′ is the point in the order $\{BAB'\}$ such that (B', A) is congruent to (A, B) and A' the point in the order $\{ABA'\}$ such that (A, B) is congruent to (B, A'), the interval $B'B$ is a diameter of the circle S and contains all points of the interior of this circle which are on the line BB'. Hence the circle T has the point A interior and the point A' exterior to the circle S. Hence they have in common by Assumption XII, two points C and C', one on each side of the line AB. The interval AC is congruent to the interval AB because they are radii of S and the interval AB is congruent to the interval BC because they are radii of T.

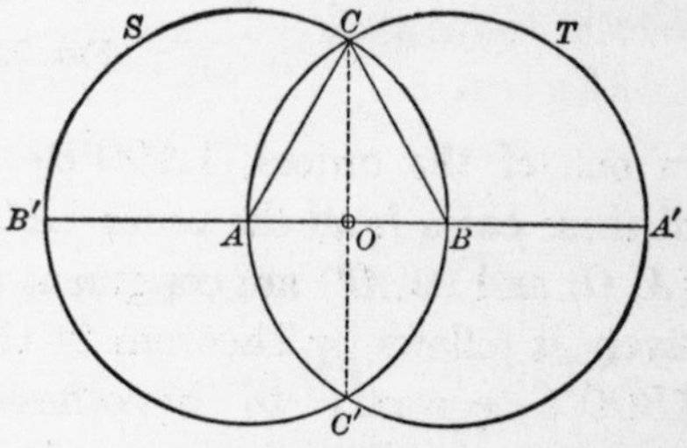

Fig. 38.

Theorem 35. Definition.† *If AB is any segment there exists one and but one of its points, O, such that (A, O) is congruent to (O, B). This point is called the* **mid-point** *of the segment or interval AB.*

Proof. Using the notation of the last theorem we have

* Cf. Euclid, I, 1.

† Cf. Euclid, I, 10.

that the segment CC' meets the line AB in a point O because C and C' are on opposite sides of the line AB. Since the point-pairs (C, B), (C', B) and (C, C') are congruent respectively to the point-pairs (C, A), (C', A) and (C, C') it follows by Theorem 30 that $\measuredangle BCO$ is congruent to $\measuredangle ACO$ and hence that (O, B) is congruent to (O, A).

Suppose now there were another point $O' \neq O$ such that AO' were congruent to $O'B$. O' could not be on a prolongation of the segment AB; for if it were in the order $\{ABO'\}$ there would be two segments $O'B$ and $O'A$ on the ray $O'B$ and congruent to the segment $O'B$; similarly it could not be in the order $\{O'AB\}$. If O' were on the segment AB it would be

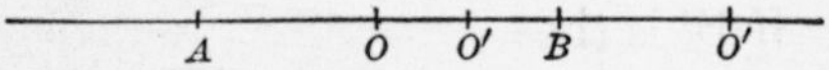

FIG. 39.

in one of the orders, $\{AOO'B\}$ and $\{AO'OB\}$. In the first of these cases from the order $\{AOO'\}$ and the hypotheses that (A, O) and (A, O') are congruent to (B, O) and (B, O') respectively it follows by Theorem 24 that we should have the order $\{BOO'\}$, contrary to hypothesis. The order $\{AO'OB\}$ is proved impossible similarly. Hence there is only one mid-point, O, and it is on the segment AB.

Theorem 36.* *If ABC is a triangle there is no point $C' \neq C$ on the same side of the line AB with C such that (A, C) and (B, C) are congruent to (A, C') and (B, C') respectively.*

Proof. By Assumption VII C' cannot be on either of the lines AC or BC. If C' exists and is not on these lines we distinguish two cases according as the line CC' does or does not meet the line AB.

In case the line CC' does meet the line AB in a point, P, the point-pairs (B, C), (C, A), (A, B), (A, P) are congruent respectively to (B, C'), (C', A), (A, B), (A, P) and hence by Theorem 30 (C, P) is congruent to (C', P). This result is, however, contrary to Assumption VII.

* Cf. Euclid, I, 7.

In case the line CC' does not meet the line AB, A and B are on the same side of the line CC'. Let O be the mid-point of the segment CC'; let P be a point in the order AOP and interior to $\measuredangle CBC'$; then by the results of V the segment PB meets the segment CC' in a point Q.

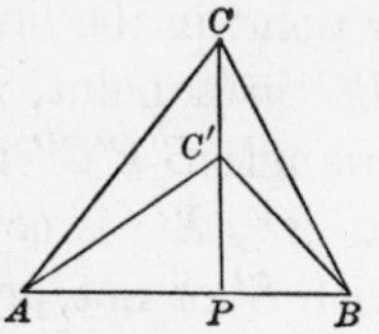

FIG. 40.

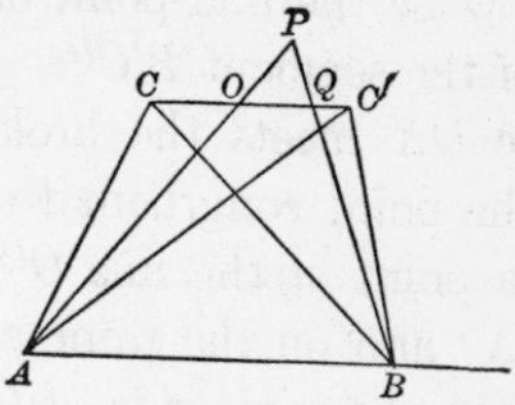

FIG. 41.

Since (O, C), (C, A), (A, O), (A, P) are congruent respectively to (O, C'), (C', A), (A, O), (A, P) it follows by Assumption XI that (C, P) is congruent to $(C' P)$. Hence $\measuredangle CBP$ is congruent to $\measuredangle C'BP$ and hence (C, Q) is congruent to $(C' Q)$. Hence Q is a mid-point of the segment CC' as well as O, contrary to Theorem 35.

Corollary. *If $\measuredangle ABC$ is congruent to $\measuredangle ABC'$ in such a way that A corresponds to itself and C' is on the same side of the line AB with C then the rays BC and BC' are identical.*

Theorem 37. *If ABC and $A'B'C'$ are any two planes they are congruent in such a way that B corresponds to B', the ray BC to the ray $B'C'$ and the half plane containing A and bounded by BC to the half plane containing A' and bounded by $B'C'$.*

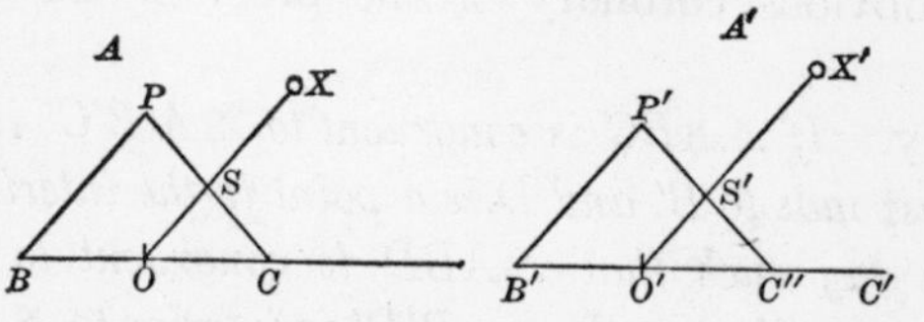

FIG. 42.

Proof. Let P be a point (Theorem 34) in the first half plane such that (P, B), (B, C), (C, P) are congruent (Theorem 34) and let C'' be a point in the ray $B'C'$ such that (B, C) is congruent to $B'C''$ and let P' be a point in the second half plane such that $P'B'$, $B'C''$, $C''P'$ are congruent. Then by Theorem 31 the triangles PBC and $P'B'C''$ are congruent and this determines a correspondence between the points of the two triangles. A correspondence between the two planes may be determined as follows:

Let O be the mid-point of the segment BC and O' the mid-point of the segment $B'C''$. If X is any point in the first plane the line OX meets the broken line PBC in a point, S. Let S' be the point congruent to S in the triangle $B'P'C''$ and let X' be a point of the line $O'S'$ such that (O', X') is congruent to (O, X) and on the same side of O' with S' or not, according as X is on the same side of O with S or not.

To complete the proof of the theorem it is necessary to show that if X_1 and X_2 correspond in this way to X_1' and X_2' then (X_1, X_2) is congruent to (X_1', X_2'). This is obvious if X_1 and X_2 are on the same line through O. If they are on different lines, let S_1 and S_2 be the points in which the lines OX_1 and OX_2 meet the broken line BPC and let S_1' and S_2' be the corresponding points on the broken line $B'P'C''$. By Theorem 31, (O, S_1), (O, S_2) and (S_1, S_2) are congruent respectively to (O', S_1'), (O', S_2'), and (S_1', S_2'). Hence by Theorem 30, $\measuredangle S_1OS_2$ is congruent to $\measuredangle S_1'O'S_2'$ and (X_1, X_2) is congruent to (X_1', X_2').

With the aid of this theorem any plane figure may be superposed upon any other to determine whether or not they are congruent.

As an obvious corollary of the proof of this theorem we have:

Corollary. *If $\measuredangle ABC$ is congruent to $\measuredangle A'B'C'$ in such a way that B corresponds to B' and D is a point in the interior of $\measuredangle ABC$ and BD' a ray such that $\measuredangle ABD$ is congruent to $\measuredangle ABD'$, B corresponding to B', then the ray $B'D'$ is interior to $\measuredangle A'B'C'$.*

Definition. An angle congruent to either of its supplementary angles in such a way that the vertex of the angle corresponds to itself is called a **right angle.** The two sides of the angle are said to be **perpendicular,** as are also the two lines containing these rays.

Corollary. *The two supplementary angles and the vertical angle of a right angle are right angles.*

Theorem 38. *If P is any point and AB any line there is one and only one line through P and perpendicular to P in any plane containing A, B and P.*

Proof. Suppose first that P is on the line AB. Let M and N be on opposite sides of P and such that (M, P) is congruent to (P, N) and let C be the third vertex of an equilateral triangle of which MN is a side. Since (C, P), (C, N), (N, P) are congruent respectively to (C, P), (C, M), (M, P) $\measuredangle CPM$ is congruent to $\measuredangle CPN$ and hence the line CP is perpendicular to the line AB.

If some other line DP were also perpendicular, D would be on the same side of the line CP with M or with N. As the two cases are treated alike, suppose that D is on the same side with N. Then the segment MD meets the line CP in a point E. Let E' be the point on the opposite side of P from E such that (P, E) is congruent to (P, E'). Also let D' be the point on the ray ME' such that (M, D) is congruent to (M, D'). Since we have the order $\{MED\}$ we also have the order $\{ME'D'\}$ (Theorem 24) and hence the segment DD' meets the line MN in a point Q different from P. By the last corollary and Theorem 30, (M, E) is congruent to (M, E'); hence (P, D) is congruent to (P, D'); hence (D, Q) is congruent to $(D'Q)$ and (D, N) is congruent to $D'N$. Since the line DP is assumed perpendicular to the line MN, (D, N) is congruent to (D, M) and it follows that (D, M), (D, N), $(D'N)$, $(D'M)$ are all congruent. Hence we have (D', D), (D', N) and (D, N) congruent to (D, D'), (D, M) and (D', M) respectively and thus have $\measuredangle ND'Q$ congruent to $\measuredangle MDQ$. Hence (M, Q)

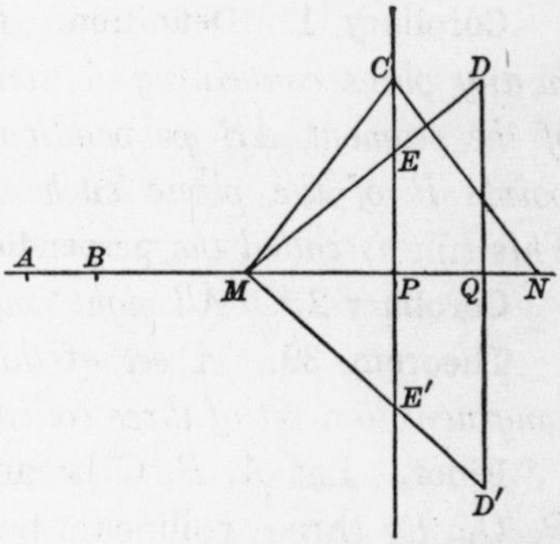

Fig. 43.

is congruent to (N, Q) although $Q \neq P$. This contradicts Theorem 35.

Thus we have shown not only that the line PC is the only perpendicular to the line MN at P but also that if D is any point off the line CP, (D, M) is not congruent to (D, N).

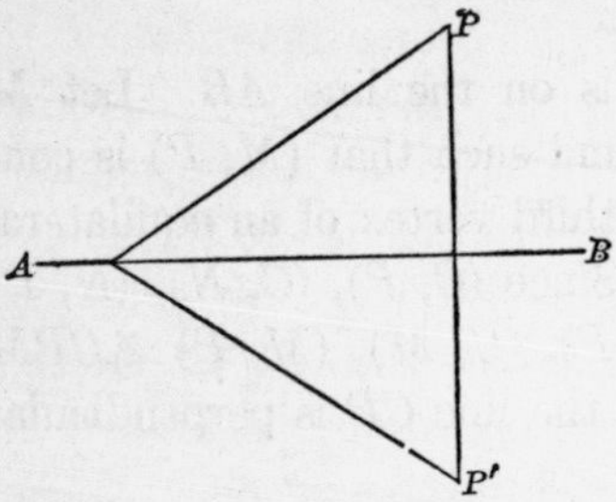

FIG. 44.

Now if P is not on the line AB, let P' be a point on the opposite side of the line AB (Theorem 37), such that $\measuredangle P'AB$ is congruent to $\measuredangle PAB$ and (P, A) is congruent to (P', A). The line PP' is easily seen to be perpendicular to the line AB.

Corollary 1. Definition. *If A and B are any two points, in any plane containing A and B the line through the mid-point of the segment AB perpendicular to the line AB contains all points P of the plane such that (P, A) is congruent to (P, B). This line is called the* **perpendicular bisector** *of (A, B).*

Corollary 2.* *All right angles are congruent to one another.*

Theorem 39. *A set of three non-collinear points cannot be congruent to a set of three collinear points.*

Proof. Let A, B, C be any three non-collinear points and P, Q, R three collinear points. If (A, B), (B, C), (C, A) were congruent respectively to (P, Q), (Q, R), (R, P) then by the theorems of VI there would be a point D on the line CA such that (A, B) and (C, B) were congruent to (A, D) and (C, D) respectively. Let M be the mid-point of (B, D). Then since (A, B) and (A, D) are congruent, the line AM is perpendicular to the line BD and since (B, C) and (D, C) are

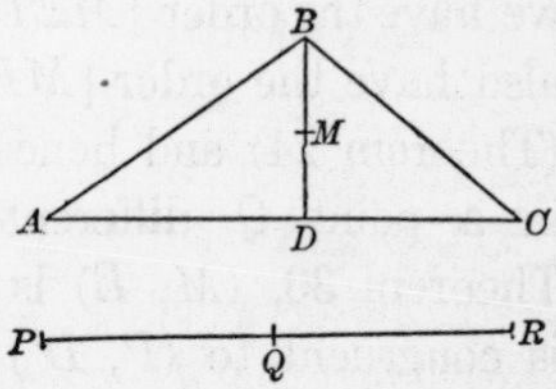

FIG. 45.

* Cf. Euclid, Postulate 4.

congruent C must be on the line AM (Theorem 38), contrary to the hypothesis that A, B and C are non-collinear.

Theorem 39 makes it possible to prove the converses of the theorems on angles and triangles in the last section. In that section we proved that two triangles were congruent if the three sides of one were congruent to the three sides of the other. We were not, however, prepared to say that if two triangles were congruent the vertices of one corresponded to the vertices of the other. It might have happened that the sides AB, BC of one triangle corresponded to the side PQ of another, and that the third side, CA, corresponded to the broken line QRP. This possibility is excluded by Theorem 39. We now easily see that if the triangle ABC is congruent to the triangle PQR that the point-pairs (A, B), (B, C), (C, A) are congruent to the three point-pairs (P, Q), (Q, R), (R, P). We shall take these converse theorems for granted without further proof.

It is also evident that Theorem 24, and the corollary of Theorem 37, may be generalized to read: *If two planar figures are congruent, the points and lines of one figure are in the same order relations as are the corresponding points and lines of the other figure.*

Theorem 40. *A line, l, containing a point interior to a circle meets the circle in two and only two points.*

Proof. Let O be the centre of the circle and I the given interior point and J the point of the line l such that the line OJ is perpendicular to it. Let Q be on the opposite side of J from O and such that (O, J) is congruent to (Q, J). We shall prove first that J is interior to the circle. If $I = J$ this is evident. If not, let I' be the point of the ray OJ such that (O, I') is congruent to (O, I). Let J' be a point of the ray OI such that

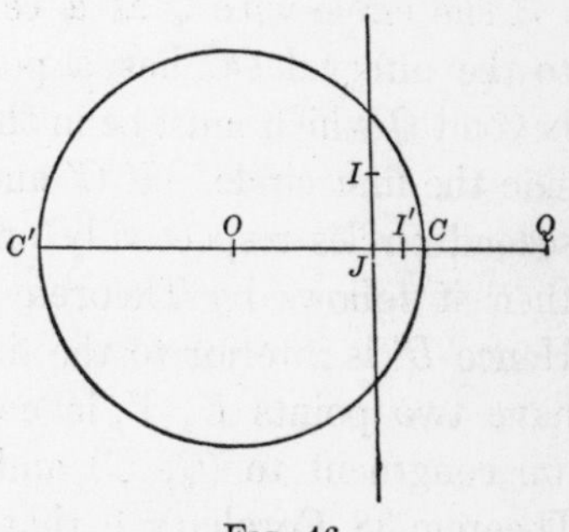

FIG. 46.

OJ is congruent to OJ'. If I' were in the order $\{OI'J\}$ then J'

would be in the order $\{OIJ'\}$. In this case let K be the mid-point of the segment JJ'. It follows that $\measuredangle J'KO$ is a right angle. Now let $J'S$ be a ray on the same side of the line JJ' with O making a right angle with JJ'. The ray $J'S$ cannot meet the interval OK because this would imply two perpendiculars to JJ' from the point of intersection. Hence the ray $J'I$ is interior to the right angle $\measuredangle JJ'S$. On the other hand the ray JJ' is exterior to the right angle $\measuredangle OJI$. But $\measuredangle JJ'I$ is congruent to $\measuredangle OJJ'$, and thus we have a contradiction with the corollary of Theorem 37. Hence we have established the order $\{OJI'\}$.

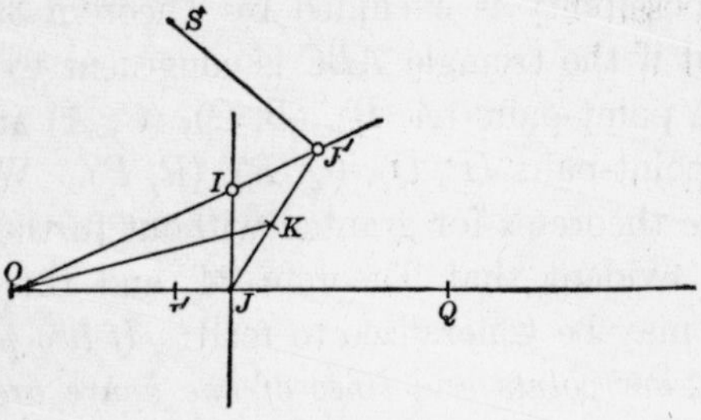

FIG. 47.

Since the point of the circle on the ray OI is on a prolongation of the segment OI the point C of the circle on the ray OJ is on the prolongation of the segment OI'. Hence J is an interior point.

The circle with Q as a centre and with a radius congruent to the interval OC has a point D on the prolongation of OQ beyond Q which must be in the order $\{OCD\}$. Hence D is outside the first circle. If C' and D' are the points of the first and second circles respectively on the prolongation of QC beyond C then it follows by Theorem 24 that we must have $\{QD'C'\}$. Hence D' is interior to the first circle. Hence the two circles have two points U, V, in common. Since (O, U) and (O, V) are congruent to (Q, U) and (QV) respectively, it follows by Theorem 38, Corollary 1, that U and V are on the line l. Since any point W common to the line l and the first circle would be such that OW is congruent to QW and hence be on the second circle there are, by Theorem 36, only two points common to the line and the first circle.

With the aid of this theorem there is no difficulty in proving that a circle decomposes its plane into two regions, the interior and the exterior. It is also easy to derive the earlier propositions of the first book of Euclid's Elements. In most cases *Euclid's* own proof can be used.

It will be an excellent exercise for the reader to work through those of the first twenty-eight propositions which we have not already taken up. It will be necessary for him to define certain terms such as addition of segments and angles which are not explicitly defined by *Euclid.* The logical bases for these definitions will be found in our development of the elementary theory of order and congruence. The propositions in question are as follows:

2. To construct* at a given point a segment congruent to a given segment.

3. Given two non-congruent segments, to cut off from the greater a segment congruent to the less.

6. If in a triangle the two angles be congruent to one another, the sides which subtend the congruent angles will also be congruent to one another.

9. To bisect a given angle.

11. To draw a line at right angles to a given line from a given point on it.

12. To a given line from a given point not on it, to draw a perpendicular line.

13. If a ray set up on a line make angles it will either make two right angles or angles equal to two right angles.

14. If with any line two rays on opposite sides of it make the adjacent angles equal to two right angles the two rays will be in the same line with one another.

16. In any triangle, if one of the sides be produced the exterior angle is greater than either of the interior and opposite angles.

---

* By means of a compass which closes when lifted from the plane.

17. In any triangle two angles taken together in any manner are less than two right angles.

18. In any triangle the greater side subtends the greater angle.

19. In any triangle the greater angle is subtended by the greater side.

20. In any triangle two sides taken together in any manner are greater than the remaining one.

21. If on one of the sides of a triangle, from its ends there be constructed two lines meeting within the triangle, the segments so constructed will be less than the remaining two sides of the triangle, but will contain a greater angle.

22. Out of three intervals congruent to three given intervals to construct a triangle: thus it is necessary that two of the intervals taken together in any manner should be greater than the remaining one.

23. On a given line at a given point to construct an angle congruent to a given angle.

24. If two triangles have the two sides congruent to two sides respectively but have one of the angles contained by the congruent sides greater than the other they will also have the base greater than the base.

25. If two triangles have the two sides congruent to two sides respectively, but have the base greater than the base, they will also have the one of the angles contained by the sides greater than the other.

26. If two triangles have the two angles congruent to two angles respectively and one side congruent to one side, namely, either the side adjacent to the congruent angles, or that subtending one of the congruent angles, they will also have the remaining sides congruent to the remaining sides and the remaining angle to the remaining angle.

27. If a line falling on two lines make the alternate angles congruent to one another, the lines will not meet.

28. If a line falling on two lines make the exterior angle congruent to the interior and opposite angle on the same side, or make the sum of the interior angles on the same side two right angles, the lines will not meet.

IX. PARALLEL LINES *

The next assumption which we shall set down is the justly famous assumption of *Euclid* about parallel lines. It has been stated in many different forms, of which the following is perhaps the simplest.

Assumption XIII. *If A is any point and a any line not passing through A, there is not more than one line through A coplanar with a and not meeting a.*

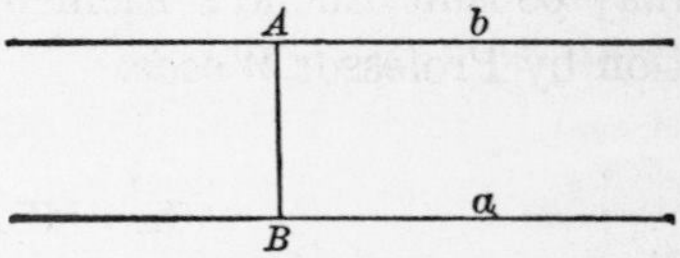

FIG. 48.

That there is at least one line through A, coplanar with a and not meeting it is easily seen by dropping a perpendicular AB from A to a, and observing that the perpendicular, b, to the line AB at the point A could not meet a without contradicting Theorem 38. The same result follows directly from *Euclid*, I, 27 or I, 28.

The assumption of parallels was stated by *Euclid* in his Postulate 5 as follows:

"If a straight line falling on two straight lines makes the interior angles on the same side less than two right angles, the two straight lines, if produced indefinitely, meet on that side on which are the angles less than the two right angles."

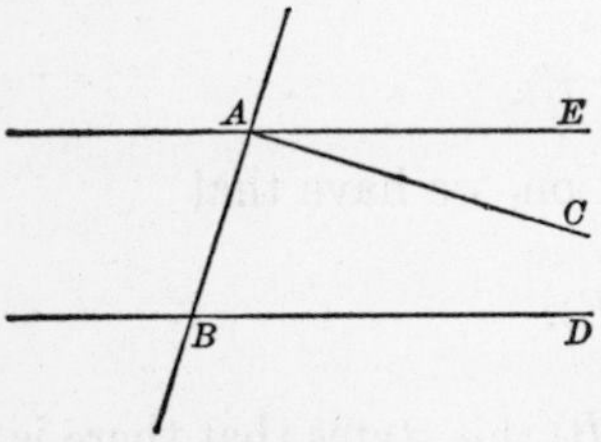

FIG. 49.

This is a consequence of our assumption, for let the rays AC and BD be such that the sum of the angles $\measuredangle CAB$ and $\measuredangle ABD$, is less than two right angles. Let AE be the ray such that the sum of $\measuredangle EAB$ and $\measuredangle ABD$ is two right angles. Then by Euclid, *I*, 28, the line AE does not meet the line BD. Hence the line AC does meet the line BD. Since the sum of the

* From this point forward the essay is a mere outline, intended to suggest how the rest of the subject may be developed.

angles $\measuredangle CAB$ and $\measuredangle ABD$ is less than two right angles and the sum of $\measuredangle EAB$ and $\measuredangle ABD$ is equal to two right angles, it follows that the ray AC falls within $\measuredangle EAB$. Hence the ray AC is on the same side of the line AE with the line BD. It is also on the same side of the line AB with the ray BD. Therefore the point of intersection of the line AC with the line BD is on the rays AC and BD.

For a further discussion of the theory of parallels the reader may consult Euclid's Elements, and the memoir in this collection by Professor *Woods.*

X. MENSURATION

Defining the sum of two segments and a multiple of a segment (or point-pair) and the terms equality and inequality of segments in the obvious way, it is easy to prove first that if A and B are any two points and n is any whole number, there is a point C on the line AB such that

$$n(A, B) \equiv (A, C),$$

and second that there is a point D such that

$$n(A, D) \equiv (A, B).$$

From this it follows that if m and n are any whole numbers there exists a point E such that

$$m(A, B) \equiv n(A, E).$$

Thus, with an extension of our definition, we have that

$$\frac{m}{n}(A, B) \equiv (A, E).$$

Calling m/n the ratio of (A, E) to (A, B) this states that there is a point-pair having to (A, B) the same ratio as that of any two whole numbers. Two such segments are said to be **commensurable.**

It is not hard to show that there are segments which are not commensurable and there is thus propounded the problem of extending the notion of ratio to incommensurable segments.

Euclid's method of doing this is a purely geometrical one, and similar methods have been preferred by nearly all the great geometers, the latest notable example being the Algebra of Segments of *Hilbert*.

The method, however, which is more or less approximated to in elementary teaching, is that of defining the ratio of two incommensurable segments as an **irrational number.** The theory of irrational numbers is taken for granted from arithmetic and algebra.

The following proposition, known as the *Postulate of Archimedes*, is fundamental in this method.

Assumption XIV. *If A, B, C are three points in the order* $\{ABC\}$ *and* B_1, B_2, $B_3, \ldots$ *are points in the order* $\{ABB_1\}$, $\{AB_1B_2\}, \ldots$ *such that* (A, B), *is congruent to each of the point-pairs* (B, B_1), (B_1, B_2), $\ldots$ *then there are not more than a finite number of the points* $B_1, B_2, \ldots$ *between A and C.*

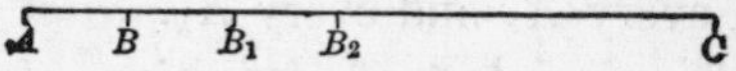

FIG. 50.

In other words, by laying off the segment AB a finite number of times in the way indicated a point is reached which is beyond C; that is to say, there exists a number n such that

$$(A, C) < n(A, B).$$

Another phrasing of this assumption would be: there exists no infinitely great interval (A, C).

A direct consequence of Assumption XIV is that if D is any point of the ray AB there exists a number n such that

$$\frac{1}{n}(A, B) < (A, D),$$

for, if not, there would exist no number n such that

$$(A, B) < n(A, D).$$

This may be expressed by saying that there is no infinitely small interval.

Let A_0 and A_1 be any two points and let us denote by $A_{\frac{m}{n}}$ that point of the ray A_0A_1 which is such that the ratio of the segment $A_0A_{\frac{m}{n}}$ to A_0A_1 is $\frac{m}{n}$. If B is any point of the ray such that (A_0, B) is incommensurable with (A_0, A_1), the points $\left[A_{\frac{m}{n}}\right]$ fall into two classes, those on the segment A_0B, which we may call $[A_x]$ and those on its prolongation which we may call $[A_y]$. The numbers, $[x]$, associated with points in the first class, are all less than the numbers $[y]$ associated with points in the second class. With the aid of

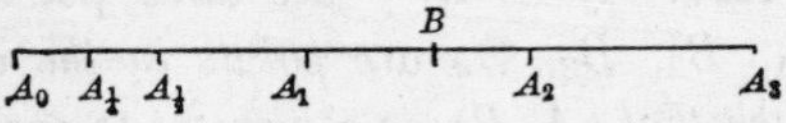

FIG. 51.

Assumption XIV it can be proved that B is the *only* point which is between every A_x and every A_y.

By Dedekind's principle* of definition of the irrational numbers there exists a unique irrational number, b, greater than every x and less than every y. This number, b, we define to be the ratio of the segments A_0B and A_0A_1.

Since any segment whatever is congruent to one of the segments A_0A_1 which have A_0 as one end, we have now established a scale of magnitudes for the comparison of segments and are in a position to develop a complete theory of proportion.

The theory of the measure (that is to say, length) of segments depends essentially on showing how to arrange segments in order of magnitude. In like manner, the theory of the measure, that is to say, of the area, of regions in the plane depends on showing how to arrange areas in an order of magnitude. For the purpose of elementary geometry we may confine attention to convex regions. A convex region **A** may be said to be less than a convex region **B**, if it is possible to decompose **A**, into a finite set of convex regions congruent to a non-overlapping set of convex regions contained in **B**, and such

---

* See Monograph IV, Appendix I.

that **B** contains at least one convex region not in this set. Two convex regions **A** and **B**, may then be said to be equivalent if neither is less than the other. In order to give this definition value it must be proved that two congruent regions are equivalent. This amounts to proving the following proposition:

It is not possible to decompose two congruent convex regions $\mathbf{R}_1$, $\mathbf{R}_2$ into convex regions so that all the regions into which $\mathbf{R}_1$ is decomposed are congruent to a subset of the regions into which $\mathbf{R}_2$ is decomposed.

By associating with an arbitrary square the number 1, a number, called the area, can now be assigned to each region in such a way that two equivalent regions have the same area, and if one region is less than another the less region has the smaller area. The theory of volumes can be developed similarly.

It has been shown by *Hilbert* that a theory of the areas of polygonal regions can be developed independently of Assumption XIV, and by *Dehn* that a fully corresponding theory for polyhedral regions does not exist. On this subject the reader should consult the second edition of *Hilbert's* Grundlagen der Geometrie * and the article by *Amaldi*, "Sulla teoria dell' equivalenza," in Questioni riguardanti la Geometria Elementare,† edited by *F. Enriques*.

XI. THREE-DIMENSIONAL SPACE

Definition. If A, B, C, D are four points not all in the same plane the set of all points on and interior to the four triangles ABC, BCD, CDA, ABD, is called a **tetrahedron.** The set of all points collinear with pairs of points of a tetrahedron is called a **three-space.**

By a discussion‡ analogous to that made in IV it is possible to prove that if $A'B'C'D'$ are any four points of a

* Leipzig, 1903.

† Bologna, 1900.

‡ Cf. Transactions of the American Mathematical Society, Volume V, page 360.

three-space $ABCD$, then the three-space $ABCD$ is identical with the three-space $A'B'C'D'$; that if two points of a line lie in a given three-space $ABCD$, then so do all points of the line; that if three points of a plane lie in a three-space, so do all points of the plane; and that if and only if two planes are in the same three-space they have a line in common. The notion of a three-dimensional region can then be defined and studied analogously to V. Congruent figures can be defined as in VI.

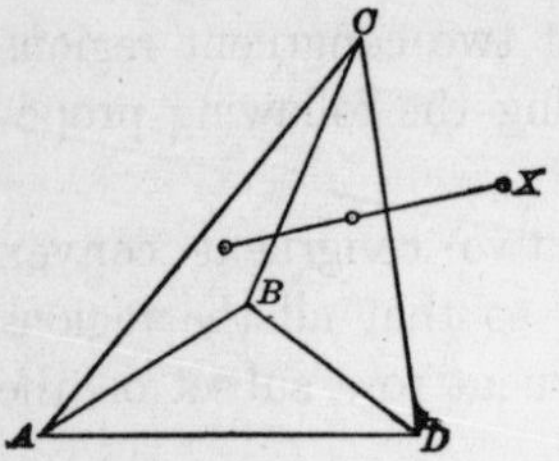

FIG. 52.

Assumption VI provided for the existence of a plane, but since nothing has as yet been said about the existence of points which are not coplanar, we add the following:

Assumption XV. *If A, B, C are three non-collinear points, there exists a point D not in the same plane with A, B and C.*

Assumption XVI. *Two planes which have one point in common have two points in common.*

Assumption XV provides for the existence of at least one three-space and from Assumption XVI it follows that all points are in the same three-space.

All the theorems of elementary three-dimensional geometry can be developed on the basis of these assumptions. But to do so would be to write a large book.*

---

* A book giving a complete and rigorous treatment of elementary geometry would be a most important influence in improving the teaching of the most ancient and perfect of sciences. Such a book could rarely, if ever, be used in the classroom, but if it were in the hands of the teachers it would serve to keep before them in something like its actual form the structure of which they are trying to give their students a first glimpse.

XII. CONCLUSION

The logically important questions as to the independence and categoricalness of our assumptions must be passed over with a reference to the two papers in the *Transactions* on which this essay is based. The ideas of consistency, independence and categoricalness (sufficiency) are explained in the essay by Professor *Huntington* in this book, and the independence of Assumption XIII is established in the essay by Professor *Woods.*

A reader who is sufficiently interested to pursue the subject further is strongly urged to go into the question of the independence of the assumptions and to try to discover for himself some of the examples which constitute the independence proofs. For convenience in this sort of study we have collected the assumptions in the following list.

I. If points A, B, C are in the order $\{ABC\}$ they are distinct.

II. If points A, B, C are in the order $\{ABC\}$ they are not in the order $\{BCA\}$.

Definition. If A and B are distinct points the **segment** AB consists of all points, X, in the order $\{AXB\}$; all points of the segment AB are said to be **between** A and B; the segment together with A and B is called the **interval** AB; the **line** AB consists of A and B and all points, X, in one of the orders $\{ABX\}$, $\{AXB,\}$ $\{XAB\}$; and the **ray** AB consists of B and all points, X in one of the orders $\{AXB\}$ and $\{ABX\}$; A is called the **origin** of the ray AB.

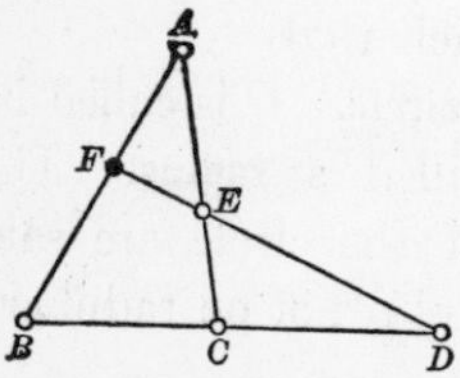

FIG. 53.

III. If points C and D $(C \neq D)$ are on the line AB, then A is on the line CD.

IV. If A and B are two distinct points, there exists a point C such that A, B and C are in the order $\{ABC\}$.

V. If three distinct points A, B and C do not lie on the same line and D and E are two points in the orders $\{BCD\}$ and $\{CEA\}$, then a point F exists in the order $\{AFB\}$ and such that D, E and F lie on the same line.

VI. There exist three distinct points, A, B, C, not in any of the orders $\{ABC\}$, $\{BCA\}$, $\{CAB\}$.

Definition. If A, B, C are three non-collinear points, the set of all points collinear with pairs of points on the intervals AB, BC, CA is called the **plane** ABC. The points X of the plane such that the interval AX does not contain a point of the line BC constitute, together with A itself, one **side** of the line BC. The other points of the plane, not on the line BC, constitute the other **side** of the line BC.

The notation (A, B) denotes a pair of distinct points.

VII. If $A \neq B$, then on any ray whose origin is C there exists one and only one point D such that (A, B) is congruent to (C, D).

VIII. If (A, B) is congruent to (C, D) and (C, D) is congruent to (E, F) then (A, B) is congruent to (E, F).

IX. If (A, B) is congruent to (A', B') and (B, C) is congruent to (B', C') and $\{ABC\}$ and $\{A'B'C'\}$, then (A, C) is congruent to (A', C').

X. (A, B) is congruent to (B, A).

XI. If A, B, C are three non-collinear points and D is a point in the order $\{BCD\}$, and if $A'B'C'$ are three non-collinear points and D' is a point in the order $\{B'C'D'\}$ such that the point-pairs (A, B), (B, C), (C, A), (B, D) are respectively congruent to (A', B'), (B', C'), (C', A'), (B', D') then (A, D) is congruent to (A', D').

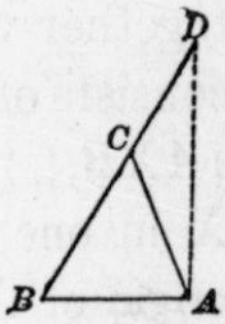

Fig. 54.

Definition. If O and X_0 are two points of a plane α, then the set of points $[X]$ of α such that (O, X) is congruent to (O, X_0) is called a **circle.** O is called its **centre** and any of the intervals OX is called a **radius.** The points, except the points $[X]$, on radii of the circle are said to be **interior** to the circle. The points of α not on radii are said to be **exterior** to the circle.

XII. A circle passing through a point, A, interior and a point, B, exterior to another circle in the same plane has in common with the other circle at least one point on each side of the line AB.

XIII. If A is any point and a any line not passing through A, there is not more than one line through A coplanar with a and not meeting a.

XIV. If A, B, C are three points in the order $\{ABC\}$ and $B_1, B_2, B_3, \ldots$ are points in the order $\{ABB_1\}, \{AB_1B_2\}, \ldots$ such that (A, B) is congruent to each of the point-pairs (B, B_1), $(B_1, B_2), \ldots$, then there are not more than a finite number of the points $B_1, B_2, \ldots$ between A and C.

XV. If A, B, C are three non-collinear points, there exists a point D not in the same plane with A, B and C.

XVI. Two planes which have one point in common have two points in common.

XIII. If A is any point and a any line not passing through A, there is not more than one line through A coplanar with a and not meeting a.

XIV. If A, B, C are three points in the order ABC, and B_1, B_2, B_3, ... are points in the order ABB_1, AB_1B_2, ... such that AB is [illegible] to each of the segments BB_1, B_1B_2, ..., then there are not more than a finite number of the points B_1, B_2, ... between A and C.

XV. If A, B, C are three non-collinear points, there exists a point D not in the same plane with A, B, and C.

XVI. Two planes which have one point in common have two points in common.

II

MODERN PURE GEOMETRY

By Thomas F. Holgate

CONTENTS

II

MODERN PURE GEOMETRY

By Thomas F. Holgate

I. INTRODUCTION

1. In Analytical Geometry conclusions are reached through the application of algebraic processes to geometric properties and relations. By making use of certain conventions the given relations are expressed in algebraic language, then certain algebraic operations are performed and the results are reinterpreted as geometric propositions. During the process the geometric concept may be entirely lost sight of and the resulting statement may bear no apparent relation to the premises from which it was derived. In Pure Geometry, on the other hand, the geometric concept is kept continually in mind throughout the reasoning process, and the steps by which a conclusion is reached from given conditions are readily traceable.

2. Pure geometry was cultivated by peoples of the earliest times. By them many important theorems were discovered on the relations of triangles and other rectilinear forms, on the properties of circles and spheres, and on areas, ratios, and the equality and similarity of geometric figures. The investigations of the ancient geometers were carried so far as to include the conic sections and certain curves of higher order whose principal properties were discovered, but the methods used were fragmentary and the results for the most part were disconnected. The ancient geometry is typified most clearly by Euclid's Elements, which was in fact a collation and systematic arrangement of the geometric knowledge of his time.

In it properties and relations are demonstrated each by itself, and little attention is paid to relations common to all forms of the same class. The method of *Euclid* has come to be known as the method of Elementary Geometry, and the subject-matter of his elements has prescribed the field of elementary geometry.

3. The methods of the ancient geometers were not materially modified till the period of the revival of learning early in the sixteenth century, when with the introduction of certain new concepts, and the application of well-known older ones, as, for example, infinitely distant elements, the harmonic division of a line segment, the principle of continuity, and the theory of imaginary intersections, the science began to take on a more generalized form. The renewed activity in geometric research resulted in the invention by *Descartes* of the analytical geometry, and for two and a half centuries investigations by purely geometric methods were for the most part pushed aside. Happily, interest in pure geometry was revived toward the close of the eighteenth century through the publications of *Monge*, and during the first half of the nineteenth century it reached its highest development at the hands of *Poncelet*, *Steiner*, *Von Staudt*, and *Chasles*.

4. Modern pure geometry differs from the geometry of earlier times not so much in the subjects dealt with as in the processes employed and the generality of the results obtained. Much of the material is old, but by utilizing the principle of projection and the theory of transversals, facts which were thought of as in no way related, prove to be simply different aspects of the same general truth. This generalizing tendency is the chief characteristic of modern geometry, and while it may perhaps be attributed largely to the influence of the analytic method, still it is true that some progress had been made in this direction before the analytic method was invented, and pure geometry has done much in recent times to enliven and heighten the interest in analysis.

II. SIMPLE ELEMENTS IN GEOMETRY

5. Points, straight lines, and planes are the simple undefined elements of pure geometry. Each of these may be thought of as having an existence independent of the others; a plane may be thought of without considering the lines and points which lie in it; we may think of a line without considering the points which lie on it or the planes which pass through it, and of a point without considering either the lines or the planes which pass through it. In fact each of these simple elements may be the base on which rest an indefinite number of elements of either of the other kinds.

III. THE PRINCIPLE OF DUALITY

6. Duality in space. Two points will fix the identity of a straight line and three points will in general determine a plane. So also two planes intersect in a straight line and three planes in general have one point in common. If three points lie in a specialized relative position, namely, in a straight line, then many planes pass through them. Similarly, if three planes be in a specialized relative position, namely, with one line in common, then many points lie in all three. But apart from such special cases the following statements may be made:

*a*1. Three points determine a plane.

*a*2. Three planes determine a point.

*b*1. Two lines which have a common point determine a plane.

*b*2. Two lines which have a common plane determine a point.

*c*1. A line and a point determine a plane.

*c*2. A line and a plane determine a point.

In these statements taken two and two there will be noted an interchangeable relation between the elements 'point' and 'plane', and between 'line' and 'line'. This is called a dual relation, and in accordance with it any geometric form will yield another by replacing every point in one by a plane in the other, and every line joining two points in one by a line the intersection of two planes in the other. If in the original figure three planes meet at a point, in the dual or reciprocal figure three points will lie in a plane; or if in the original figure four lines lie in a plane, in the reciprocal four lines will meet in a point.

7. Examples of duality. A cube consists of eight vertices (points), six plane faces, and twelve edges each the intersection of two faces and joining two vertices. Its dual or reciprocal figure, therefore, consists of eight plane faces, six points (ver tices), and twelve edges each joining two vertices and the intersection of two faces. In the original figure the faces meet by threes in the vertices, and also the edges meet by threes in the vertices, while four edges lie in each face. In the reciprocal figure, the vertices must lie by threes in the faces, and also the edges lie by threes in the faces, while four edges meet in each vertex. This reciprocal figure is readily seen to be an octahedron.

The cube and the octahedron may thus be spoken of as dual or reciprocal figures. In the same way it will be seen that the dual of a tetrahedron is again a tetrahedron, and the dual of a dodecahedron is an icosahedron.

8. This principle, by which a theorem on points, lines, and planes may be deduced from another on planes, lines, and points, by simple interchange is called the **principle of duality.** It was made much use of by *Poncelet*, but was first announced as an independent principle by *Gergonne* (1826), and plays an important part in modern geometry. Its application is to purely descriptive properties and not in general to properties involving measurement.

9. Duality in a plane. If the forms under consideration are confined to a single plane, that is, if we are dealing only with plane geometry, the duality is between point and line, since in plane geometry two points determine a line and two lines determine a point. To any number of points on a line in one of two reciprocal plane figures there will correspond in the other an equal number of lines through a point, and if three or more lines are concurrent in the one, their reciprocal points are collinear in the other.

10. As an illustration of reciprocal figures in a plane the following will serve:

Four points (vertices) A, B, C, D, of which no three are collinear, determine six lines (sides), namely, the lines joining the vertices two and two. The lines AB and CD may be called **opposite sides** in the figure, and similarly AC and BD are opposite sides, as are also AD and BC. The pairs of opposite sides determine three points P, Q, R—**diagonal points**—the vertices of what may be called the **diagonal triangle.** The figure so constructed is known as a **complete quadrangle.**

On the other hand, four lines (sides) a, b, c, d, of which no three are concurrent, determine six points (vertices), namely, the intersections of the sides two and two. The points ab and cd may be called **opposite vertices** in the figure, and similarly ac and bd are opposite vertices as are also ad and bc. The pairs of opposite vertices determine three lines p, q, r—**diagonals**—the sides of what may be called the **diagonal triangle.** This figure is known as a **complete quadrilateral.**

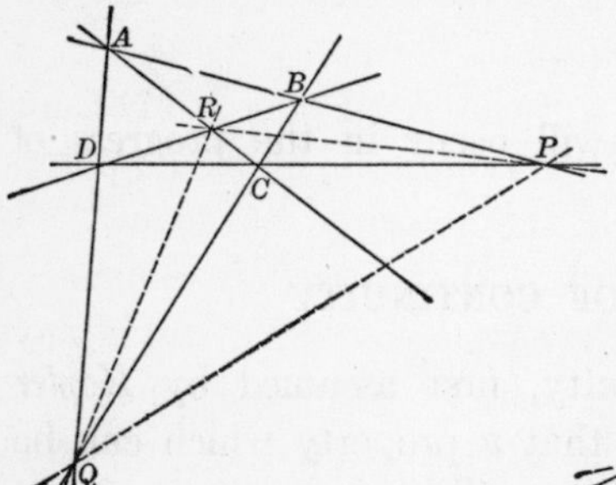

FIG. 1.

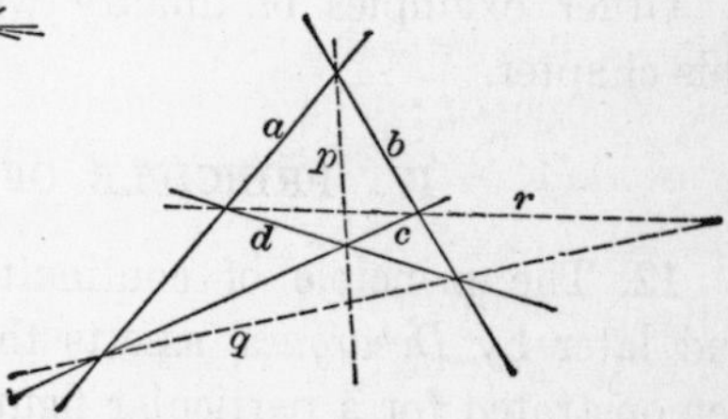

FIG. 2.

A complete quadrangle (Fig. 1) thus consists of four vertices, six sides, and three diagonal points; a complete quadrilateral (Fig. 2) consists of four sides, six vertices, and three diagonal lines. Similarly, a **complete pentangle** (pentagon) has five vertices and ten sides intersecting by fours in the vertices, while there may be found fifteen points in which only two sides intersect. A **complete pentalateral** on the other hand, has five sides and ten vertices lying by fours on the sides, while there may be drawn fifteen lines on which only two vertices lie.

11. As an illustration of how one theorem may be deduced from another by the principle of duality the following example will serve. The theorem on the left is well known, having been stated by *Pappus* in the fourth century. That on the right is not so familiar, but follows immediately by interchange of point and line, or it may be demonstrated independently.

If three points A, C, E be chosen at random on a straight line p, and three others B, D, F, be chosen at random on a straight line q, and these be joined in order AB, BC, CD, DE, EF, FA, by straight lines 1, 2, 3, 4, 5, 6, then the intersections of 1 and 4, 2 and 5, 3 and 6, lie on a straight line r.

If three straight lines, a, c, e, be drawn at random through a point P, and three others b, d, f, be drawn at random through a point Q, and the intersections of these two and two in order ab, bc, cd, de, ef, fa, be denoted by 1, 2, 3, 4, 5, 6, then the lines 14, 25, 36, pass through one point R.

Other examples of duality will occur in the progress of this chapter.

IV. PRINCIPLE OF CONTINUITY

12. The principle of continuity, first assumed by *Kepler* and later by *Desargues*, asserts that a property which can be demonstrated for a particular figure will hold true if the figure should change its form in any manner subject to the conditions under which it was first constructed. This principle makes necessary an enlargement of the significance of many geometric terms so as to include what are called imaginary elements, and by the aid of these it permits the statement of general facts or theorems which otherwise would be subject to exceptions and limitations. The geometer makes no attempt to construct imaginary elements, but contents himself with the acceptance of their existence and of the principle that though by continuous change in a figure a property once proved may become unmeaning through the loss of real elements, it is still true when imaginary elements are taken into consideration.

13. Imaginary intersections. As an illustration it may be stated that a straight line drawn through a fixed point P intersects a circle in two points. If the point P lies within the circle, the intersections are always real no matter how far the line rotates about P. If, however, the point is chosen outside the circle, the line in the first instance may cut the circle in two real points, but as it rotates about P the intersections will move so as first to fall together or become coincident, and after that they will disappear or become imaginary. To say that the line in this last phase intersects the circle may be without meaning under the ordinary conventions; yet it is assumed true, and the imaginary points of intersection play the same part in any general theorem as do the real points of intersection of the earlier phases. Thus the theorem that the product of the segments of a chord or secant of a circle remains constant while the secant rotates about a point comes to have an interpretation for all positions of the secant.

V. POINTS AT INFINITY

14. Infinitely distant elements. The introduction into geometry of the notion of infinitely distant elements has aided greatly in the process of generalization with which modern methods are chiefly concerned. Many exceptional cases which under earlier conditions would require special treatment, by the addition of this concept are brought into conformity with a general statement.

15. Infinitely distant elements come most easily into view from the following considerations.

Suppose a straight line b (Fig. 3) passing through a fixed point O, intersects the line a, in a point P: and suppose the line b rotates about O as indicated by the arrow. The point of intersection P will move along the line a to the right until it is lost to view and then will immediately appear at the far left, moving along the line in the same sense as before.

The assumption is made that the two lines have not at any time ceased to intersect, and that the point P has moved continuously along the line a, disappearing at the far right and reappearing at the far left after passing through but a single position which lies outside the accessible region of the plane. In other words, it is assumed that on the line a, and so on any other straight line of the plane, or for that matter, on any straight line of the finite region, there is one and only one infinitely distant point. It is also assumed that this point makes the line continuous, so that we can pass from any one point of the line to any other point of the line by moving continuously along the line either to the right or to the left.*

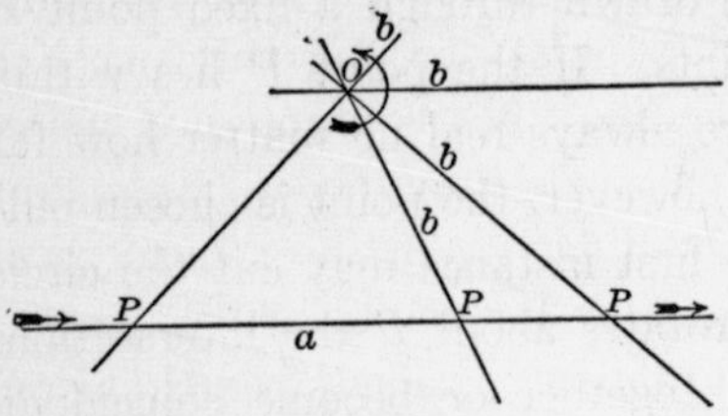

FIG. 3.

16. Two points will thus divide a straight line into two segments on one of which lie only finite points, while on the other lies the infinitely distant point. The first of these is sometimes called the **internal segment,** the second, the **external segment.** From this it follows that a point on a straight line cannot be separated from another point by a single third point. It requires two points to separate one point from another, just as on a ring or closed curve.

17. The assumption of a single infinitely distant point on the line a is equivalent to the assumption that through a point O there can be drawn one and only one straight line which does not meet a given line in the finite region, and that these lines do intersect in an infinitely distant point. This assumption

* The present monograph deals only with the so-called Euclidean geometry. For the assumptions of non-Euclidean geometry, see Monograph III.

makes possible the statement that any two straight lines of a plane intersect somewhere; if not in the finite region, then in an infinitely distant point.

Definition. Lines which intersect in an infinitely distant point are called **parallel lines.**

18. Postulate of parallels. Euclid's twelfth axiom, which is more properly speaking a postulate, was his starting point for proving that through a given point one and only one line can be drawn parallel to a given line. Its assumption is consequently equivalent to that of a single infinitely distant point on a straight line. Most of the difficulty in the treatment of parallels which perplexed geometers for centuries was caused by the failure to recognize that this so-called twelfth axiom was an assumption and not a self-evident truth.

19. A single infinitely distant point on a straight line, or what is the same thing, a single line through a given point parallel to a given line, leads at once to the conclusion that all the infinitely distant points of a plane lie on one straight line and that any two parallel lines of a plane intersect in a point of this line. The following considerations will make this clear. If a line p should rotate about a point P, every point of the line would describe a continuous path in the plane, and this may be assumed also for the infinitely distant point. The infinitely distant path described by this point contains all the infinitely distant points of the plane and is such that it is cut by any straight line in only one point. It is therefore itself a straight line.

From this it follows that any two parallel planes intersect in an infinitely distant straight line common to the two.

VI. FUNDAMENTAL THEOREM

20. In the development of modern geometry there have been differences among investigators as to the best mode of attack. Some geometers, *Steiner* and *Chasles*, for instance, have preferred to base their fundamental notions on certain metric properties, while others, notably *Von Staudt*, and after him

Reye, and in a modified form *Cremona*, have preferred to use as starting point a purely positional relation, and thus avoid the necessity of recognizing measurement as fundamental.

21. Perspective triangles. Following the latter method we announce as our fundamental fact the theorem on perspective triangles which was stated by *Desargues* early in the seventeenth century, but which was known much earlier, probably by *Euclid*.

DIRECT THEOREM

If two triangles ABC and $A_1B_1C_1$ are so situated that the lines AA_1, BB_1, and CC_1 meet in a point S, then the pairs of corresponding sides c and c_1, b and b_1, a and a_1, intersect in points of one straight line.

DUAL THEOREM

If two triangles abc and $a_1b_1c_1$ are so situated that the sides a and a_1, b and b_1, c and c_1, intersect in points of one straight line s, then the lines joining pairs of corresponding vertices AA_1, BB_1, CC_1 meet in a point.

The truth of this theorem is evident if the triangles be chosen in different planes p and p_1. For then the lines AA_1 and BB_1 meeting at S, determine a plane in which AB and A_1B_1 lie. These lines therefore intersect, and can meet only on the common line of the planes p and p_1. Similarly AC and A_1C_1, also BC and B_1C_1, meet in points of this same straight line.

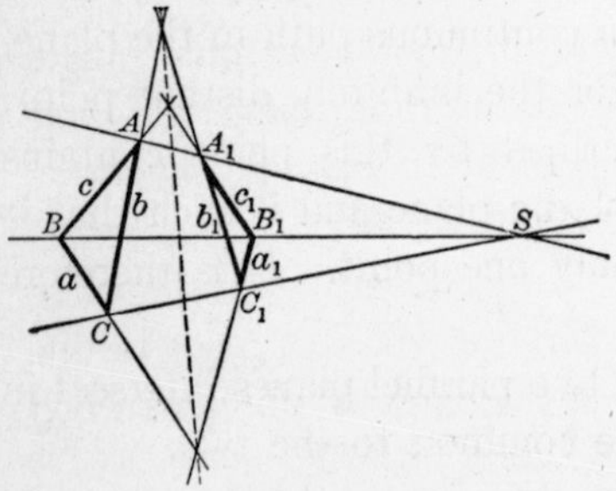

FIG. 4.

That the theorem is true also when the triangles lie in the same plane is seen most easily by projecting the original figure, that is the two given triangles, the lines joining corresponding vertices and meeting in S, and the line of intersection of the planes p and p_1, from some point O, the eye for instance, thus forming a figure of ten lines and ten planes intersecting at O. In each plane will lie three of the lines and through each line will pass three of the planes. Any plane section of this projection will yield a figure consisting of two triangles so situated that the lines joining pairs of corresponding vertices intersect in one point while the pairs of corresponding sides intersect in points of one straight line.

The process of projecting a figure from some chosen centre and then taking a plane section, thus securing a new diagram, is a favorite one in modern geometry. The properties which remain unchanged by this process are called projective properties, and they are found to be numerous. Magnitudes are changed but, as will be seen later, certain relations among magnitudes remain unchanged, as do also properties of intersections, contact, collineation, and the like.

22. Perspective quadrangles. By repeated applications of the theorem on perspective triangles the following theorem on complete quadrangles is proved to be true:

"If two complete quadrangles are so situated that five pairs of corresponding sides intersect in points of one straight line then the sixth pair will also intersect in a point of that line."

Remembering that the reciprocal of a complete quadrangle is a complete quadrilateral made up of four lines and their six points of intersection, the dual theorem may be stated as follows:

"If two complete quadrilaterals are so situated that five of the lines joining pairs of corresponding vertices meet in one point, then the line joining the sixth pair of corresponding vertices will also pass through that point."

23. Harmonic points. Let *ABCD* be any complete quadrangle (Fig. 5) and let *PQ* be a line joining two diagonal points while *R* and *S* are the points in which the third pair of sides intersect *PQ*. Construct any other quadrangle such that one pair of sides will intersect in *P*, a second pair will intersect in *Q*, and a fifth side will pass through *R*. This is readily possible if the two sides through *P* be drawn at random and likewise the side through *R* be drawn at random cutting the two already drawn at A' and C', respectively. Then QA' and QC' will determine the vertices D' and B'.

Now, in these two quadrangles, one of which was drawn wholly at random, five pairs of sides intersect in points of the straight line PQ, hence the sixth pair BD and $B'D'$ must also intersect on PQ. In other words, if two points P and Q on a straight line be such that pairs of sides of a complete quadrangle intersect in them, while a fifth side passes through a third point R of this line, then the sixth side will of necessity pass through a definite point S determined by the first three. These four points on the line are said to be **harmonically related,** or it may be said that the line segment PQ is **harmonically divided** at R and S, and we thus have a purely positional definition of the harmonic relation.

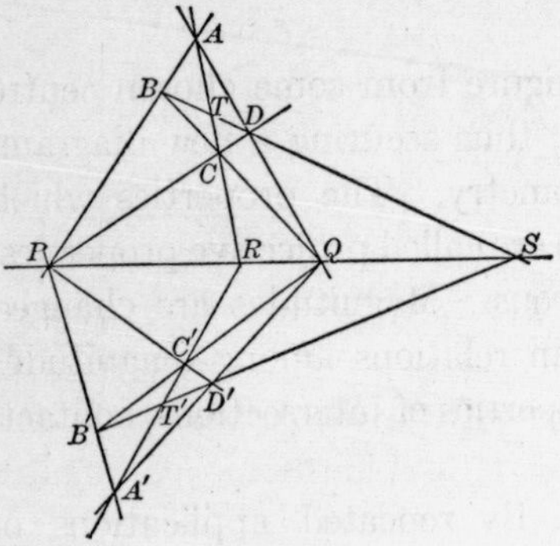

FIG 5.

Definition. Four points on a straight line are **harmonic** when they are so situated that in two of them pairs of opposite sides of a complete quadrangle may intersect while the remaining sides pass through the other two.

In the diagram (Fig. 5) it should be noted that not only the points $PQRS$, but also the points $ATCR$ fulfil the conditions specified for "harmonic points," as do also the points $DTBS$.

24. If the intersection of the sides AC and BD be the point T, and if PT intersect BC and AD in L and N respectively, and QT intersect AB and CD in K and M respectively, then the line KL must pass through R since $KBLT$ is a quadrangle of which one pair of opposite sides intersect in P, a second pair intersect in Q, while a fifth side passes through S. Similarly, NM passes through R, while KN and LM both pass through S. $KLMN$ is thus a complete quadrangle with one pair of opposite sides intersecting in R, one pair in S, a fifth side passing through

P, and the sixth side through Q. The points R and S in this modified diagram play exactly the same part as P and Q in the original diagram, while P and Q in the modified diagram play the same part as R and S in the original. Thus, if the segment PQ is harmonically divided at R and S, so also the segment RS is harmonically divided at P and Q. The points P and Q are harmonic conjugates with respect to R and S, and in the same way, R and S are harmonic conjugates with respect to P and Q.

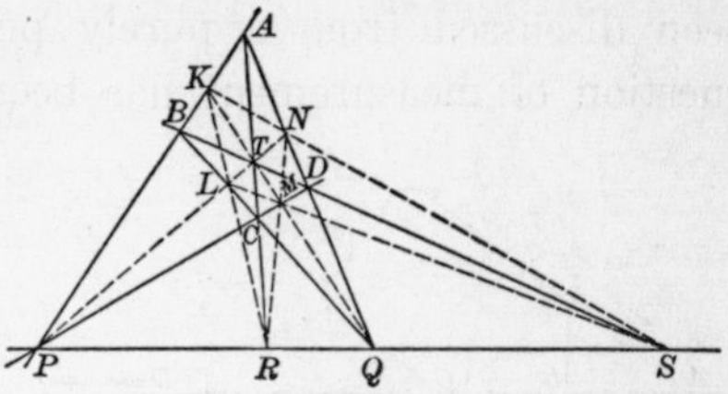

FIG. 6.

25. It is not difficult to show that the pairs of points P, Q and R, S must actually separate each other if they form a harmonic set, and that if P and Q remain fixed while R traverses the segments from Q to P internally, then S will traverse the segment from Q to P externally. From this it follows that if two pairs of points R, S, and R', S' are harmonically separated by the same points P and Q, then R, S, and R', S' cannot separate each other. Conversely, it is not difficult to show that if two pairs of points be chosen on a straight line so as not to separate each other, then a single pair may be found which will harmonically separate both pairs.

26. Suppose now the complete quadrangle $ABCD$ with the harmonic points P, Q, R, S, is projected from some point O outside the plane, and that a section is taken by a plane cutting the projection in a new quadrangle $A'B'C'D'$, of which two sides intersect in a point P', two sides in Q', a fifth side passes through R', and the sixth side through S'. Then the points $P'Q'R'S'$, any section of the rays OP, OQ, OR, OS, are harmonic. Hence if four harmonic points P, Q, R, S, be projected from a centre O, any section $P'Q'R'S'$ of the four projecting rays is a harmonic set of points. The rays OP, OQ, OR, OS, are themselves also said to be harmonic.

VII. METRIC PROPERTIES

27. Thus far the harmonic relation of points on a line has been discussed from a purely positional standpoint and no question of measurement has been considered. To introduce magnitudes into our discussion let us assume the theorem that the diagonals of a parallelogram bisect each other. Then if AC be one diagonal of a parallelogram, $ALCN$, bisected by the other diagonal LN at B, and if the pairs of opposite sides be produced to meet at the infinitely distant points K and M, respectively, $KLMN$ may be looked upon as a complete quadrangle with one pair of sides KL and MN intersecting at A, a second pair KN and LM intersecting at C, a fifth side LN passing through B, and the sixth side KM (the infinitely distant line) intersecting AC in the infinitely distant point D. Then the segment AC is harmonically divided by the mid-point B and the infinitely distant point D.

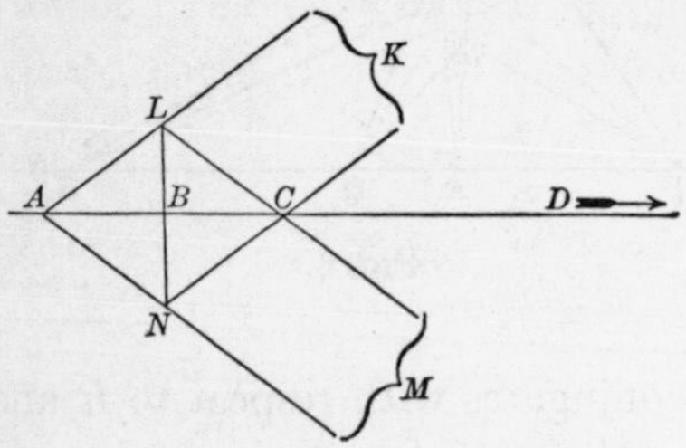

FIG. 7.

Thus any line-segment PQ is bisected at a point R when the harmonic conjugate of R with respect to P and Q is at infinity; or, the harmonic conjugate of the mid-point of a line-segment with respect to the extremities of the segment is the infinitely distant point of the line.

28. If a set of harmonic points $ABCD$ be projected from any point O by rays OA, OB, OC, OD, and a section of these rays $A'BC'D'$ be taken by a line drawn through B parallel to OD, the segment $A'B$ will equal the segment BC', since D' is at infinity and the four points are harmonic.

By similar triangles it follows at once that

$$\frac{AB}{AD}=\frac{BA'}{DO}=\frac{BC'}{DO}=\frac{BC}{CD},$$

or, interchanging the order of segments and giving attention to direction,

$$\frac{AB}{BC} = -\frac{AD}{DC}.$$

That is, the segment AC is divided internally at B and externally at D in the same ratio, a relation which is frequently taken as the definition of harmonic points.

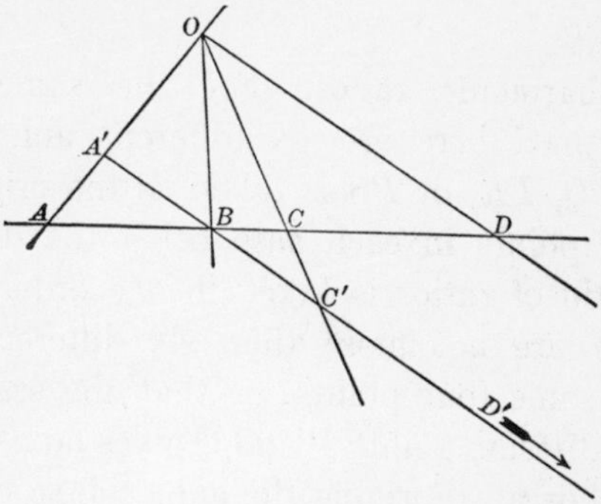

FIG. 8.

It should be noted that by another interchange in the order and direction of segments, the ratio

$$\frac{AB}{BC} = -\frac{AD}{DC} \quad \text{becomes} \quad \frac{BA}{AD} = -\frac{BC}{CD},$$

which shows that not only is the segment AC divided at B and D in equal ratios, but also that the segment BD is divided at A and C in equal ratios, as has been already pointed out.

29. From this property of harmonic points it is not difficult to demonstrate the following two:

(1) $\frac{1}{AB} + \frac{1}{AD} = \frac{2}{AC}$, from which immediately comes the identity of geometric harmonics with the algebraic harmonical progression; and

(2) $MB \cdot MD = MC^2$, where M is the mid-point of the segment AC.

VIII. ANHARMONIC RATIOS

30. Definition. If a line-segment PQ is divided by any two points R and S, and the ratios $\frac{PR}{RQ}$ and $\frac{PS}{SQ}$ be formed and again the ratio of these two ratios be taken, we obtain the ratio $\frac{PR \cdot SQ}{PS \cdot RQ}$, which is called the **cross-ratio,** or the **anharmonic ratio,** of the four points.

31. Six anharmonic ratios. For the same four points it is evident that there are six different anharmonic ratios according as PQ, PR, or PS is taken as the original segment, the other two points in each case being the division points, and as the ratio of ratios is taken in one order or the other.

That there are not more than six different anharmonic ratios for the same four points, or that the segment RS, for example, with division points P and Q gives no new anharmonic ratio is easily shown. Forming the anharmonic ratio as before, with RS as initial segment, it takes the form $\frac{RP \cdot QS}{RQ \cdot PS}$, and this by reversal of segments is identical with the one previously written.

Three of the anharmonic ratios of four points are reciprocals of the other three since they are formed by taking the ratio of ratios in the reverse order. The six ratios therefore are $\frac{PR \cdot SQ}{PS \cdot RQ}$, $\frac{PQ \cdot SR}{PS \cdot QR}$, $\frac{PQ \cdot RS}{PR \cdot QS}$, and their reciprocals. These six anharmonic ratios involve only the quantities $PQ \cdot RS$, $PR \cdot SQ$, $PS \cdot QR$, and their negatives.

Now for any four points, P, Q, R, S, on a straight line it may be easily shown that $PQ \cdot RS + PR \cdot SQ + PS \cdot QR = O$. From this we derive

$$PQ \cdot SR = PS \cdot QR + PR \cdot SQ$$

or

$$\frac{PQ \cdot SR}{PS \cdot QR} = 1 - \frac{PR \cdot SQ}{PS \cdot RQ}.$$

Also $$PQ \cdot RS = PR \cdot QS + PS \cdot RQ,$$

or $$\frac{PQ \cdot RS}{PR \cdot QS} = 1 - \frac{PS \cdot RQ}{PR \cdot SQ}.$$

Hence if the anharmonic ratio $\dfrac{PR \cdot SQ}{PS \cdot RQ} = k$, the ratio

$$\frac{PQ \cdot SR}{PS \cdot QR} = 1 - k; \text{ and } \frac{PQ \cdot RS}{PR \cdot QS} = 1 - \frac{1}{k}.$$

Therefore, if one of the anharmonic ratios of four points on a straight line be equal to k, the remaining five are

$$\frac{1}{k}, \ 1-k, \ \frac{1}{1-k}, \ 1-\frac{1}{k}, \text{ and } \frac{k}{k-1}.$$

In speaking of an anharmonic ratio it is clearly necessary to distinguish which of the six ratios is meant, and when the ratio has been formed in one order that order must be retained throughout the discussion in hand.

32. Take $\dfrac{PQ \cdot RS}{PR \cdot QS}$ as the anharmonic ratio of four given points. If two of the points P and S, and also the other two Q and R, be interchanged, the ratio becomes $\dfrac{SR \cdot QP}{SQ \cdot RP}$ which by reversal of segments is equal to the original ratio. Or if any other two, and also the remaining two, be interchanged, the ratio is unaltered. Hence

"If the anharmonic ratio of four points is formed in any order, the ratio is unchanged when we interchange two of the points and also the other two."

If the anharmonic ratio $\dfrac{PQ \cdot RS}{PR \cdot QS} = -1$, then $\dfrac{PQ}{QS} = -\dfrac{PR}{RS}$, or the segment PS is divided at Q and R in the same ratio and the four points are harmonic. In this case P and S must be separated by Q and R.

33. Take four points, A, B, C, D, on a line and project them from any centre O. Let p be the length of the perpendicular from O on the line.

Now the area of the triangle OAB

$$=\tfrac{1}{2}p\cdot AB=\tfrac{1}{2}OA\cdot OB\cdot\sin AOB,$$

and there are similar relations for the other triangles. Hence the anharmonic ratio $\dfrac{AB\cdot CD}{AC\cdot BD}=\dfrac{\sin AOB\cdot\sin COD}{\sin AOC\cdot\sin BOD}$, a quantity independent of p, and hence independent of the position of the line relative to the rays of OA, OB, OC, OD. Therefore

"If A', B', C', D', be a projection of the points A, B, C, D, from any centre O, the anharmonic ratio of the former set of points is equal to the corresponding anharmonic ratio of the latter set; or, the anharmonic ratio of four points is unaltered by projection."

IX. ELEMENTARY GEOMETRIC FORMS

34. The whole system of points on a straight line is called a **range of points** and the system of lines through a point, these lines being confined to one plane, is called a **sheaf or pencil of rays.** The system of planes passing through a line is a **sheaf of planes.** The aggregate of lines through a point, not confined to one plane, is called a **bundle of rays,** and the aggregate of planes through a point is a **bundle of planes.**

In plane geometry, the range of points and the sheaf of rays are reciprocal forms, while in three-dimensional geometry the range of points is reciprocal to the sheaf of planes and the sheaf of rays is reciprocal to itself. The bundle of rays and bundle of planes are reciprocal respectively to the rays of a plane and the points of a plane.

X. CORRELATION OF ELEMENTARY FORMS

35. Two ranges of points may be so correlated that to every point of one range there corresponds one and only one of the other. For example, two sections of the same sheaf of rays are correlated in this way if to each point of one range is correlated that point of the other which lies on the same ray. Similarly, two sheaves of rays may be correlated, one to one, if they project the same range of points. These are perhaps the simplest examples of one to one correlation, but other more complicated examples will readily occur to the reader.

Definition. When two elementary forms—ranges of points, sheaves of rays, or sheaves of planes—are so correlated that to every set of harmonic elements in one of them there corresponds a set of harmonic elements in the other, the forms are said to be **related to each other projectively.**

It is readily seen that if two forms are the first and last of a series, each of which is a projection or a section of the next preceding or next following, they fulfil the conditions of this definition, and hence are projectively related.

36. From the definition it follows without great difficulty (see *Reye*, Geometry of Position, §80*) that to any orderly sequence of elements in one of two projectively related forms there corresponds always an orderly sequence of elements in the other, and also that the anharmonic ratio of any set of four points in one form is equal to the anharmonic ratio of the corresponding four in the other.

37. Two projectively related simple forms which have the same base—for example, two projective ranges of points which lie on the same straight line—may have two elements of the one which correspond to themselves in the other; but if more than two, then every element of the one corresponds to itself in the other, and the two forms are identical.

That there may be two self-corresponding elements in the superposed forms may be seen as follows: Let $A, B, C, D, \ldots$ be points of a range u projected from S_1, by rays $a_1, b_1, c_1, d_1, \ldots$ and from S_2, by rays $a_2, b_2, c_2, d_2, \ldots$ Let V cut the rays $a_1, b_1, c_1, d_1, \ldots$ in points $A_1, B_1, C_1, D_1, \ldots$ and cut the rays $a_2, b_2, c_2, d_2, \ldots$ in points $A_2, B_2, C_2, D_2, \ldots$ The ranges $A_1, B_1, C_1, D_1, \ldots$ and $A_2, B_2, C_2, D_2, \ldots$, both lying on the line v, are projectively related, since any set of har-

---

* The reference is to *Reye's* Geometry of Position. English translation. This is now out of print, but readily accessible in libraries.

monic points in one corresponds to a set of harmonic points in the other, and in general corresponding points are distinct. The ray S_1S_2, however, cutting the line u at the point S, will determine on v two corresponding points which coincide. Also the rays of S_1 and S_2 which project the point of u in which that line is intersected by v, determine on v two coincident corresponding points. So that, in two superposed projective forms, two self-corresponding elements are possible without requiring that all elements should be self-corresponding.

But if three elements are self-corresponding, then all elements are self-corresponding. It is readily seen that certainly in this case an indefinite number of points will coincide with their corresponding points, namely, the harmonic conjugate of each of the three given points with respect to the remaining two, and so on indefinitely. But for a proof that every point must coincide with its corresponding point the reader is referred to *Reye*, §84.

38. Let us apply this property to some simple example.

(1) If two projective ranges of points A_1, B_1, C_1, . . . lying on the line u_1 and A_2, B_2, C_2, . . . lying on the line u_2 are so situated that the rays AA_1, BB_1, and CC_1, or any three such rays, pass through one point S, then all rays joining pairs of corresponding points will pass through S, and the common point of the two ranges must be self-corresponding.

For S is the centre of two superposed projective sheaves of rays having three self-corresponding rays, hence all rays are self-corresponding,

(2) If two projective sheaves of rays a_1, b_1, c_1, . . . , with centre S_1, and a_2, b_2, c_2, . . . , with centre S_2, are so situated that the points of intersection a_1a_2, b_1b_2, and c_1c_2, or any three such points of intersection, lie on one straight line s, then all points of intersection of pairs of corresponding rays will lie on s, and the common ray of the two sheaves must be self-corresponding.

For s is the base of two superposed projective ranges of points having three self-corresponding points; hence all points are self-correspond-

and the ray joining any point P_1 to S must coincide with the ray joining P_2 to S, or, the ray P_1P_2 must pass through S.

ing and the intersection of any ray p_1 with s must coincide with the intersection of p_2 with s, or, p_1 and p_2 must intersect on S.

Definition. When two projective ranges of points are so situated that the lines joining pairs of corresponding points all pass through one point, they are said to be **perspective to each other,** or to be **in perspective position,** and this will happen whenever three lines joining pairs of corresponding points pass through one point.

Definition. When two sheaves of rays are so situated that the points of intersection of pairs of corresponding rays all lie on one straight line, they are said to be **perspective to each other,** or to be **in perspective position,** and this will happen whenever three points of intersection of pairs of corresponding rays lie on one line.

For brevity, the symbol $\barwedge$ is frequently used for **is projective to** and we shall use the symbol $\doublebarwedge$ for **is perspective to.** It should be noted that forms which are perspective to each other are also projective, but lie in a special relative position.

(3) Two projective ranges of points, A_1, B_1, C_1, . . . lying on the line u_1 and A_2, B_2, C_2, . . . lying on the line u_2, are perspectively related if the common point of u_1 and u_2 is self-corresponding.

For, if A_1A_2 and B_1B_2 intersect in S and the two ranges are projected from this point, then in the two projective sheaves of rays whose centre is S there are three self-corresponding rays, namely, SAA_1, SBB_1, and SK where

(4) Two projective sheaves of rays, a_1, b_1, c_1 . . . with centre S_1 and a_2, b_2, c_2 . . . with centre S_2, are perspectively related if the common ray of the two sheaves, S_1S_2, is self-corresponding.

For, if s is the line joining intersections a_1a_2 and b_1b_2, and a section of each sheaf of rays by this line is taken, then in the two projective ranges of points lying on this line there will be three self-corresponding points, namely,

K is the common point of u_1 and u_2. Hence all rays of S are self-corresponding and the two ranges are perspective.

a_1a_2, b_1b_2, and the point where s cuts S_1S_2. Hence all points of these two ranges are self-corresponding, or, in other words, all pairs of corresponding rays of the two sheaves intersect on s, and the two sheaves are perspective.

(5) Two fixed straight lines u_1 and u_2 intersect at O and there are two fixed points S_1 and S_2 collinear with O. A line v rotates about a fixed point V and intersects u_1 and u_2 in A_1 and A_2 respectively. The locus of the intersection of S_1A_1 and S_2A_2 is a straight line.

For the line v rotating about V marks out on the lines u_1 and u_2 two perspective ranges of which A_1 and A_2 are corresponding points and O is a self-corresponding point. The two sheaves, of which S_1A_1 and S_2A_2 are corresponding rays, are therefore projective, and since S_1O and S_2O are identical, i.e., S_1S_2 is self-corresponding, the two sheaves are perspective and the locus of the intersection of pairs of corresponding rays is a straight line.

39. Construction of corresponding elements. From what has been said it appears that two elementary forms may be correlated projectively as soon as there are known three elements in the one form which correspond to three given elements in the other. Let S_1 and S_2 be the centres of two sheaves of rays lying in the same plane, which are to be correlated projectively. Let the rays a_1, b_1, c_1, of the first sheaf correspond respectively to the rays a_2, b_2, c_2, of the second sheaf. The problem is to find in the second sheaf the ray d_2 which corresponds to any chosen ray d_1 of the first sheaf.

If a_1, a_2 intersect at A, b_1, b_2, at B, and c_1, c_2 at C, and these three points lie on a straight line v, the two sheaves are perspective and any pair of corresponding rays will intersect on v. But, if A, B, and C are not collinear, we must find a sheaf of rays to which each of the given sheaves is perspective and so arrive at a correlation of them.

Through one of the points of intersection, A, draw two secants, u_1 and u_2, and consider the first, u_1, a section of the sheaf S_1, the second, u_2, a section of the sheaf S_2. These two ranges of points therefore will be projectively related, and they are perspective since A is a self-corresponding point. If $B'C'$ and $B''C''$, are the points in which b_1, c_1, and b_2, c_2, are cut respectively by the lines u_1 and u_2, the intersection of $B'B''$ and $C'C''$, or S, is the centre of a sheaf of rays of which both u_1 and u_2 are sections. Hence the sheaves S_1 and S are perspective since corresponding rays intersect on the straight line u_1, and S_2 and S are perspective since corresponding rays intersect on the straight line u_2.

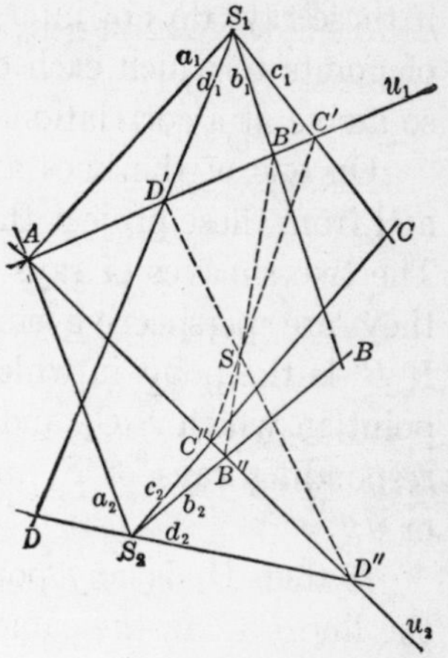

FIG. 9.

If then d_1 is any ray of the sheaf S_1 which cuts u_1 at D', the ray SD' will cut u_2 in a point D'' in which the ray d_2 of the sheaf S_2 also cuts it. Thus the ray d_2 of S_2 corresponding to any ray d_1 of S_1 is determined and the correlation is complete.

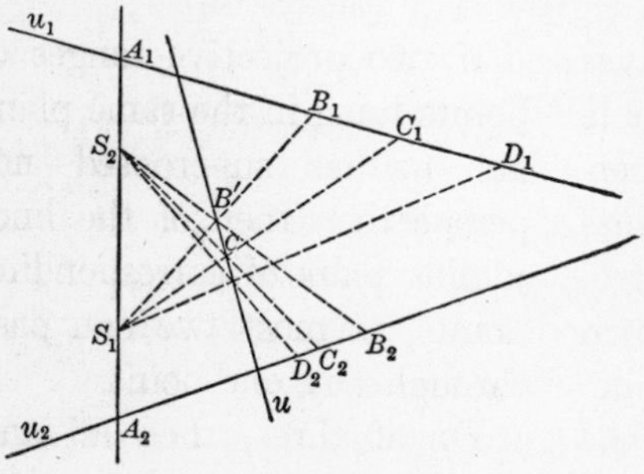

FIG. 10.

40. On the other hand, let u_1 and u_2 be two ranges of points lying in the same plane which are to be correlated projectively, and let the points A_1, B_1, C_1, of the first range correspond respectively to the points A_2, B_2, C_2, of the second range. The problem is to find the point D_2 of the second range corresponding to any chosen point D_1 of the first range.

If the rays A_1A_2, B_1B_2, C_1C_2 pass through one point V, the two ranges are perspective and all pairs of corresponding points in the two ranges will lie on rays through V. But if these rays do not intersect in one point we must find a range of points to which each of the given ranges is perspective, and so arrive at a correlation.

On one of the lines as A_1A_2 choose two centres S_1 and S_2, and from these project the given ranges u_1 and u_2, respectively. The two sheaves of rays S_1 and S_2 will thus be projective, and they are perspective since S_1S_2 is a self-corresponding ray. If B' is the point in which S_1B_1 and S_2B_2 intersect, and C' the point in which S_1C_1 and S_2C_2 intersect, then all pairs of corresponding rays of S_1 and S_2 will intersect on the line $B'C'$ or u.

If then D_1 is any point of the range u_1, S_1D_1 will intersect the line $B'C'$ in the same point as does S_2D_2. Thus the point D_2 of u_2 corresponding to any point D_1 of u_1 is determined and the correlation is complete.

It should be noted that both the problem and the process of sec. 40 are the reciprocals or duals of those of sec. 39.

XI. CURVES AND SHEAVES OF RAYS OF THE SECOND ORDER

41. If two projective sheaves of rays lying in the same plane are neither concentric nor perspective, then of the points of intersection of pairs of corresponding rays, at most two can lie on any straight line.

For if three, then all and the two sheaves would be perspective.

If two projective ranges of points lying in the same plane are neither superposed nor perspective, then of the lines joining pairs of corresponding points, at most two can pass through any one point.

For if three, then all and the two ranges would be perspective.

42. Since a continuous series of elements in one of two projective forms corresponds always to a continuous series in the other, the locus of the point of intersection of corresponding rays in two projective sheaves is a continuous series of points, or a **curve,** and the locus of the line joining corresponding points in two projective ranges is a continuous series of rays, or an **envelope.**

If the two projective sheaves of rays are not perspective, the generated curve is such that not more than two of its points lie on any straight line. Such a curve is called a **curve of the second order.**

If the two ranges of points are not perspective, the generated envelope is such that not more than two of its rays pass through any one point. Such an envelope is called a **sheaf of rays of the second order.**

A curve of the second order is generated by two projective sheaves of rays lying in the same plane, which are not perspective.

A sheaf of rays of the second order is generated by two projective ranges of points lying in the same plane, which are not perspective.

43. The centres of the sheaves generating a curve of the second order are themselves points of the curve, since the ray S_1S_2 of the sheaf S_1 meets its corresponding ray at S_2, and the ray S_2S_1 of the sheaf S_2 meets its corresponding ray at S_1. These corresponding rays have each only one point in common with the curve, namely, S_2 and S_1 respectively, while all other rays through these centres meet the curve at S_2 or S_1 and also elsewhere. These rays are consequently called **tangents** to the curve at these points.

The lines on which lie ranges of points generating a sheaf of rays of the second order are themselves rays of the sheaf, since each joins a point in itself to the corresponding point in the other, namely, the common point of the two lines. Through the point of u_1 which corresponds to the point of u_2 lying on u_1, there passes but one ray of the sheaf, namely, u_1 itself, while through all other points of u_1 there pass two rays of the sheaf. The same is true for that point of u_2 which corresponds to the point of u_1 lying on u_2. These points are consequently called **points of contact** on the two rays.

44. A curve of the second order may thus be generated from two given points S_1 and S_2 and three rays through each correlated to three rays through the other, in other words, from

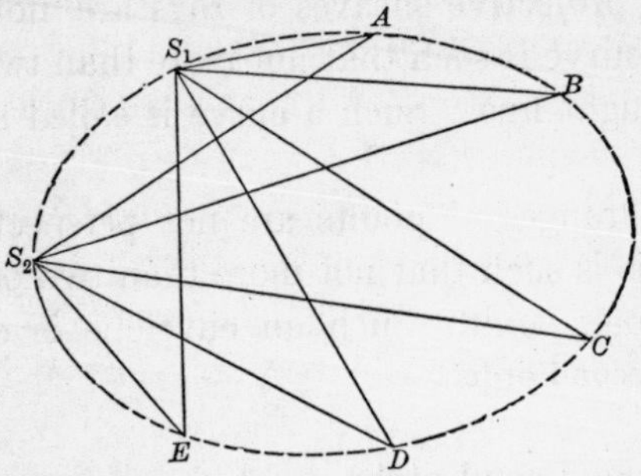

FIG. 11.

five given points of the curve. The problem of constructing a curve of the second order from five given points is then the problem of determining pairs of corresponding rays in two projective sheaves when three pairs are given.

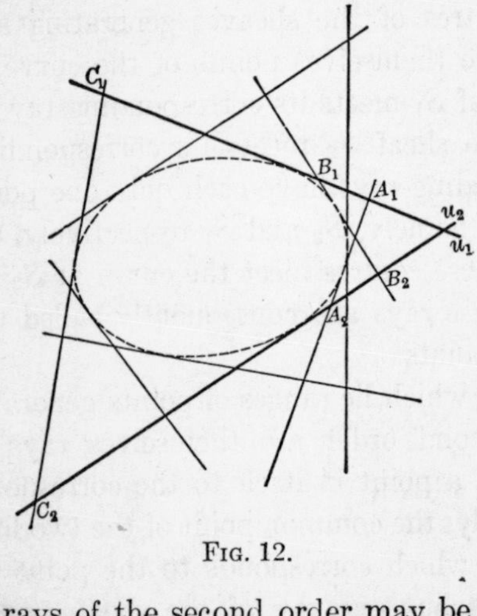

FIG. 12.

A sheaf of rays of the second order may be generated from two given rays u_1 and u_2 and three points on each correlated to three points on the other; in other words, from five given rays of the sheaf. The problem of constructing a sheaf of rays of the second order from five given rays is then the problem of determining pairs of corresponding points in two projective ranges when three pairs are given.

45. That the points S_1 and S_2, the centres of the generating sheaves, are not particular points of the curve, or that the curve could as well be generated with any other two of its points for centres, follows without great difficulty, but the demonstration is omitted. The same is true regarding the lines u_1 and u_2 in the sheaf of rays. Accepting this, it follows that:

"A curve of the second order may be projected from any two of its points by projective sheaves of rays and a sheaf of rays of the second order is cut by any two of its rays in projective ranges of points."

46. A circle is a curve of the second order, since if two points S_1 and S_2 on it be chosen for centres and other points

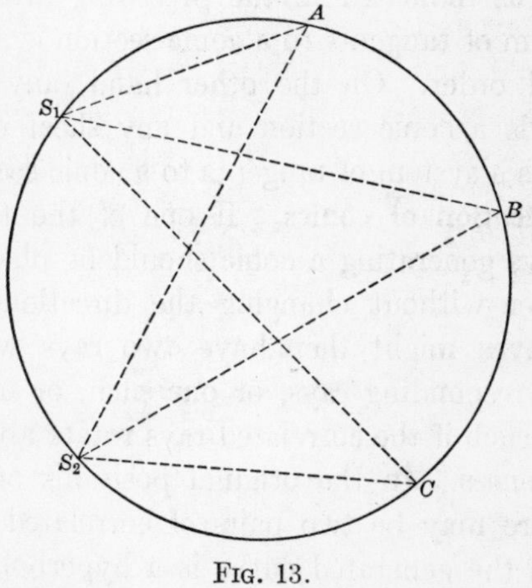

FIG. 13.

$A, B, C, \ldots$ be projected from these, the angle AS_1B equals the angle AS_2B, and so on, so that the two sheaves of rays S_1 and S_2 might be placed the one on the other so that pairs of corresponding rays would coincide. Hence the sheaves are projective and the points of the circle are points of intersection of pairs of corresponding rays.

Similarly the tangents to a circle form a sheaf of rays of the second order. If u_1 and u_2 are any two tangents to a circle, and other tangents cut these two in points A_1, A_2; B_1, B_2,. . . respectively, the angle A_1OB_1 equals the angle A_2OB_2, and so on, so that the ranges of points u_1 and u_2 are sections of two identically equal sheaves of rays having the same centre O. Hence these two ranges of points are projective and the system of tangents is a sheaf of rays of the second order.

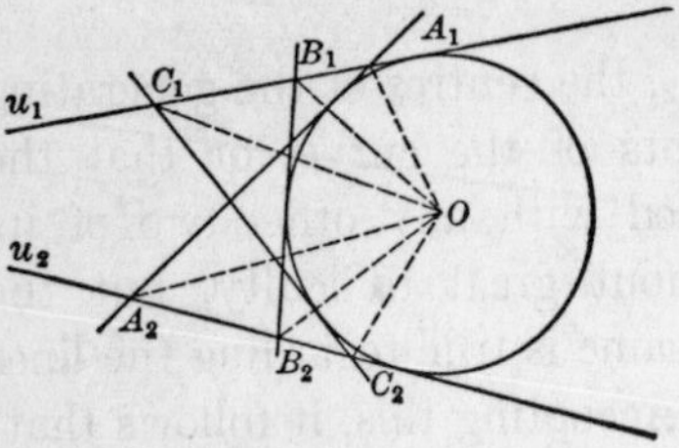

FIG. 14.

47. From considerations such as these, it may be shown that every conic section is a curve of the second order and may be generated as indicated in the preceding articles, and also that the system of tangents to a conic section is a sheaf of rays of the second order. On the other hand, any curve of the second order is a conic section and any sheaf of rays of the second order is a system of tangents to a conic section.

48. Classification of conics. If one of the two projective sheaves of rays generating a conic should be placed concentric with the other without changing the directions of its rays, the two sheaves might then have two rays which coincide with their corresponding rays, or one such, or none such, but certainly two such if the correlated rays rotate about the centre in opposite senses. In the original positions of the sheaves, therefore, there may be two pairs of correlated rays parallel, in which case the generated curve is a hyperbola, having two points at infinity; or one pair, in which case the curve is a parabola; or no corresponding rays parallel, in which case the curve is an ellipse. If the five given points from which the curve is generated lie so that one is within the quadrangle formed by the other four, the resulting curve is necessarily a hyperbola.

XII. PASCAL'S AND BRIANCHON'S THEOREMS

49. The diagram for the construction of pairs of corresponding rays in two projective sheaves (sec. 39), may be extended so far as to show that the ray S_1S of the sheaf S_1 cuts the line u_2 in a point M of the curve determined by the two sheaves. Similarly, S_2S of the sheaf S_2 cuts the line u_1 in a point L of the curve. Now S_1, S_2, A, D, L, and M are arbitrary points of the curve and lines connecting them in order, S_1DS_2LAM, form a hexagon inscribed in the curve of second order such that the pairs of opposite sides S_1D and LA, DS_2 and AM, S_2L and MS_1 necessarily intersect in points of a straight line $D'SD''$. Hence

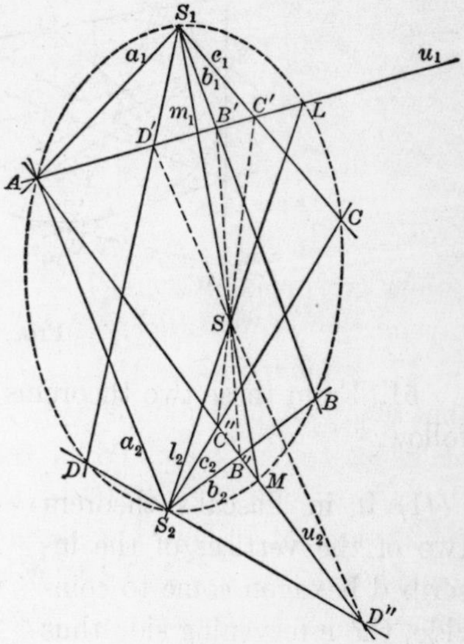

FIG. 15.

"The points of intersection of the three pairs of opposite sides of a hexagon inscribed in a conic lie on one straight line."

This is the well-known theorem of *Pascal* enunciated in 1640, when the author was but a lad of sixteen years.

50. On the other hand, the diagram for the location of pairs of corresponding points in two projective ranges (sec. 40) may be extended to show that the lines S_2R_1 and S_1Q_2 are rays of the sheaf of second order determined by the given ranges, R_1 and Q_2 being the points in which the line $B'C'$, or u, intersects u_1 and u_2, respectively. Now $S_1S_2R_1D_1D_2Q_2$ are vertices of a hexagon whose sides are arbitrary rays of the sheaf of second order, and it is such that the lines joining pairs of opposite vertices necessarily intersect in one point. Hence

"The lines joining pairs of opposite vertices of a hexagon circumscribed to a conic intersect in one point."

This is Brianchon's theorem, the exact dual or reciprocal of Pascal's theorem, but not discovered till 1806.

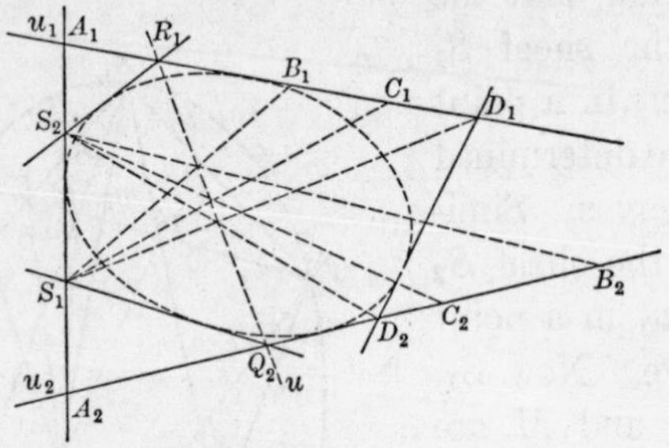

FIG. 16.

51. From these two theorems many important consequences follow.

(1) If in Pascal's theorem two of the vertices of the inscribed hexagon come to coincide, the intervening side thus becoming the tangent at that vertex, the theorem takes the form: A pentagon inscribed in a conic is such that the intersections of two pairs of non-adjacent sides and of the fifth side with the tangent at the opposite vertex lie on one straight line.

(2) If in Brianchon's theorem two of the sides of the circumscribed hexagon come to coincide, the intervening vertex thus becoming the point of contact of that side, the theorem takes the form: A pentagon circumscribed to a conic is such that the lines joining two pairs of non-adjacent vertices and the line joining the fifth vertex to the point of contact of the opposite side pass through one point.

(3) If further the hexagon is reduced to an inscribed quadrilateral and tangents at two opposite vertices, we have: In any quadrilateral inscribed

(4) If further the hexagon is reduced to a circumscribed quadrilateral and the points of contact on two opposite sides, we have: In any quad-

in a conic, the intersections of pairs of opposite sides and of tangents at opposite vertices are collinear.

rilateral circumscribed to a conic the lines joining pairs of opposite vertices and pairs of points of contact in opposite sides are concurrent.

(5) For the inscribed triangle Pascal's theorem becomes: The sides of a triangle inscribed in a conic intersect the tangents at the opposite vertices in points of one straight line.

(6) For the circumscribed triangle Brianchon's theorem becomes: The lines joining the vertices of a triangle circumscribed to a conic to the points of contact of the opposite sides intersect in one point.

52. Pascal's theorem yields itself at once to the construction of a conic of which there are given five points, or four points and the tangent at one of them, or three points and the tangents at two of them. In the case of five points being given, if these are A, B, C, D, E, and they are joined in order, while an arbitrary line through A is drawn for sixth side of the inscribed hexagon, the hexagon is determined excepting only the fifth side and the sixth vertex. Of this hexagon AB and DE are opposite sides, CD and the arbitrary line through A are opposite sides, and the intersections of these determine the Pascal line. The sides BC and the side EF, where F is on the arbitrary line through A, intersect also on the Pascal line, hence the point F, an arbitrary point of the conic, is determined.

In the same way, Brianchon's theorem yields itself to the construction of tangents to a conic when there are given either five tangents, four tangents and the point of contact of one of them, or three tangents and the points of contact of two of them.

XIII. POLE AND POLAR THEORY

53. In the plane of a conic is a point *P*, and through it are drawn two secants of the conic as in the diagrams (Figs. 17 and 18), cutting the conic in the points *A*, *B*, and *C*, *D*. If these points are joined two and two so as to form the inscribed quadrangle *ACBD*, the pairs of opposite sides *AC* and *BD*, *AD* and *BC*, will intersect on a line *p*, on which also intersect the tangents at opposite vertices *A* and *B*, *C* and *D* (Pascal's

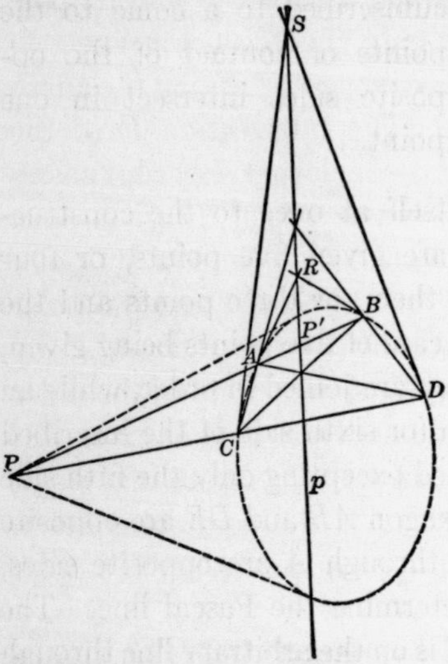

FIG. 17.

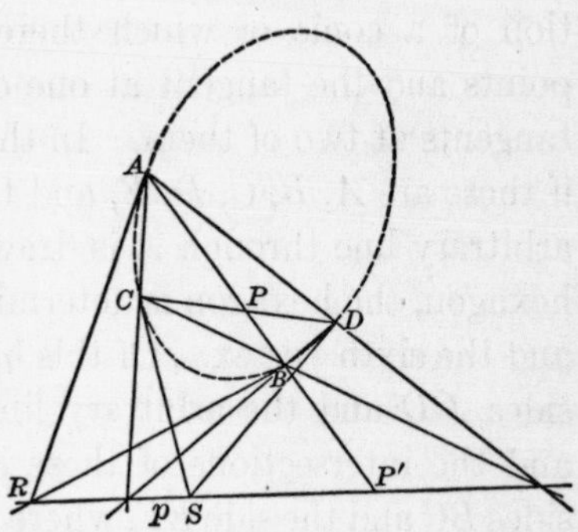

FIG. 18.

theorem). The line *p* is called the **polar** of the point *P* with respect to the conic, and the point *P* is the **pole** of the line *p*.

If the secant *PAB* cuts the polar at the point *P'* it is readily seen that the points *PAP'B* are harmonic, hence *P'* could be found as the harmonic conjugate of *P* with respect to *A* and *B*. Also the tangents at *A* and *B* intersect on the polar, consequently two points of the polar can be found from a single secant. Hence the position of the polar is independent of the second secant, that is, the polar of a point is independent of the process of constructing it, and it therefore bears a fixed relation to the point and the curve.

54. On the polar of a point P with respect to a conic there will lie:

(1) The intersections of chords joining the extremities of pairs of secants through P. (By extremities we mean the points of intersection with the curve.)

(2) The intersections of tangents at the extremities of secants through P.

(3) All points harmonically separated from P by the curve.

(4) The points of contact of tangents from P.

55. If a straight line p is given and we wish to find its pole with respect to a given conic, we may choose on the line two points R and S, and from these draw tangents meeting the curve at A, B, and C, D, respectively. The intersection P of the chords AB and CD is such that its polar necessarily passes through both R and S. Hence P is the pole of the given line.

56. If a point P lies inside a conic, all points of its polar lie outside, since chords through P cut the conic, and the polar passes through all points harmonically separated from P by the curve. If P lies outside the conic, some points of the polar must lie inside and the polar necessarily cuts the curve. If P is a point of the conic its polar is the tangent at that point and, conversely, the pole of a tangent is the point of contact. This follows as a limiting case of the construction for the polar in sec. 53.

Incidentally, it may be stated by way of definition that a point lies inside of a closed curve when all straight lines through it cut the curve, and a point lies outside of a closed curve when through it straight lines can be drawn which do not cut the curve in real points.

57. Conjugate points and lines. If a point Q lies on the polar of a point P, relative to a conic, then P lies on the polar of Q.

For if P lies outside the curve, Q may be chosen either inside or outside, but in either case, the polar of P is a secant through Q, the tangents at whose extremities intersect in a point of the polar of Q. But they intersect at P, hence P is a point of the polar of Q. If P lies inside the curve, Q must lie outside and QP necessarily cuts the curve in real points. Now Q and P are harmonically separated by the curve, since Q lies on the polar of P, but for this same reason P must lie on the polar of Q. If P lies on the curve, and Q is a point of its polar, namely a point of the tangent at P, the polar of Q evidently passes through P.

Two points are called **polar conjugates** when one, and consequently each, lies on the polar of the other; and two lines are "polar conjugates" when one, and consequently each, passes through the pole of the other.

Thus a point is conjugate to all the points of its polar and a line is conjugate to all the lines through its pole.

58. Centre and diameters. In the diagram for the construction of the polar of a point (sec. 53), if P should lie at infinity, and consequently the secants through it be parallel, the polar becomes the locus of the mid-points of a system of parallel chords, each mid-point being harmonically separated from P.

The locus of the mid-points of a system of parallel chords of a conic is thus a straight line—the polar of the infinitely distant point at which the chords intersect—and this line is called a **diameter** of the curve.

The intersection of any two diameters of a conic is the pole of the infinitely distant line, and is called the centre of the conic.

The centre of an ellipse lies inside the curve since the infinitely distant line of the plane lies wholly outside and all diameters cut the curve in real points. For a parabola, the infinitely distant line is tangent to the curve, hence the centre lies at infinity on the curve, and all diameters are parallel. The infinitely distant line cuts a hyperbola in two real points, hence the centre lies outside the curve and there are some diameters which cut the curve in real points while others do not. The tangents to the curve at infinity are called **asymptotes.** They pass through the centre and are hence diameters.

XIV. CONCLUSION

59. In this brief chapter it is hoped that enough of the spirit of modern pure geometry has been exhibited to encourage the reader to continue its study. The field yields rich results in applications to more elementary subjects and is not too difficult or forbidding for the isolated reader. By continuing the methods here indicated a complete study can be made not only of the conic sections, but of the relations of conics to each other and of many curves of higher order. The pole and polar theory in reference to a conic relates every point of the plane to a line and every line to a point in such a way as to give concreteness to the principle of duality and to make it possible so to reciprocate systems of points and lines as to yield definite sets of lines and points. By projection from a point outside the plane all the conclusions here reached can be transferred directly to cones of the second order and their tangent planes, and many interesting theorems develop which are not simple projections and which have not more than an analogy in a plane figure. Ruled surfaces of the second order appear from a consideration of two projectively related ranges of points which do not lie in the same plane, or from two projective sheaves of planes whose axes do not intersect.

Perhaps the easiest and most attractive approach to the study is through *Reye's* Geometrie der Lage, but the English translation of Part I of this work, made some years ago, is now out of print. *Cremona's* Projective Geometry, English translation by *Leudesdorf*, has always been a popular text. The classic treatises on modern geometry are *Chasles's* Géométrie Supérieure, *Steiner's* Systematische Entwicklung, etc., *Poncelet's* Propriétés Projectives, and *Von Staudt's* Geometrie der Lage. Of these the last, though perhaps the most systematic, should be read only after a considerable knowledge and comprehension of the subject has been obtained.

III

NON-EUCLIDEAN GEOMETRY

By Frederick S. Woods

CONTENTS

III

NON-EUCLIDEAN GEOMETRY

By Frederick S. Woods

I. INTRODUCTION

1. The fifth postulate of *Euclid* reads as follows: "If a straight line falling on two straight lines makes the interior angles on the same side less than two right angles, the two lines, if produced indefinitely, meet on that side on which are the angles less than two right angles."

Under the term **non-Euclidean geometry** we shall understand a system of geometry which is built up without the use of this postulate. Strictly speaking, perhaps, the same name might be given to any geometry the basis of which differs in any essential particular from that of *Euclid*, but usage has decreed otherwise.

The conception of a non-Euclidean geometry came into being only after centuries of vain attempts to prove the truth of Euclid's postulate. There is no place here to review the history of such attempts.* It is sufficient to note that all inevitably failed. Some writers, however, especially *Saccheri* (1667–1733), *Lambert* (1728–77), and *Legendre* (1752–1833) made important contributions to what is now recognized as

---

* See, for example: *Engel-Staeckel*, Theorie der Parallellinien von Euklid bis auf Gauss, Leipzig, 1895. A shorter account is found in *Bonola*, Die nichteuklidische Geometrie, Vol. IV, of the series, Wissenschaft und Hypothese, Leipzig, 1908. See also the Historical Note, in *Manning*, Non-Euclidean Geometry, Boston, 1901; and *Heath*, The Thirteen Books of Euclid's Elements, Vol. I, p. 202, Cambridge, 1908.

the non-Euclidean geometries, though each failed to see the true meaning of the results he obtained.

Finally, nearly simultaneously though quite independently, a Russian, *Lobachevsky,* a Hungarian, *J. Bolyai,* and a German, *Gauss,* reached the conclusion not only that the parallel postulate could not be proved, but that a logical system of geometry could be constructed without its use. The work of *Gauss* is only partly revealed by extracts from his correspondence and fragments of his posthumous papers. That of *Lobachevsky* is contained in several articles published between 1833 and 1855, and that of *Bolyai* in an appendix to a work of his father published in 1832–35. The system of geometry common to these three writers we shall call the Lobachevskian geometry, since *Lobachevsky* was the mathematician to develop it most fully.*

The Lobachevskian geometry remained for a time the sole type of a non-Euclidean geometry. In 1854, however, *Riemann,* working from the standpoint of the differential calculus, discovered a new type to which we shall give the name of the Riemannian geometry.

Besides the three types of geometry, the Euclidean, the Lobachevskian, and the Riemannian, there are also three methods by which the geometries may be developed. The first is by elementary methods similar to those of *Euclid,* and was used by *Lobachevsky, Bolyai,* and *Gauss.* The second is by use of *Cayley's* system of projective measurement and has been largely employed by *Klein.* The third is that of the calculus, and has been used by *Riemann.* We shall begin by employing the first method, but shall later make some reference to the other two.

It does not lie within the plan of this paper to examine the assumptions which must be made before any form of a parallel postulate can be introduced. This work has been done by

---

* English readers will find the simplest introduction to *Lobachevsky's* own work in the little book written in German and translated into English by *G. B. Halsted* under the title, "Geometrical researches on the theory of parallels." More complete is *Engel's* translation: *Lobatschefskij*, Zwei geometrische Abhandlungen aus dem Russischen übersetzt mit Anmerkungen and mit einer Biographie des Verfassers, Leipzig, 1879.

Professor *Veblen* in his paper* contained in the present collection and the results of that paper will be assumed as known and freely referred to. It is believed, however, that this paper may be easily read by any reader who prefers to start from the original definitions, common notions, and postulates, stated or implied, of *Euclid*.

II. PARALLEL LINES

2. We assume Euclid's fundamentals with the exception of the parallel postulate, or make *Veblen's* assumptions I–XII and XIV. The first twenty-eight propositions of the first book of *Euclid* (*Veblen*, VIII) are then true. We proceed to give a definition of parallel lines more general than that of *Euclid*.

Let PQ (Fig. 1) be any straight line and A any point not on PQ. Through A there passes a set of lines intersecting PQ,

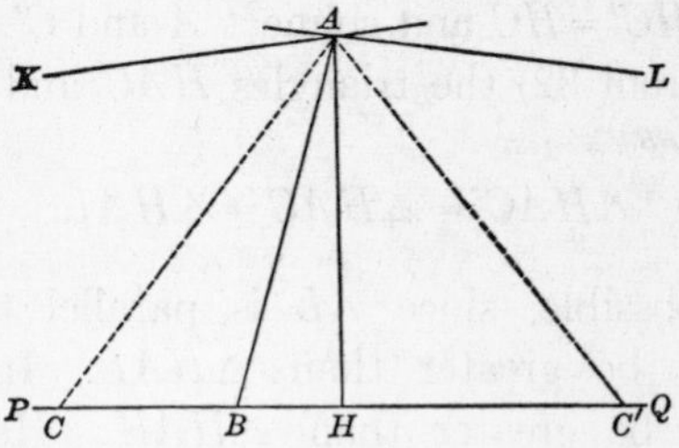

FIG. 1.

since any point on PQ may be joined to A. It is conceivable that there may be other lines through A which do not intersect PQ. In that case, there will be lines such as AL and AK, not intersecting PQ and forming the boundaries of the set of lines which meet PQ. Such lines are said to be parallel to PQ.

Otherwise expressed: *Let AB be any line through A intersecting PQ. The line AL is said to be parallel to PQ at the point A, if*

(1) *AL does not intersect PQ no matter how far produced.*

---

* Monograph No. I.

(2) *Any line through A in the angle opening BAL does intersect PQ.*

It is evident that this definition considers only those portions of the lines AL and PQ which lie on the same side of AB. In other words, the directions of the lines are important. We shall indicate the directions of parallel lines in the usual way by the order in which the letters at these extremities are named. Thus we shall say that AL is parallel to PQ and AK is parallel to QP.

The line AB may be any line through A intersecting PQ. It is often convenient, however, to use the line AH perpendicular to PQ. We may then show that

$$\measuredangle HAK = \measuredangle HAL.$$

For if $\measuredangle HAK$ were greater than $\measuredangle HAL$, we could draw AC meeting QP in C so that $\measuredangle HAC = \measuredangle HAL$. Now take C' on HQ so that $HC' = HC$ and connect A and C'. By *Euclid*, I, 4 (*Veblen*, Theorem 32) the triangles HAC and HAC' are congruent, and hence

$$\measuredangle HAC' = \measuredangle HAC = \measuredangle HAL.$$

This is impossible, since AL is parallel to HQ. Hence $\measuredangle HAK$ cannot be greater than $\measuredangle HAL$. In like manner, $\measuredangle HAL$ cannot be greater than $\measuredangle HAK$. Hence $\measuredangle HAK = \measuredangle HAL$.

The angle HAL is called the **angle of parallelism** for the distance AH.

In the definition, the point A plays apparently a unique role. We shall show this to be unessential by the theorem of the next section.

3. *A straight line maintains the property of parallelism at all its points.*

Let AK (Fig. 2) be parallel to BQ at the point A and let A_1 be any point on AK. We wish to show that AK is parallel to BQ at the point A_1.

Connect A_1 and B and draw through A_1 any line A_1C in the angle opening BA_1K. Take D any point on A_1C and connect D with A. The line AD prolonged will meet BQ at some point F since AK is parallel to BQ. Hence A_1C will meet BQ in some point between B and F (*Veblen,* Theorem 17). That is, any line through A_1 in the angle opening BA_1K intersects BQ. But A_1K does not intersect BQ. Hence it is parallel to BQ.

The proof also holds that if A_1 is taken on the backward extension of AK, but, in that case D must be taken on the backward extension of A_1C.

We shall now show that the property of parallelism is reciprocal.

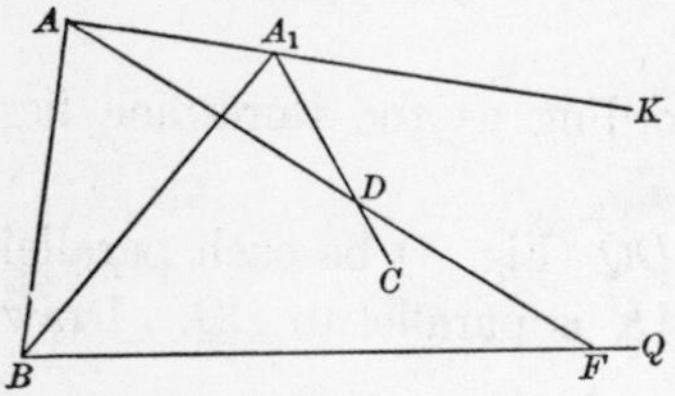

Fig. 2.

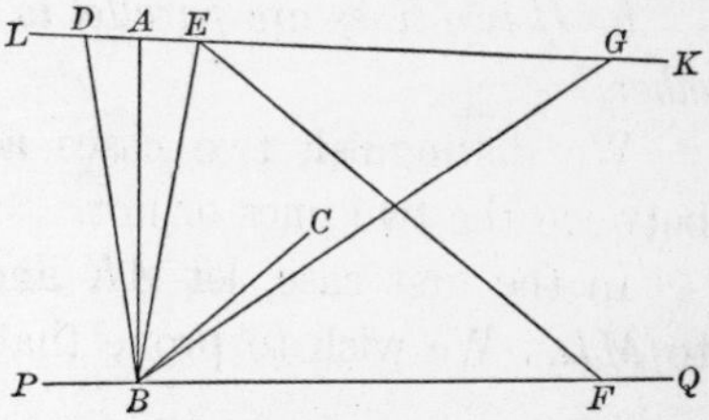

Fig. 3.

4. *If a line is parallel to another line the second line is parallel to the first.*

Let LK (Fig. 3) be parallel to PQ. We wish to prove that PQ is parallel to LK. From A draw a line perpendicular to LK. This perpendicular will meet PQ at some point B since LK is parallel to PQ. Draw through B any line BC in the angle opening QBA. Construct the two angles ABE and ABD so that

$$\measuredangle ABE = \measuredangle ABD < \tfrac{1}{2} \measuredangle QBC.$$

Then $\qquad BD = BE, \qquad$ (Euclid, I, 26)

$$\measuredangle BEK > \measuredangle BDK. \qquad \text{(Euclid, I, 16)}$$

Hence we may draw in the angle BEK a line EF so that

$$\measuredangle BEF = \measuredangle BDK,$$

and EF will meet HQ since LK is parallel to PQ. Now take $DG = EF$ and draw BG. Then the two triangles BEF and DBG are congruent and therefore

$$\measuredangle DBG = \measuredangle EBF.$$

But $$\measuredangle DBE < \measuredangle QBC.$$

Therefore $$\measuredangle EBG > \measuredangle EBC.$$

Hence the line BC meets LK at some point between E and G. But BC is any line through B in the angle opening QBA and LK and BQ do not meet. Therefore BQ is parallel to LK.

5. *If two lines are parallel to a third, they are parallel to each other.*

We distinguish two cases according as the third line lies between the two lines or not.

In the first case, let AK and DQ (Fig. 4) be each parallel to ML. We wish to prove that AK is parallel to DQ. Draw

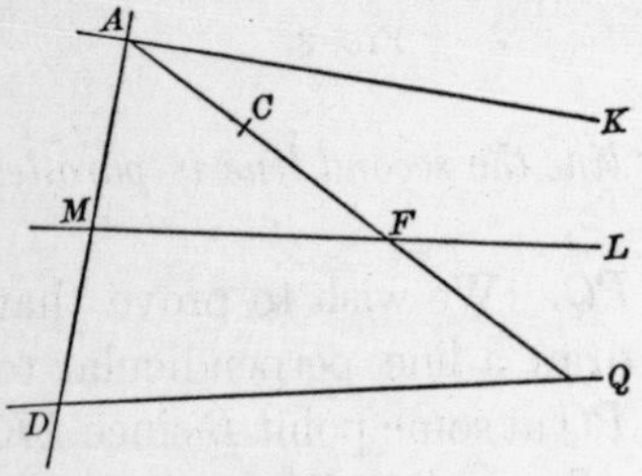

FIG. 4.

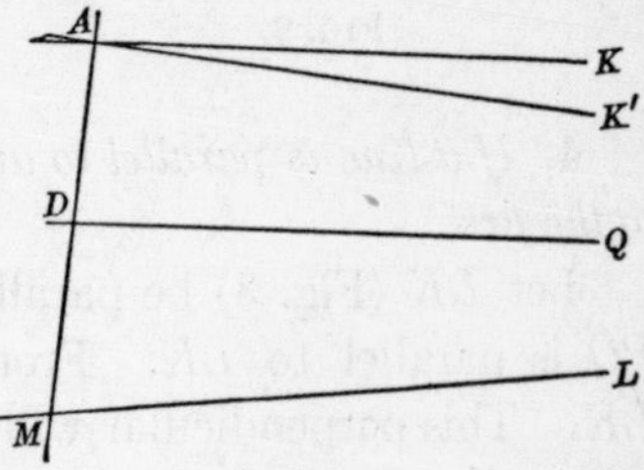

FIG. 5.

AC any line through A in the angle opening DAK. AC will meet ML in some point F since AK is parallel to ML. CF produced will also meet DQ, since ML and DQ are parallel.

Hence any line through A in the angle opening DAK meets DQ. On the other hand AK cannot meet DQ since it cannot meet ML. Hence AK and DQ are parallel.

In the second case, let AK and DQ (Fig. 5) be each parallel to ML. We wish to prove that AK is parallel to DQ. Draw through A the line AK' parallel to DQ. Then by the first case AK' is parallel to ML and hence coincides with AK.

III. THE EUCLIDEAN ASSUMPTION

6. We may replace Postulate 5 of *Euclid* or Assumption XIII of *Veblen* by the following assumption while retaining all the other assumptions of either author.

Through any point in the plane there goes one and only one line parallel to a given line.

That one parallel exists, is, in fact, proved in the twenty-eighth proposition of the first book of *Euclid* (*Veblen*, VIII). To assume that only one parallel exists is equivalent to assuming that in Fig. 1 the lines AL and AK form one and the same straight line. Hence

$$\measuredangle HAL = \measuredangle HAK = \text{rt. } \measuredangle.$$

Take now M (Fig. 6), the middle point of AB and draw MD perpendicular to PQ and intersecting AL in C. Then as

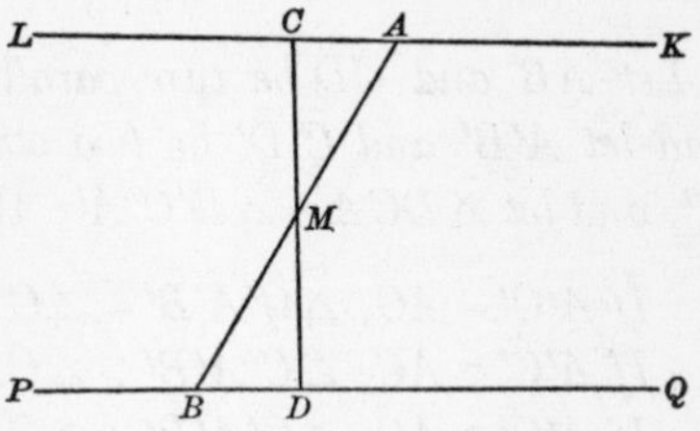

FIG. 6.

just shown, $\measuredangle DCK$ is a right angle. The two right triangles AMC and BMD are congruent and $\measuredangle CAB = \measuredangle ABD$. Therefore

$$\measuredangle QBA + \measuredangle BAK = 2 \text{ rt. } \measuredangle\text{s}.$$

By our definition of parallels, any line through A in the angle BAK meets PQ.

Hence our assumption is equivalent to *Euclid's* Postulate 5. From this follows the Euclidean geometry.

IV. THE LOBACHEVSKIAN ASSUMPTION

7. While retaining all the other assumptions of the Euclidean geometry, we will replace Postulate 5 of *Euclid* or Assumption XIII of *Veblen* by the following assumption due to *Lobachevsky.*

Through any point in the plane there go two lines parallel to a given line.

It follows that, in Fig. 6,

$$\measuredangle QBA + \measuredangle BAK < 2 \text{ rt. } \measuredangle\text{s.}$$

For if the sum of the angles QBA and BAK were greater than two right angles we could draw through A in the angle BAK a line not meeting BQ by Euclid I, 28. This is contrary to our assumption that AK and BQ are parallel.

On the other hand, if the sum of the angles were equal to two right angles we should have the Euclidean assumption.

8. The following theorems are of vital importance in subsequent proofs.

Theorem I. *Let AB and CD be two parallel lines cut by a third line CD and let $A'B'$ and $C'D'$ be two other parallel lines cut by a line $A'C'$, and let $\measuredangle DCA = \measuredangle D'C'A'$;* then

(1) *If* $A'C' = AC$, $\measuredangle C'A'B' = \measuredangle CAB$
(2) *If* $A'C' < AC$, $\measuredangle C'A'B' > \measuredangle CAB$
(3) *If* $A'C' > AC$, $\measuredangle C'A'B' < \measuredangle CAB$

Consider first the case $A'C' = AC$ (Fig. 7).

If $\measuredangle C'A'B'$ were less than $\measuredangle CAB$ draw AK so that $\measuredangle CAK = \measuredangle C'A'B'$. Then AK meets CD in some point K. Take K' on

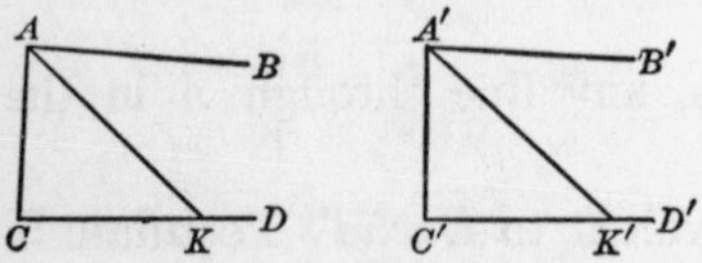

FIG. 7.

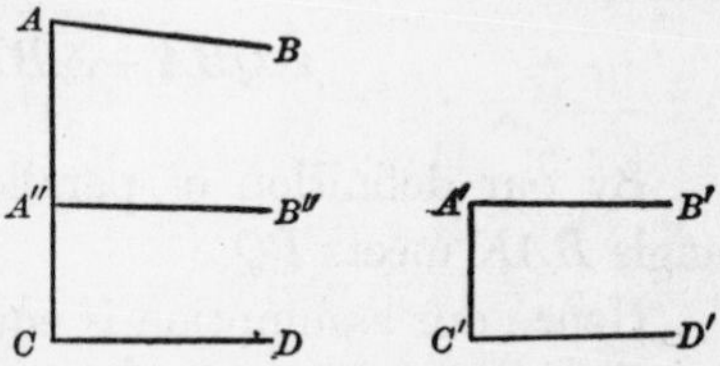

FIG. 8.

$C'D'$ so that $C'K' = CK$ and draw $A'K'$. Then the triangles ACK and $A'C'K'$ are congruent (Euclid I, 4) and $\measuredangle C'A'K' = \measuredangle CAK$

$=\measuredangle C'A'B'$. This is impossible, since $A'B'$ does not meet $C'D'$. Hence $\measuredangle C'A'B'$ cannot be less than $\measuredangle CAB$. Similarly $\measuredangle CAB$ cannot be less than $\measuredangle C'A'B'$ and hence $\measuredangle C'A'B'=\measuredangle CAB$.

Consider secondly the case $A'C'< AC$ (Fig. 8).

On CA take CA'' equal to $C'A'$ and draw $A''B''$ parallel to CD. Then $\measuredangle CA''B''=\measuredangle C'A'B'$, as just shown, and AB and $A''B''$ are parallel (sec. 5). Therefore, by sec. 7,

$$\measuredangle B''A''A+\measuredangle A''AB< 2 \text{ rt. } \measuredangle\text{s}.$$

But $\measuredangle B''A''A+\measuredangle CA''B''=2 \text{ rt. } \measuredangle\text{s}$,

whence $\measuredangle A''AB< \measuredangle CA''B''$;

that is $\measuredangle CAB< \measuredangle C'A'B'$.

The third case $A'C' >AC$, is handled like the second case.

Theorem II. *Let AB and CD be two parallel lines cut by a third line AC and let $A'B'$ and $C'D'$ be two other parallel lines cut by a line $A'C'$, and let $\measuredangle CAB=\measuredangle C'A'B'$ and $\measuredangle ACD=\measuredangle A'C'D'$, then $AC=A'C'$.*

For each of the suppositions $AC< A'C'$ and $AC >A'C'$ contradicts Theorem I.

If in Theorem I we take $\measuredangle DCA=\measuredangle D'C'A'=\text{rt. }\measuredangle$, the angles CAB and $C'A'B'$ are the angles of parallelism for the distance AC and $A'C'$ respectively (sec. 2). Theorem I includes then, as a special case, the following:

Theorem III. *The angle of parallelism is fixed for a fixed distance and decreases as the distance increases.*

If we denote the distance AH (Fig. 1) by p, the angle of parallelism HAL is denoted in *Lobachevsky's* notation by $\Pi\ (p)$. Theorem III asserts that $\Pi\ (p)$ is a decreasing function of p. The exact determination of $\Pi\ (p)$ will be given in sec. 33. We may note, however, that $\Pi\ (p)$ is always less than a right angle. In other words,

Theorem IV. *If two lines have a common perpendicular they neither intersect nor are parallel.*

The converse of IV is also true, as we shall now show.

9. *Two straight lines which neither intersect nor are parallel have a common perpendicular.**

Let LM and EF (Fig. 9) be two straight lines which neither intersect nor are parallel. We wish to show that they have a common perpendicular. Take A and B any two points on LM and draw AH and BK perpendicular to EF. If $AH=BK$ the existence of a common perpendicular to LM and EF follows quickly, as shown below. Suppose then that

$$BK < AH.$$

Draw KS parallel to LM. Place † the rt. $\measuredangle$ FKB on the rt. $\measuredangle$ FHA so that K falls on H, KF takes the direction HF

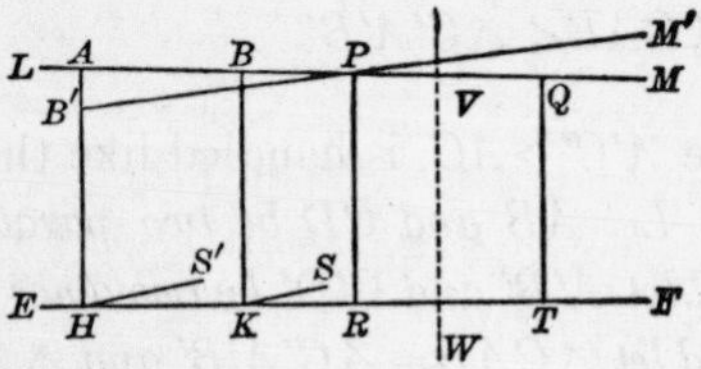

FIG. 9.

and KB takes the direction HA. The point B falls at B' between H and A, BM takes the position $B'M'$ and KS the position HS', parallel to $B'M'$.

Since $\measuredangle FKS = \measuredangle FHS'$ a line parallel to KS (and hence to LM) drawn through H lies in the angle opening FHS' (sec. 7). Hence HS' intersects LM and therefore $B'M'$ intersects LM at some point P (*Veblen*, Theorem 17).

Draw PR perpendicular to EF. Place the right angle FHB' on the right angle FKB. Then the line PR takes the position QT, where $QT=PR$ and QT is perpendicular to EF.

Take now W halfway between R and T and draw WV

* The proofs in this and the following section are due to *Hilbert*, Neue Begründung der Bolyai-Lobatschefkyschen Geometrie, Math. Ann., Vol. LVII.

† Here and subsequently, we use the principle of superposition to abbreviate the proof. The theorems on congruence may of course be employed without the aid of any idea of mechanical motion.

perpendicular to EF. Fold the figure TWV on WV. Then T falls on R, TQ coincides with RP, and $\measuredangle WVQ$ coincides with $\measuredangle WVP$. Hence WV is the required common perpendicular to EF and LM.

10. *Any angle is an angle of parallelism belonging to a certain distance.*

Let KAE (Fig. 10) be any given α. We wish to find a distance p for which α is the angle of parallelism.

Construct $LAE = \alpha$ and on AK and AL take two points B and C so that $AB = AC$. Connect B and C and draw BL' parallel to BL and CK' parallel to CK. Draw also CF bisecting $\measuredangle LCK'$ and BG bisecting $\measuredangle KBL'$. It is evident that the figure is symmetric with respect to the line AE.

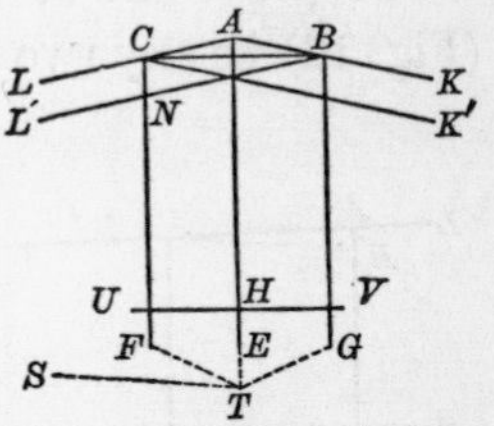

Fig. 10.

The lines CF and BG cannot intersect. For if they did intersect at a point T, we could draw TS parallel to AL and BL' and then, since $\measuredangle LCT = \measuredangle L'BT$ and $CT = BT$, we should have $\measuredangle STC = \measuredangle STB$ (sec. 8, I) which is impossible.

Also CF and BG cannot be parallel, for if they were, since $\measuredangle LCF = \measuredangle L'BG$ and $\measuredangle CNL' = \measuredangle BNF$, we should have $CN = NB$ (sec. 8, II) and therefore $\measuredangle NCB = \measuredangle NBC = \measuredangle K'CB$, which is impossible.

Since FC and BG neither intersect nor are parallel, they have (sec. 9) a common perpendicular UV, which is also, by the symmetry of the figure, perpendicular to AE at H. We assert that UV is parallel to AK.

If UV were not parallel to AK we could draw from each of the points U and V a line parallel to AK and CK'. Since $CU = BV$ and $\measuredangle UCK' = \measuredangle VBK$, these two parallels would make equal angles with UV (sec. 8, I) which is impossible.

Hence the angle KAE is the angle of parallelism for the distance AH.

11. *Two parallel lines approach each other continually and their distance apart eventually becomes less than any assigned quantity.*

Let LK and PQ (Fig. 11) be two parallel lines, and A and B two points on LK, the point B lying from A in the direction of parallelism. From A and B draw AH and BM perpendicular to PQ. We wish to prove $BM < AH$.

Take R half way between H and M and draw the line RC perpendicular to PQ. The angle RCB is less than a right angle, since it is an angle of parallelism. Therefore $\measuredangle RCB < \measuredangle RCA$. Hence, if the quadrilateral $RMBC$ is folded over on RC as an axis, the line MB takes the position HB' where $MB = HB' < HA$. Hence the lines LK and PQ continually approach each other.

To prove the second part of the theorem, let AK and HQ (Fig. 12) be any two parallel lines and AH a perpendicular from

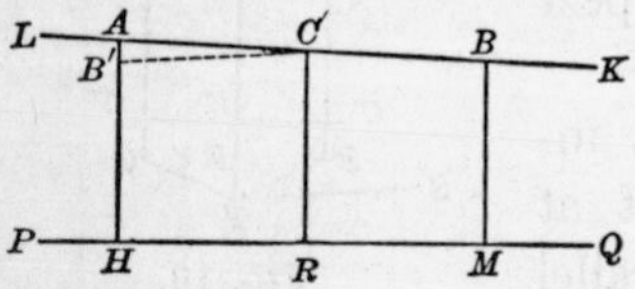

FIG. 11.

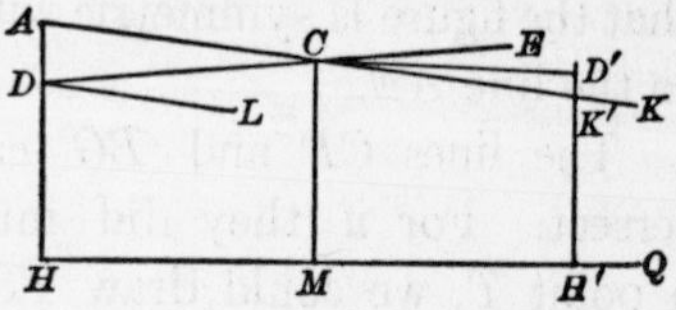

FIG. 12.

A to HQ. Let ε be any assigned quantity and lay off on AH the distance $HD < \varepsilon$. Draw DL parallel to HQ and AK. Then $\measuredangle HDL <$ rt. $\measuredangle$. Hence the line DE drawn from D perpendicular to AH will meet AK in some point C. From C draw CM perpendicular to HQ. Now $\measuredangle MCD > \measuredangle MCK$, for $\measuredangle MCK$ is the angle of parallelism for the distance CM, and the line CD and MH neither intersect nor are parallel, since they have a common perpendicular (sec. 8).

Hence if the quadrilateral $MHCD$ is folded over on MC as an axis, it takes the position $MH'D'C$ where CK lies between CD' and MQ. Then CK meets $H'D'$ in some point K' where $H'K' < H'D' = HD$. Hence $H'K' < \varepsilon$.

12. *If two lines are not parallel they will diverge if sufficiently far produced, and their distance apart will eventually become greater than any assigned quantity.*

Consider first two intersecting straight lines AM and AN (Fig. 13). Let B and D be two points on AM such that $AD > AB$, and let BC and DE be drawn perpendicular to AN. We wish to prove $DE > BC$.

Suppose if possible that $DE = BC$. Then a line drawn perpendicular to AN at the middle point of CE would be also perpendicular to AM, which is impossible, since AM and AN intersect (sec. 8, IV).

Suppose, if possible, that $DE < BC$. Take AF less than each of the distances DE and AB and draw FG perpendicular to N. Then $FG < AF < DE$. But $BC > DE$. Hence at some point K between G and C there is a perpendicular HK such that $HK = DE$. But this is impossible, as just shown. Therefore $DE > BC$.

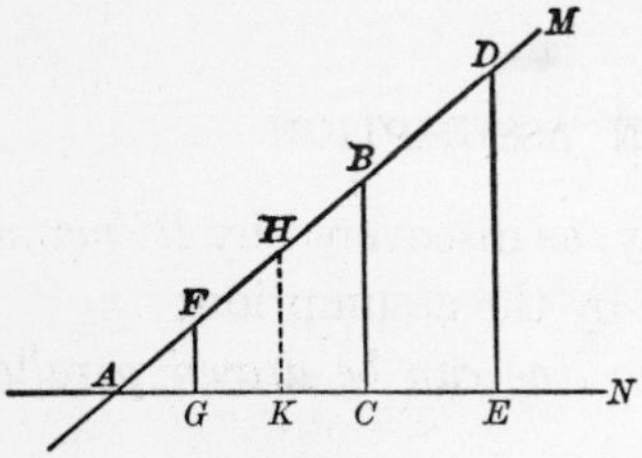

FIG. 13.

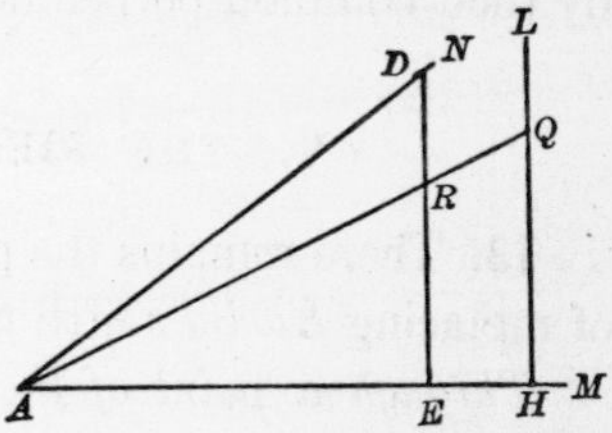

FIG. 14.

To show that there is no superior limit to the length of ED, take AH (Fig. 14) so that $\measuredangle MAN$ is the angle of parallelism for AH (sec. 10) and draw HL perpendicular to AM. Then AN and HL are parallel. Let a be any quantity, no matter how large, and take Q on HL so that $HQ = 2a$. Connect Q and A, and at E, a point between A and H, draw a line perpendicular to AH, intersecting AQ in R. We can take E so near H that RE will differ from HQ by as little as we please and certainly so that $RE > a$. But RE will intersect AN in a point D, since the angle of parallelism for AE is greater than $\measuredangle HAN$ (sec. 8, III). Then $DE > RE > a$. Since a is any positive number, there is no superior limit to the length of DE.

Consider now two non-intersecting lines MN and PQ (Fig. 15). At A, any point on MN draw AK parallel to PQ. Since AK and MN intersect, their distance apart eventually becomes greater than any assigned quantity. But the distance between

AK and PQ eventually becomes less than any assigned quantity (sec. 11). Hence the distance between AN and PQ eventually becomes greater than any assigned quantity.

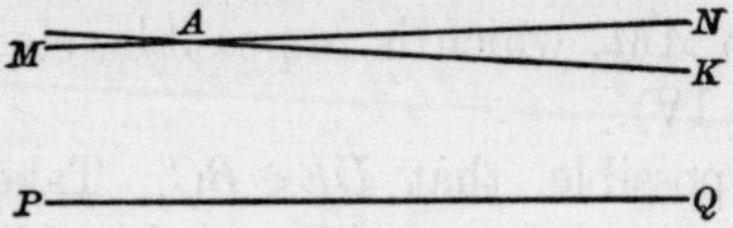

FIG. 15.

It is of course possible that AN and PQ approach each other for a time, but they eventually diverge. In fact the shortest distance between them may be shown to be measured by their common perpendicular.

V. THE RIEMANNIAN ASSUMPTION

13. There remains the possibility, as discovered by *Riemann*, of replacing *Euclid's* fifth postulate by the assumption:

Through a point of the plane no line can be drawn parallel to a given line.

In other words all lines of the pencil with its vertex at A (Fig. 1) intersect PQ.

This assumption contradicts proposition 28 of *Euclid's* first book, so that it is necessary to modify the assumptions upon which that theorem depends. Proposition 28 depends upon proposition 16, which in turn depends upon the tacit assumption that two straight lines cannot enclose a space. This assumption is satisfied when applied to objective space in the domain of experience. We will accordingly assume that *the Euclidean assumptions, with the exception of the parallel postulate, are valid in a sufficiently restricted portion of space,* that is, in a portion of space in which no straight line can be drawn of greater length than some fixed line of length M.

We may proceed similarly with the *Veblen* assumptions. Let $[S]$ be our space, for which all the assumptions, except II, are made. And let $[S_0]$ be a subset of points of $[S]$ for which, in addition, Assumption II is made. Then in $[S_0]$ we have all the theorems proved by *Veblen*, and in [S] those theorems which do not depend upon Assumption II. The assumptions and theorems concerning congruence enable us to compare geometric configurations in [S_0] with others which lie outside of [S_0]. In particular, the theorems on the congruence of triangles are independent of the positions of the triangles.

With this preparation, we may proceed to examine the results of the Riemannian assumption.

14. *All lines perpendicular to the same straight line meet in a point at a constant distance from the straight line.*

Let LK (Fig. 16) be any straight line and A and B any two points upon it. By the Riemannian hypothesis AO and BO, perpendicular to LK, meet in a point O. Since it is conceivable that the perpendiculars may meet more than once we assume explicitly that the two perpendiculars have no common point on the segment AO or BO. We assume also that the triangle ABO lies in the region [S_0] of sec. 13, so that in particular only one straight line can be drawn from O to any point of the segment AB.

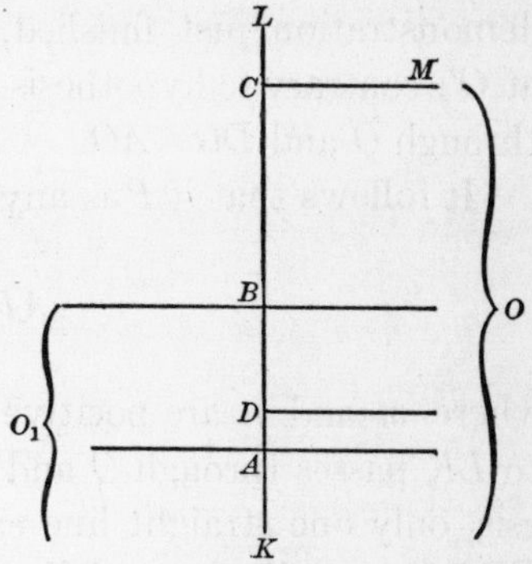

FIG. 16.

Since

$$\measuredangle BAO = \measuredangle ABO,$$

$$BO = AO$$

by Euclid, I, 6.

Construct $\measuredangle BOM = \measuredangle AOB$. Then by the Riemannian hypothesis the line OM meets LK in a point C. The triangle BOC has two angles and an included side congruent respectively to two angles and an included side of the triangle AOB. Hence

$$\measuredangle BCO = \measuredangle ABO = \text{rt. } \measuredangle$$

and $$OC = OB = OA.$$

By repeating this demonstration, we prove that if P is a point on LK such that

$$AP = m \cdot AB,$$

where m is a positive integer, the line OP is perpendicular to LK at P and $PO = AO$. But only one perpendicular can be drawn at P to LK. Hence this perpendicular passes through O.

Now take D, so that

$$AB = n \cdot AD,$$

where n is a positive integer, and draw a line perpendicular to LK at D. If this perpendicular should intersect either BO or AO at a point O' in the segments BO or AO, then, by the demonstration just finished, BO and AO would also intersect at O', contrary to hypothesis. Hence this perpendicular passes through O and $DO = AO$.

It follows that if P is any point on LK such that

$$AP = \frac{m}{n} AB,$$

where m and n are positive integers, the perpendicular at P to LK passes through O and $PO = AO$. Also, since by hypothesis, only one straight line can be drawn from P to O, the line PO is perpendicular to LK.

Now let P_1 be a point such that

$$AP_1 = \lambda AB,$$

where λ is an irrational number. Take P such that $AP = \frac{m}{n} AB$, draw OP and OP_1, and let $\frac{m}{n}$ pass through rational values approaching λ as a limit.

$$\measuredangle AP_1O = \lim \measuredangle APO, \qquad P_1O = \lim PO.$$

But APO is always a right angle and PO is always equal to AO. Hence $\measuredangle AP_1O = \text{rt. } \measuredangle$ and $P_1O = AO$.

Our theorem is therefore proved for the line LK. If $L'K'$ is any other line, we may take A' and B' any two points on it, and draw the perpendiculars $A'O'$ and $B'O'$, intersecting at O'. Take AB on LK so that $AB = A'B'$. The two triangles ABO and $A'B'O'$ are congruent and $A'O' = AO$. The distance AO is therefore independent of the line LK or of the position of the point A on the line. We will place $OA = \Delta$.

A corollary of our theorem is *that all straight lines are of constant length.* For, from the proof we have used, it is evident that, if P is any point on AB,

$$\frac{AP}{AB} = \frac{\measuredangle AOP}{\measuredangle AOB}.$$

Now if $\measuredangle AOP = 2\pi$, the line OA coincides with OP, and AP becomes l, the total length of the line. Then

$$l = \frac{2\pi \cdot AB}{\measuredangle AOB}.$$

15. *All lines which pass through a point O meet again in a point O_1 such that the distance O_1 is constant.*

Let O (Fig. 16) be any point and OA any line through O. Take $OA = \Delta$ (sec. 14) and draw LK perpendicular to AO. Let OB be any other line through O intersecting LK in B. Then OB is perpendicular to LK (sec. 14). Prolong AO to O_1 so that $AO_1 = AO$ and draw O_1B. The triangles AOB and AO_1B are congruent, since two sides and the included angle of one are congruent respectively to two sides and the included angle of the other. Hence

$$\measuredangle ABO_1 = \measuredangle ABO = \text{rt. } \measuredangle,$$

and

$$O_1B = OB = OA.$$

Therefore the line OBO_1 is a straight line and

$$OO_1 = 2\Delta.$$

Since all lines are of finite length (sec. 14) any line through O returns through O_1 to O. Two cases are usually considered.

First, the point O_1 may coincide with O. The total length of a straight line is then 2Δ and any two lines have only one point in common.

Secondly, the point O_1 may be distinct from O, but the lines OO_1 continued through O_1 meet again in O. The total length of a line is then 4Δ and two lines meet in two points. The Riemannian geometry in this case is the same as the geometry on the surface of a sphere.

VI. THE SUM OF THE ANGLES OF A TRIANGLE

16. Consider any triangle ABC (Fig. 17). Take E, the middle point of AB, F the middle point of AC, and draw a straight line EF. From A, B, and C draw the lines AG, BK, and CL perpendicular to EF.

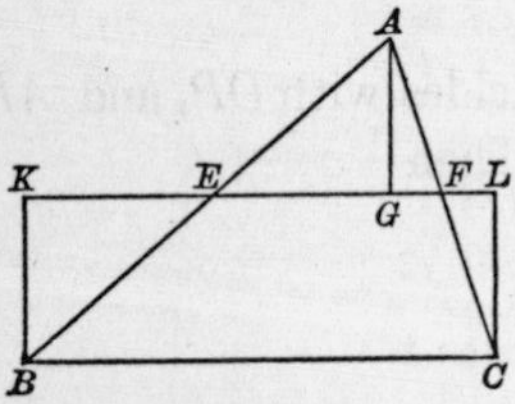

FIG. 17.

In the right triangles AEG and EBK, $EA = EB$ and $\measuredangle GEA = \measuredangle BEK$. Hence the two triangles are congruent and

$$BK = AG, \quad \measuredangle KBE = \measuredangle GAE.$$

Similarly, the right triangles AGF and FLC are congruent and

$$AG = CL, \quad \measuredangle FCL = \measuredangle GAF.$$

If we *define* **equivalent figures** *as those which may be divided into parts which are congruent in pairs*, it appears that the triangle ABC is equivalent to the quadrilateral $BCLK$. Also, the sum of the angles of the triangle ABC is equal to the sum of the angles KBC and LCB of the quadrilateral $BCLK$.

This quadrilateral $BCLK$ has two right angles, L and K, and two equal sides, KB and LC, adjacent to the right angles and opposite to each other. Such a figure we shall call an **isosceles birectangular quadrilateral.**

The study of the sum of the angles and of the area of a triangle is thus reduced to the study of an equivalent isosceles birectangular quadrilateral.

17. Let $ABCD$ (Fig. 18) be an isosceles birectangular quadrilateral with right angles at A and B. For convenience, we shall call AB the **base,** CD the **summit,** and C and D the **summit angles** of the quadrilateral.

Take L the middle point of the base and draw LK perpendicular to the base. Fold $LBDK$ on LK as an axis. It is clear that the point D falls on C. Hence, *the summit angles of an isosceles birectangular quadrilateral are equal.* Also, LK is perpendicular to CD at its middle point K and the quadrilateral $LBDK$ has three right angles.

Now through H, the middle point of LK, draw EF perpendicular to LK. Fold $HFDK$ on HF as an axis. The point D will fall at B', B, or B'' according as KD is less than, equal to,

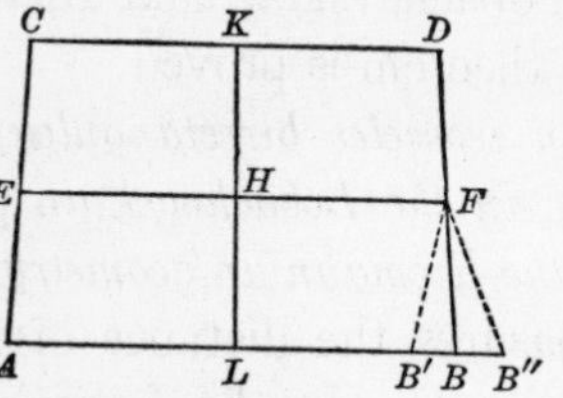

FIG. 18.

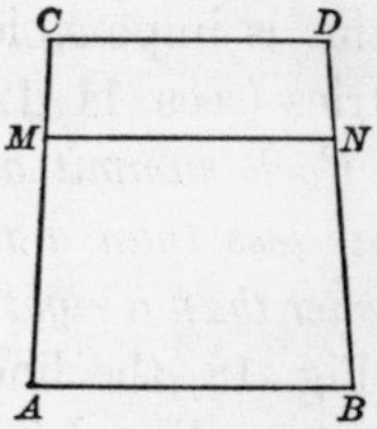

FIG. 19.

or greater than LB. In these three cases $\measuredangle D$ is greater than, equal to, or less than, $\measuredangle B$ respectively. Hence:

Each summit angle of an isosceles birectangular quadrilateral is less than, equal to, or greater than, a right angle, according as the summit of the quadrilateral is greater than, equal to, or less than, the base.

18. *In the Euclidean geometry each summit angle of an isosceles birectangular quadrilateral is equal to a right angle.*

This is a familiar proposition of the Euclidean geometry and need not be proved here. We shall prove, however, the following theorem:

In the Lobachevskian and Riemannian geometries, a summit-angle of an isosceles birectangular quadrilateral cannot equal a right angle.

Let $ABCD$ (Fig. 19) be an isosceles birectangular quadrilateral with right angles at A and B. If possible, suppose $\measuredangle C = \measuredangle D =$ rt. $\measuredangle$. Then (sec. 17) $CD = AB$. Take two points

M and N on AC and BD respectively so that $CM = DN$ and draw MN.

Then $ABMN$ is an isosceles birectangular quadrilateral with right angles at A and B. $MNDC$ is an isosceles birectangular quadrilateral with right angles at C and D. Then MN must be perpendicular to AC and BD or we should have, by sec. 17, MN greater than one and less than the other of the two equal lines AB and CD, which is absurd.

Since M is any point between A and C it appears that the segments AC and BD are equidistant. By prolonging the lines AC and BD and considering congruent segments, it appears that the lines AC and BD are equidistant throughout their extent. Since this is impossible in the Lobachevskian and Riemannian geometries (secs. 11, 12, 13) the theorem is proved.

19. *Each summit angle of an isosceles birectangular quadrilateral is less than a right angle in the Lobachevskian geometry and greater than a right angle in the Riemannian geometry.*

In Fig. 18, the line CK measures the distance of the line AC from the line LK at the point C. In the Lobachevskian geometry, if the line AC is taken sufficiently long, $CK > AL$ (sec. 12). If, therefore, CK were in any position less than AL, there would exist at least one other position in which $CK = AL$. This is impossible (sec. 18) and hence CK is always greater than AL and the angle C less than a right angle (sec. 17).

In the Riemannian geometry the lines AC and LK eventually intersect. Hence, if AC is sufficiently long $CK < AL$, and therefore CK is always less than AL and the angle C greater than a right angle.

20. *In the Euclidean, Lobachevskian, and Riemannian geometries respectively the sum of the angles of a triangle is equal to, less than, and greater than, two right angles.*

We have seen in sec. 16 that the sum of the angles of a triangle is equal to that of the summit angles of an isosceles birectangular quadrilateral.

The theorem then follows from secs. 18, 19.

VII. AREAS

21. According to the definition already given (sec. 16) two polygons are equivalent, or equal in area, if they can be divided into the same number of triangles which are congruent in pairs. We have proved (sec. 16) that a triangle is equivalent to an isosceles birectangular quadrilateral having its summit equal to one side of the triangle, and each summit angle equal to half the sum of the angles of the triangle.

Now, in either the Lobachevskian or the Riemannian geometry an isosceles birectangular quadrilateral is fully determined by its summit and summit angles, for if *ABCD* (Fig. 20)

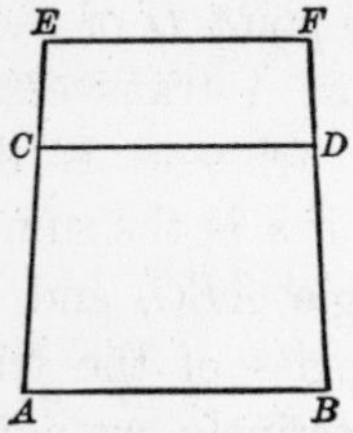

FIG. 20.

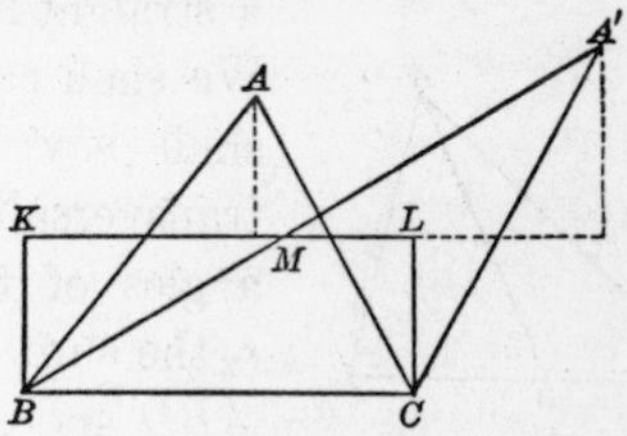

FIG. 21.

and *ABEF* are two isosceles birectangular quadrilaterals with the same summit *EF* and the same summit angles *E* and *F*, their bases *CD* and *AB* must coincide. Otherwise, the quadrilateral *ABCD* would have four right angles, which is impossible (sec. 18). Hence follows the theorem:

In the Lobachevskian and Riemannian geometries, two triangles are equivalent if a side and the sum of the angles of one are equal to a side and the sum of the angles of another.

22. A triangle may be constructed having the same area and the same angle sum as a given triangle, and having one side arbitrarily assumed within certain wide limits.

Let *ABC* (Fig. 21) be a given triangle and *BCKL* the isosceles birectangular quadrilateral constructed as in sec. 16. Let l be a given length. With $\frac{1}{2}l$ as a radius and *B* as a center described an arc of a circle cutting *KL* in *M*. Connect *B* and

M and prolong BM to A' so that $MA' = BM$. Connect A' and C. Then $A'BC$ is the required triangle, as is readily shown.

That the construction may be possible, it is necessary, on the one hand, that $BM > BK$, a condition which is certainly met if $l > AB$.

On the other hand, it is necessary, in the Riemannian geometry, that l should be less than the constant 2Δ (sec. 15).

If, now, we have two triangles with the same angle sum, we may take l greater than one side of each, and replace each by an equivalent one with the same angle sum and a side equal to l. The two new triangles are equivalent (sec. 21). Hence:

Any two triangles with the same angle sum are equivalent.

23. Consider any triangle ABC (Fig. 22) and draw from A a straight line to any point D of the base. We shall call this line a transversal and shall say that the triangle is divided transversally. Now if s is the sum of the angles of the triangle ABC, and s_1 and s_2 the sum of the angles of the triangles ABD and ADC respectively, we have

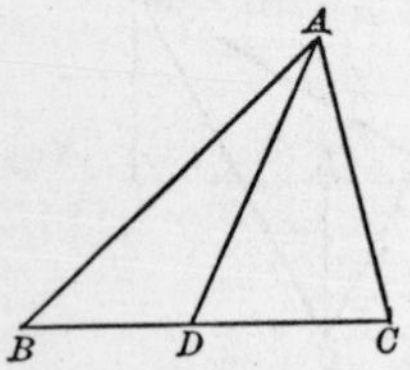

FIG. 22.

$$s = s_1 + s_2 - 2 \text{ rt. } \measuredangle\text{s}.$$

If we adopt such a unit of angle measure that a right angle shall have the measure $\frac{\pi}{2}$, the above equation may be written in either of the forms

$$\pi - s = (\pi - s_1) + (\pi - s_2)$$

or

$$s - \pi = (s_1 - \pi) + (s_2 - \pi).$$

In the Lobachevskian geometry, $\pi - s$ is positive (sec. 20) and is called the **defect** of the triangle. In the Riemannian geometry $s - \pi$ is positive and is called the **excess** of the triangle. Hence we may state the theorem:

If a triangle is divided transversally, the sum of the defects, or excesses, of the parts, is equal to the defect, or excess, of the triangle.

The theorem evidently remains true if the triangle is further subdivided by successive transversals of the parts, as shown, for example, in Fig. 23. Further *Hilbert* * has shown that any division of a triangle may be reduced to transverse divisions. We have accordingly the more general theorem:

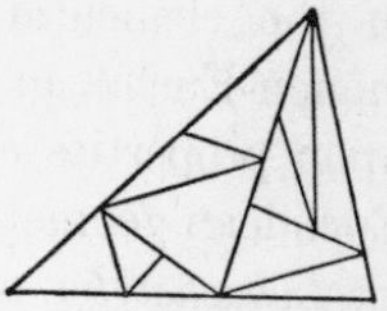

Fig. 23.

In the Lobachevskian and Riemannian geometries the defect, or excess, of any triangle is equal to the sum of the defects, or excesses, of triangles which are formed from it by any system of division.

24. Since equivalent triangles may be divided into the same number of triangles congruent in pairs (sec. 21), and since obviously congruent triangles have the same defect, or excess, it follows that *any two equivalent triangles have the same defect, or excess.* The converse theorem has been proved in sec. 22.

We are now enabled to take the defect, or excess, of a triangle as the measure of its area, since the essential properties of a measure of area are that two triangles with the same area have the same measure, that two triangles with the same measure have the same area, and that the measure of a whole is the sum of the measure of its parts. Hence we may say:

In the Lobachevskian geometry the area of a triangle is equal to a constant times its defect. In the Riemannian geometry, the area of a triangle is equal to a constant times its excess.

The value of the constant depends evidently upon the unit of area employed.

The area of a polygon is found by dividing it into triangles.

---

* Grundlagen der Geometrie, Vol. VII of Wissenschaft und Hypothese, Leipzig, 1909.

VIII. NON-EUCLIDEAN TRIGONOMETRY

25. The definitions of the trigonometric functions as given in the elementary trigonometry are evidently not available in non-Euclidean geometries, since these definitions are based upon properties of similar triangles which are true only in the Euclidean geometry.

Lobachevsky met this difficulty by the construction of a "limit-surface," or horisphere, on which the Euclidean geometry and trigonometry are valid at the same time that the Lobachevskian geometry is valid on the plane. By the aid of this surface and the sphere he obtained the formulas which will be found in sec. 34.

This method, however, cannot be applied to the Riemannian geometry. We shall therefore follow a more general method which has also the advantage of operating entirely in the plane. The method, however, is not as elementary as the other, and we shall be obliged to state some results without proof and to give a mere outline of other proofs.*

We start with the purely analytic definitions of the trigonometric functions. That is, e^x being defined by the series

$$e^x = 1 + \frac{x}{1} + \frac{x^2}{2!} + \frac{x^3}{3!} + \cdot \cdot,$$

the trigonometric functions are defined by the equations

$$\sin x = \frac{e^{xi} - e^{-xi}}{2i},$$

$$\cos x = \frac{e^{xi} + e^{-xi}}{2},$$

$$\tan x = \frac{1}{i} \frac{e^{xi} - e^{-xi}}{e^{xi} + e^{-xi}},$$

where $i = \sqrt{-1}$. These functions obey all the formulas of trigometry and if x is a real number they are real.

---

* For complete proofs and historical notes consult *Coolidge*, The Elements of Non-Euclidean Geometry, Oxford, 1909, expecially Chapter IV, where all the requirements of rigor are met.

If x is pure imaginary, the above equations lead to the hyperbolic functions, which are defined by the following equations:

$$-i \sin ix = \frac{e^x - e^{-x}}{2} = \sinh x,$$

$$\cos ix = \frac{e^x + e^{-x}}{2} = \cosh x,$$

$$-i \tan ix = \frac{e^x - e^{-x}}{e^x + e^{-x}} = \tanh x.$$

If x is real, the hyperbolic functions are real, and formulas for this use are readily obtained, if needed, from the trigonometric functions.

The following properties of $\cos x$ are important for us:

If $\cos x < 1$, x is real; if $\cos x > 1$, x is pure imaginary, except perhaps for multiples of the period 2π which may always be added.

If we place $\cos mx = f(x)$, $f(x)$ satisfies the functional equation

$$f(x+y) + f(x-y) = 2f(x)f(y).$$

Conversely, if $f(x)$ is a continuous function of x satisfying the above equation, then $f(x) = \cos mx$, m being a constant, real or complex.

26. The sine and cosine of an acute angle may be defined as follows. The extension to angles of any size is then made as in the ordinary trigonometry.

Let A (Fig. 24) be any acute angle and MP the perpendicular from any point P of one side to the other side, then it may be shown that $\frac{AM}{AP}$ approaches a limit as AP approaches zero, and that $\lim \frac{AM}{AP}$ is a continuous function of A, which satisfies the functional equation of sec. 25. Hence $\lim \frac{AM}{AP} = \cos mA$ Since $AM < AP$, the coefficient m is real, and if we adopt a system of measurement of angle by which a right angle has the measure $\frac{\pi}{2}$, we may place $m=1$. Hence, finally,

$$\lim \frac{AM}{AP} = \cos A.$$

In a similar manner

$$\lim \frac{MP}{AP} = \sin A.$$

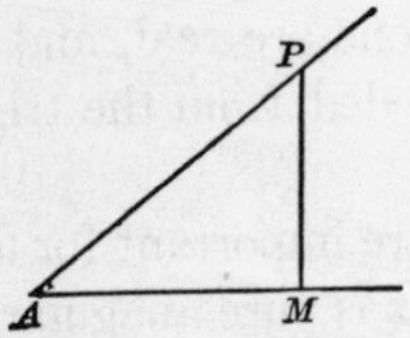

FIG. 24.

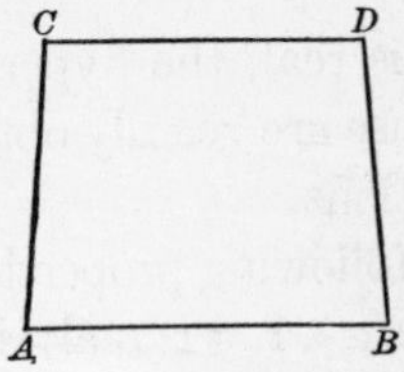

FIG. 25.

27. Let AC (Fig. 25), be any straight line of given length a. From A draw AB perpendicular to AC and take AB any length. At B draw BD perpendicular to AB, take $BD=AC$, and complete the isosceles birectangular quadrilateral $ABCD$. Then it may be shown that $\frac{CD}{AB}$ approaches a limit, as AB approaches zero, and that this limit is a continuous function of a, satisfying the functional equation of sec. 25. Hence

$$\lim \frac{CD}{AB} = \cos ma.$$

In the Lobachevskian geometry, $CD > AB$ and m is pure imaginary. In this case, we place $m = \frac{i}{k}$, where k is real, and have

$$\lim \frac{CD}{AB} = \cos \frac{ia}{k} = \cosh \frac{a}{k}.$$

In the Riemannian geometry, $CD<AB$ and m is real. In this case, we place $m=\frac{1}{k}$, and have

$$\lim \frac{CD}{AB}=\cos \frac{a}{k}.$$

There appears here a striking property of the non-Euclidean geometries in the existence of functions of distances analogous to functions of angles. The constant k depends upon the unit of distance employed.

If we apply the construction of this article to the Euclidean geometry we obtain the trivial result $\lim \frac{CD}{AB}=1$. It is worth noting that this comes out of the previous results by placing $k=\infty$.

28. We shall indicate in this section a method by which a fundamental formula connecting the sides of a right triangle may be obtained.

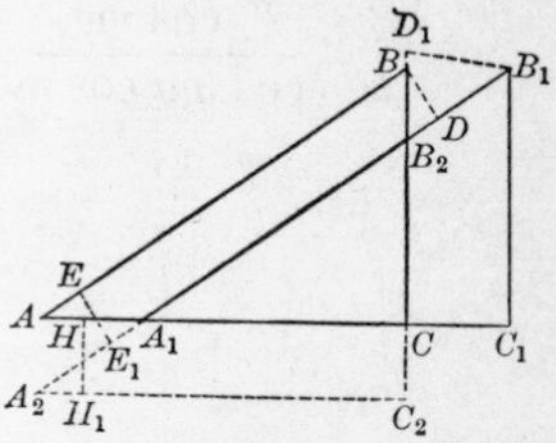

FIG. 26.

Let ABC (Fig. 26), be a triangle with the right angle at C and with the sides $AB=c$, $AC=b$, $CB=a$. Take AA_1 a small distance on AC and prolong AC to C_1 so that

$$AA_1=CC_1,$$

and construct the triangle $A_1B_1C_1$ congruent to ABC. Let B_2 be the point of intersection of A_1B_1 and BC. Prolong B_1A_1 and BC so that

$$A_1A_2=B_1B_2,$$

and

$$CC_2=BB_2,$$

and construct the triangle $A_2B_2C_2$ which differs slightly from ABC.

From B_1 draw B_1D_1 perpendicular to BC, and from B draw BD perpendicular to A_1B_1. Also draw HH_1, the common perpendicular to AC and A_2C_2, and EE_1 the common perpendicular to AB and A_2B_2. EE_1 evidently bisects AA_1, and HH_1 passes near the middle point of A_1A_2. Then as AA_1 approaches zero as a limit it may be shown that

$$\lim \frac{BD}{EE_1} = \cos mc,$$

$$\lim \frac{B_1D_1}{CC_1} = \cos ma,$$

$$\lim \frac{CC_2}{HH_1} = \cos mb.$$

In fact, from the definition of sec. 27, the reader will have no difficulty in seeing that these relations are, at least, approximately true. The rigorous demonstration may be found in the book by *Coolidge* just cited.

We have, then,

$$\frac{\cos mc}{\cos ma \cos mb} = \lim \frac{BD}{EE_1} \cdot \frac{CC_1}{B_1D_1} \cdot \frac{HH_1}{CC_2}$$

$$= \lim \frac{BD}{EE_1} \cdot \frac{AA_1}{B_1D_1} \cdot \frac{HH_1}{BB_2}$$

$$= \lim \frac{BD}{BB_2} \cdot \frac{AA_1}{EE_1} \cdot \frac{HH_1}{A_1A_2} \cdot \frac{B_1B_2}{B_1D_1}.$$

Now it may be shown that

$$\sin B = \lim \frac{BD}{BB_2} = \lim \frac{B_1D_1}{B_1B_2},$$

$$\sin A = \lim \frac{HH_1}{A_1A_2} = \lim \frac{EE_1}{AA_1},$$

as may be seen approximately from Fig. 26, and the definition of sec. 26.

We have, accordingly,

$$\frac{\cos mc}{\cos ma \cos mb} = \sin B \cdot \frac{1}{\sin A} \cdot \sin A \cdot \frac{1}{\sin B};$$

or

$$\cos mc = \cos ma \cos mb.$$

29. Let ABC (Fig. 27) be a triangle with right angle at C and $AC=b$, $BC=a$, $AB=c$. Take any point D on AC and draw BD, and DE perpendicular to AB. Let $BD=l$, $DE=p$, $AE=q$, $AD=k$. Then (sec. 28)

$$\begin{aligned}\cos ml &= \cos ma \cos m(b-k)\\ &= \cos mc \cos mk + \cos ma \sin mb \sin mk\\ \cos ml &= \cos mp \cos m(c-q)\\ &= \cos mc \cos mk + \cos mp \sin mc \sin mq,\end{aligned}$$

whence

$$\cos ma \sin mb \sin mk = \cos mp \sin mc \sin mq.$$

By use of the relations $\cos mc = \cos ma \cos mb$ and $\cos mk = \cos mp \cos mq$, we find readily

$$\frac{\tan mb}{\tan mc} = \frac{\tan mq}{\tan mk}.$$

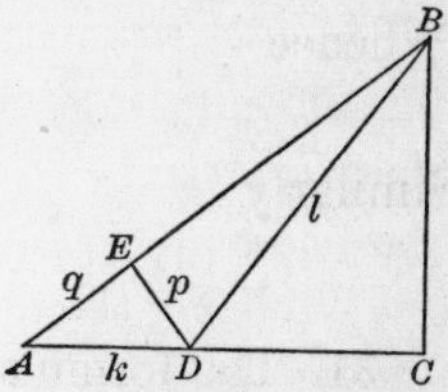

Fig. 27.

Now as k approaches zero as a limit, q approaches zero also, and $\lim \dfrac{\tan mq}{\tan mk} = \lim \dfrac{q}{k} = \cos A$.

Hence

$$\frac{\tan mb}{\tan mc} = \cos A.$$

30. From the result of sec. 29, we have

$$\begin{aligned}\sin^2 A &= \frac{\tan^2 mc - \tan^2 mb}{\tan^2 mc}\\ &= \frac{\sin^2 mc - \tan^2 mb \cos^2 mc}{\sin^2 mc}\\ &= \frac{1-(1+\tan^2 mb)\cos^2 mc}{\sin^2 mc}\\ &= \frac{1-\dfrac{\cos^2 mc}{\cos^2 mb}}{\sin^2 mc} = \frac{1-\cos^2 ma}{\sin^2 mc}.\end{aligned}$$

Since A is an acute angle, we have

$$\sin A = \frac{\sin ma}{\sin mc}.$$

Similarly

$$\sin B = \frac{\sin mb}{\sin mc}.$$

From sec. 29 and these results we have

$$\frac{\cos A}{\sin B} = \frac{\cos mc}{\cos mb} = \cos ma.$$

Whence

$$\cos A = \cos ma \sin B.$$

Similarly

$$\cos B = \cos mb \sin A.$$

31. The formulas obtained in secs. 28–30 are applicable to both the Lobachevskian and the Riemannian geometries. For the Riemannian geometry, we place $m = \frac{1}{k}$ and make the following collection of the formulas:

$$\cos \frac{c}{k} = \cos \frac{a}{k} \cos \frac{b}{k}$$

$$\sin \frac{a}{k} = \sin \frac{c}{k} \sin A$$

$$\tan \frac{a}{k} = \tan \frac{c}{k} \cos B$$

$$\cos A = \cos \frac{a}{k} \sin B$$

$$\sin \frac{b}{k} = \sin \frac{c}{k} \sin B$$

$$\tan \frac{b}{k} = \tan \frac{c}{k} \cos A$$

$$\cos B = \cos \frac{b}{k} \sin A.$$

32. We obtain from secs. 28–30 the formulas for the Lobachevskian geometry by placing $m=\frac{i}{k}$ and replacing the trigonometric functions by the hyperbolic ones. We have

$$\cosh\frac{c}{k}=\cosh\frac{a}{k}\cosh\frac{b}{k}$$

$$\sinh\frac{a}{k}=\sinh\frac{c}{k}\sin A$$

$$\tanh\frac{a}{k}=\tanh\frac{c}{k}\cos B$$

$$\cos A=\cosh\frac{a}{k}\sin B$$

$$\sinh\frac{b}{k}=\sinh\frac{c}{k}\sin B$$

$$\tanh\frac{b}{k}=\tanh\frac{c}{k}\cos A$$

$$\cos B=\cosh\frac{b}{k}\sin A.$$

It is worth noticing that the formulas for the Euclidean trigonometry come out of those in sec. 31 or sec. 32 as limit cases when $k=\infty$ (cf. also sec. 43).

33. The formulas of sec. 32 may be used to obtain an expression for the angle of parallelism belonging to a distance x.

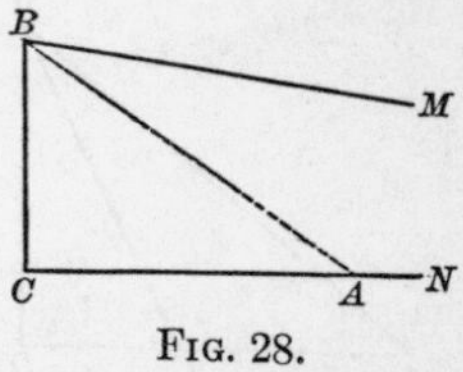

FIG. 28.

Let BM (Fig. 28) be parallel to CN and BC perpendicular to CN. The figure $NCBM$ may be regarded as the limit of a right triangle ABC in which $BC=x$ is constant, A approaches zero and B approaches $\Pi(x)$.

The formula

$$\cos A=\cosh\frac{x}{k}\sin B \quad \text{(sec. 32)}$$

goes over into

$$\sin\Pi(x)=\frac{1}{\cosh\frac{x}{k}}=\frac{2}{e^{\frac{x}{k}}+e^{-\frac{x}{k}}},$$

whence

$$\cos \Pi(x)=\frac{e^{\frac{x}{k}}-e^{-\frac{x}{k}}}{e^{\frac{x}{k}}+e^{-\frac{x}{k}}}=\tanh\frac{x}{k}.$$

Then

$$\tan \tfrac{1}{2}\Pi(x)=\frac{\sin \Pi(x)}{1+\cos \Pi(x)}=e^{-\frac{x}{k}}.$$

34. If we substitute in the formulas of sec. 32 the values of $\cosh\frac{x}{k}$ and $\tanh\frac{x}{k}$ found in sec. 33, and make certain simple reductions, the formulas of sec. 32 take the following forms:

$$\begin{aligned}
\sin \Pi(c)&=\sin \Pi(a)\sin \Pi(b),\\
\tan \Pi(c)&=\tan \Pi(a)\sin A,\\
\cos \Pi(a)&=\cos \Pi(c)\cos B,\\
\sin B&=\sin \Pi(a)\cos A,\\
\tan \Pi(c)&=\tan \Pi(b)\sin B,\\
\cos \Pi(b)&=\cos \Pi(c)\cos A,\\
\sin A&=\sin \Pi(b)\cos B.
\end{aligned}$$

These are the forms found by *Lobachevsky*, except that he writes $A=\Pi(\alpha)$, $B=\Pi(\beta)$, where α and β are the distances corresponding to the angles of parallelism A and B respectively. We shall make no use of these equations, but have given them to facilitate comparison with *Lobachevsky's* own work.

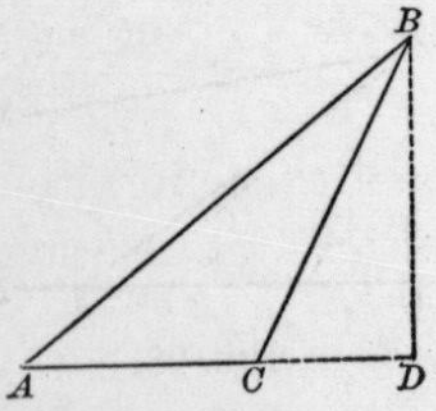

FIG. 29.

35. The above formulas are for right triangles. We shall now obtain one for oblique triangles.

Let ABC (Fig. 29) be any triangle with the angles A, B, and C, and the opposite sides a, b, and c, respectively. Draw BD perpendicular to AC and let $BD=h$, $AD=k$. Then

$$\begin{aligned}
\cos ma&=\cos mh\cos m(k-b)\\
&=\cos mc\cos mb+\sin mb\sin mk\cos mh\\
&=\cos mc\cos mb+\sin mb\tan mk\cos mc\\
&=\cos mc\cos mb+\sin mb\sin mc\cot A.
\end{aligned}$$

IX. NON-EUCLIDEAN ANALYTIC GEOMETRY

36. Let OX and OY (Fig. 30) be two axes of coordinates intersecting at right angles and MP and NP the perpendiculars from any point P to OX and OY respectively. We shall take

$$OM = x, \ ON = y$$

as the coordinates of P. To every point P corresponds a single set of coordinates (x, y) and to any set of coordinates corresponds not more than one point P. But if x and y are assumed arbitrarily there is not necessarily a corresponding point P in the Lobachevskian geometry, since the two perpendiculars at M and N may be parallel or non-intersecting.

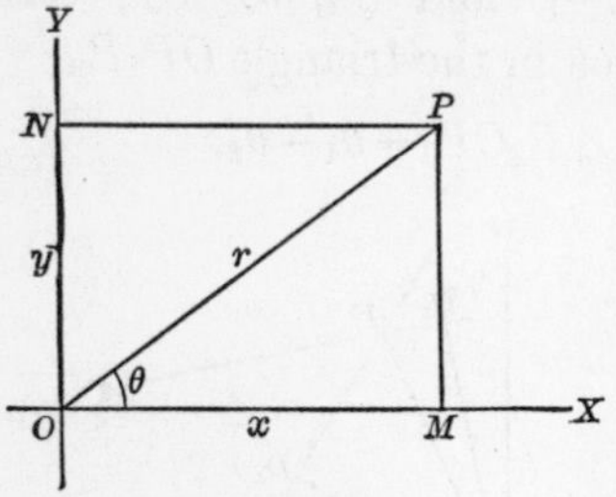

FIG. 30.

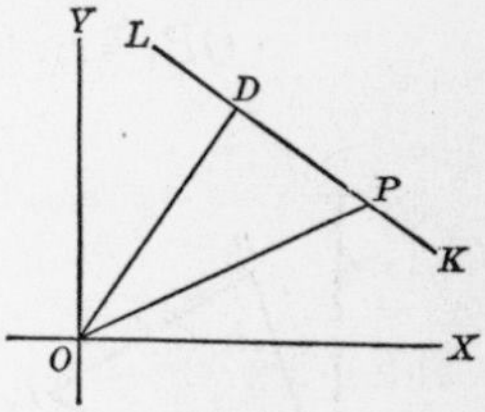

FIG. 31.

By drawing the line OP, we may take

$$OP = r, \ \measuredangle XOP = \theta,$$

as the polar coordinates of P.

Between the two sets of coordinates there exist, in either the Riemannian or the Lobachevskian geometry, the relations (sec. 29)

$$\tan mx = \tan mr \cos \theta,$$
$$\tan my = \tan mr \sin \theta,$$

whence $$\tan^2 mx + \tan^2 my = \tan^2 mr.$$

37. The equation of a straight line may be obtained as follows:

Let LK (Fig. 31) be any straight line determined by the parameters p and α, where p is the length of the perpendicular OD from the origin and α the angle made by OD with the positive direction of OX. Let $P(x, y)$ be any point on LK and draw OP. Then in the triangle OPD,

$$OD = p,\ OP = r,\ \measuredangle POD = \theta - \alpha$$

where (r, θ) are the polar coordinates of P. Hence (sec. 29)

$$\tan mr \cos(\theta - \alpha) = \tan mp,$$

whence (sec. 36)

$$\tan mx \cos\alpha + \tan my \sin\alpha = \tan mp,$$

the required equation.

38. The distance between two points may be found as follows:

Let $P_1(x_1, y_1)$ and $P_2(x_2, y_2)$ (Fig. 32) be any two points with the polar coordinates (r_1, θ_1) and (r_2, θ_2) respectively. Draw OP_1, OP_2, and P_1P_2. Then in the triangle OP_1P_2

$$OP_1 = r_1,\ OP_2 = r_2,\ \measuredangle P_2OP_1 = \theta_1 - \theta_2.$$

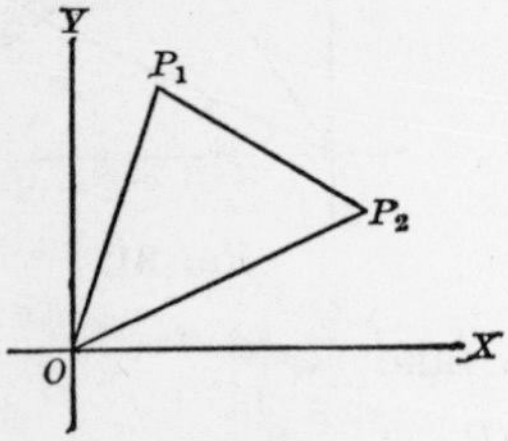

FIG. 32.

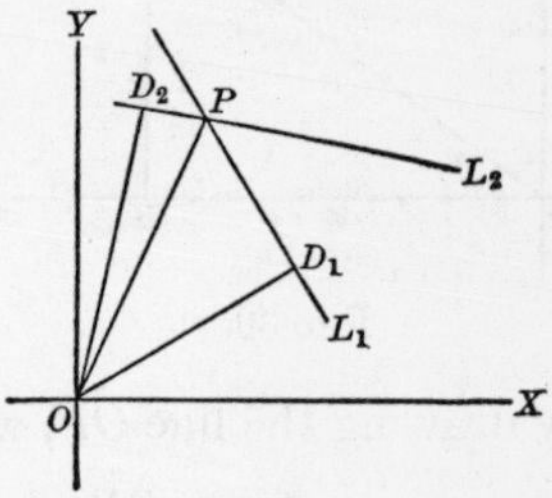

FIG. 33.

Hence (sec. 35),

$$\cos m\,\overline{P_1P_2} = \cos mr_1 \cos mr_2 + \sin mr_1 \sin mr_2 \cos(\theta_1 - \theta_2)$$
$$= \cos mr_1 \cos mr_2[1 + \tan mr_1 \tan mr_2 \cos(\theta_1 - \theta_2)].$$

By use of the formulas of sec. 36, this reduces readily to

$$\cos m\,\overline{P_1P_2} = \frac{1 + \tan mx_1 \tan mx_2 + \tan my_1 \tan my_2}{\sqrt{1 + \tan^2 mx_1 + \tan^2 my_1}\sqrt{1 + \tan^2 mx_2 + \tan^2 my_2}},$$

the required formula.

39. The angle between two lines may be determined as follows:

Let PL_1 and PL_2 (Fig. 33) be two straight lines intersecting at P. Draw from O the two perpendiculars OD_1 and OD_2 on PL_1 and PL_2 respectively, and (as in sec. 37), let

$$OD_1 = p_1, \quad \measuredangle XOD_1 = \alpha_1,$$
$$OD_2 = p_2, \quad \measuredangle XOD_2 = \alpha_2.$$

Draw OP and place $OP = \text{r}$, $\measuredangle XOP = \theta$, $\measuredangle OPD_1 = \beta_1$, $\measuredangle OPD_2 = \beta_2$, and $\measuredangle L_1PL_2 = \phi = \pi - (\beta_1 + \beta_2)$.

Now from the right triangles OPD_1 and OPD_2, we have (sec. 30),

$$\sin \beta_1 = \frac{\sin mp_1}{\sin mr}, \quad \sin \beta_2 = \frac{\sin mp_2}{\sin mr},$$

$$\cos \beta_1 = \cos mp_1 \sin (\theta - \alpha_1), \quad \cos \beta_2 = \cos mp_2 \sin (\alpha_2 - \theta),$$
$$= -\cos mp_2 \sin (\theta - \alpha_2)$$

Therefore,

$$\cos \phi = \cos mp_1 \cos mp_2 \sin (\theta - \alpha_1) \sin (\theta - \alpha_2) + \frac{\sin mp_1 \sin mp_2}{\sin^2 mr} \quad (1)$$

But (sec. 37)

$$\cos (\theta - \alpha_1) \tan mr = \tan mp_1,$$
$$\cos (\theta - \alpha_2) \tan mr = \tan mp_2,$$

whence

$$0 = \cos mp_1 \cos mp_2 \cos (\theta - \alpha_1) \cos (\theta - \alpha_2) - \frac{\sin mp_1 \sin mp_2}{\tan^2 mr}.$$

Adding this equation to equation (1), we have

$$\cos \phi = \cos mp_1 \cos mp_2 \cos (\alpha_1 - \alpha_2) + \sin mp_1 \sin mp_2$$
$$= \frac{\cos \alpha_1 \cos \alpha_2 + \sin \alpha_1 \sin \alpha_2 + \tan mp_1 \tan mp_2}{\sqrt{1 + \tan^2 mp_1} \sqrt{1 + \tan^2 mp_2}},$$

which gives the required angle in terms of the functions which enter into the equations of the lines.

40. The formulas of secs. 36–39 apply to either the Riemannian or the Lobachevskian geometry. It is now convenient to separate the two cases.

In the Riemannian geometry, where $m = \frac{1}{k}$, we will introduce, instead of x and y, the new coordinates ξ and η, where

$$\xi = k \tan \frac{x}{k}, \quad \eta = k \tan \frac{y}{k}. \quad . \quad . \quad . \quad . \quad . \quad (1)$$

The equation of the straight line (sec. 37) becomes

$$\xi \cos \alpha + \eta \sin \alpha = k \tan \frac{p}{k},$$

or, more generally,

$$a\xi + b\eta + c = 0\ , \quad . \quad . \quad . \quad . \quad . \quad . \quad . \quad (2)$$

where

$$\cos \alpha = \frac{a}{\sqrt{a^2+b^2}}, \quad \sin \alpha = \frac{b}{\sqrt{a^2+b^2}}, \quad k \tan \frac{p}{k} = \frac{-c}{\sqrt{a^2+b^2}}. \quad (3)$$

Conversely, any equation of form Eq. (2) represents a straight line, since α and p can always be obtained from Eqs. (3).

In particular, the equation

$$\eta = c$$

represents a line perpendicular to OY and intersecting OX at the point where $\xi = \infty$. But, from Eq. (1), $\xi = \infty$, when $x = \frac{k\pi}{2}$. By sec. 15, two lines perpendicular to the same line intersect at a distance Δ. Hence $k = \frac{2\Delta}{\pi}$. *This fixes the constant k in terms of Δ.*

The formulas for distance (sec. 38), and angle (sec. 39), become respectively

$$\cos \frac{P_1P_2}{k} = \frac{k^2 + \xi_1\xi_2 + \eta_1\eta_2}{\sqrt{k^2 + \xi_1{}^2 + \eta_1{}^2}\sqrt{k^2 + \xi_2{}^2 + \eta_2{}^2}}. \quad . \quad . \quad . \quad . \quad (4)$$

$$\cos \phi = \frac{k_2(a_1a_2 + b_1b_2) + c_1c_2}{\sqrt{k_2(a_2{}^2 + b_1{}^2) + c_1{}^2}\sqrt{k^2(a_2{}^2 + b_2{}^2) + c_2{}^2}}. \quad . \quad (5)$$

In Eq. (4) let us place $\xi_1 = \xi$, $\eta_1 = \eta$, $\xi_2 = \xi + d\xi$, $\eta_2 = \eta + d\eta$. The right-hand side of the equation becomes, as far as infinitesimals of the second order are concerned,

$$1 - \tfrac{1}{2}\frac{k^2(d\xi^2 + d\eta^2) + (\eta d\xi - \xi d\eta)^2}{(k^2 + \xi^2 + \eta^2)^2}.$$

The left-hand side of the same equation becomes, if we place $P_1P_2 = ds$, and expand,

$$1 - \tfrac{1}{2}\frac{(ds)^2}{k^2} + \ldots$$

Hence

$$ds = \frac{k\sqrt{k^2(d\xi^2 + d\eta^2) + (\eta d\xi - \xi d\eta)^2}}{k^2 + \xi^2 + \eta^2}. \quad . \quad . \quad . \quad (6)$$

which gives the element of arc of any curve.

We may transform Eq. (6) to polar coordinates by placing

$$\xi = k \tan \frac{r}{k} \cos \theta, \quad \eta = k \tan \frac{r}{k} \sin \theta.$$

It becomes

$$ds = \sqrt{dr^2 + k^2 \sin^2 \frac{r}{k} d\theta^2}.$$

Therefore the circumference C of the circle $r = a$ is

$$C = k \sin \frac{a}{k} \int_0^{2\pi} d\theta = 2\pi k \sin \frac{a}{k}.$$

41. To modify the formulas secs. 36–39 for the Lobachevskian geometry where $m = \frac{i}{k}$, we place

$$\xi = -ik \tan \frac{ix}{k} = k \tanh \frac{x}{k},$$

$$\eta = -ik \tan \frac{iy}{k} = k \tanh \frac{y}{k}.$$

The equation of the straight line (sec. 37) becomes

$$\xi \cos \alpha + \eta \sin \alpha = k \tanh \frac{p}{k},$$

or

$$a\xi + b\eta + c = 0, \quad . \quad . \quad . \quad . \quad . \quad . \quad . \quad (2)$$

where

$$\cos \alpha = \frac{a}{\sqrt{a^2 + b^2}}, \quad \sin \alpha = \frac{b}{\sqrt{a^2 + b^2}}, \quad k \tanh \frac{p}{k} = \frac{-c}{\sqrt{a^2 + b^2}}. \quad (3)$$

Now, if p is real, $\tanh \frac{p}{k} < 1$; hence from Eq. (2)

$$c^2 < k^2(a^2+b^2).$$

Conversely, Eq. (2) represents a straight line provided $c^2 < k^2(a^2+b^2)$, for then α and p may be determined from Eq. (3).

The formulas for distance (sec. 38) and angle (sec. 39), become respectively

$$\cosh \frac{P_1P_2}{k} = \frac{k^2 - \xi_1\xi_2 - \eta_1\eta_2}{\sqrt{k^2-\xi_1^2-\eta_1^2}\sqrt{k^2-\xi_2^2-\eta_2^2}}, \quad . \quad . \quad . \quad . \quad (4)$$

$$\cos \phi = \frac{k^2(a_1a_2+b_1b_2) - c_1c_2}{\sqrt{k^2(a_1^2+b_1^2)-c_1^2}\sqrt{k^2(a_2^2+b_2^2)-c_2^2}}. \quad . \quad .(5)$$

If in Eq. (4) we place $\xi_1 = \xi$, $\eta_1 = \eta$, $\xi_2 = \xi + d\xi$, $\eta_2 = \eta + d\eta$, $P_1P_2 = ds$, it becomes, as far as infinitesimals of the second order are concerned

$$1 + \frac{(ds)^2}{k^2} + \ldots = 1 + \tfrac{1}{2}\frac{k^2(d\xi^2+d\eta^2) - (\eta d\xi - \xi d\eta)^2}{k^2-\xi^2-\eta^2} + \ldots$$

whence the element of arc of any curve is given by the formula

$$ds = \frac{k\sqrt{k^2(d\xi^2+d\eta^2) - (\eta d\xi - \xi d\eta)^2}}{k^2-\xi^2-\eta^2}.$$

In polar coordinates, this becomes

$$ds = \sqrt{dr^2 + k^2 \sinh^2 \frac{r}{k} d\theta^2},$$

whence the circumference of the circle $r = a$ is

$$C = k \sinh \frac{a}{k} \int_0^{2\pi} d\theta = 2\pi k \sinh \frac{a}{k} = k\pi\left(e^{\frac{a}{k}} - e^{-\frac{a}{k}}\right).$$

42. We may now complete the discussion of area given in secs. 21–24. The unit of angle being such that a right angle has the measure $\frac{\pi}{2}$, we will take the unit of area such that, α, β, and γ being the angles of a triangle ABC, we have in the Riemannian geometry

$$\text{Area } ABC = k^2(\alpha+\beta+\gamma-\pi).$$

and in the Lobachevskian geometry

$$\text{Area } ABC = k^2(\pi-\alpha-\beta-\gamma),$$

Consider now in the Riemannian plane a trirectangular quadrilateral (Fig. 34) formed by the axes OX and OY and the lines $MP(\xi=c_1)$ and $NP(\eta=c_2)$.

Denote the area of $OMPN$ by A and the angle MPN by ψ. Then, by dividing $OMPN$ into two triangles

$$A=k^2\left(\psi-\frac{\pi}{2}\right);$$

whence

$$\sin\frac{A}{k^2}=-\cos\psi.$$

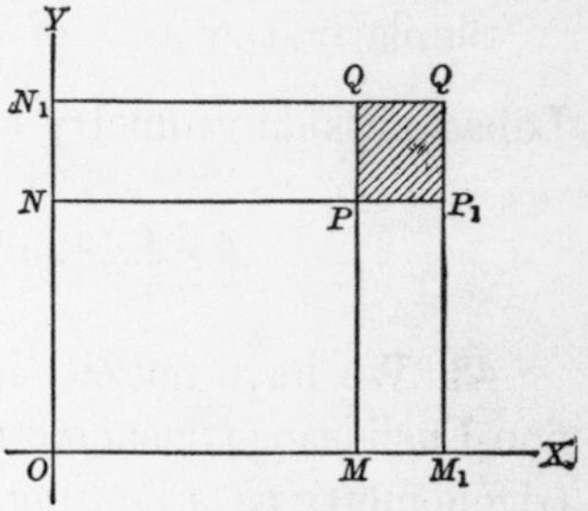

FIG. 34.

Therefore, by sec. 40,

$$\sin\frac{A}{k^2}=\frac{c_1c_2}{\sqrt{k^2+c_1^2}\sqrt{k^2+c_2^2}}=\frac{\xi\eta}{\sqrt{k^2+\xi^2}\sqrt{k^2+\eta^2}}, \quad . \quad (1)$$

the positive signs of the radicals being taken since $\frac{A}{k^2}<\frac{\pi}{2}$.

Let us now increase ξ by $d\xi$, corresponding to MM_1 in the figure. The corresponding differential of area, $d_\xi A$, represented by MM_1PP, is found by differentiating Eq. (1). We have

$$d_\xi A=\frac{k^3\eta d\xi}{(k^2+\xi^2)\sqrt{k^2+\xi^2+\eta^2}}. \quad . \quad . \quad . \quad . \quad (2)$$

The differential of this area caused, by a change of $d\eta$ in η is represented in the figure by PP_1QQ_1. We shall call this area dA and obtain it by differentiating Eq. (2) with respect to η. There results

$$dA=\frac{k^3d\eta d\xi}{(k^2+\xi^2+\eta^2)^{\frac{3}{2}}}. \quad . \quad . \quad . \quad . \quad . \quad . \quad . \quad (3)$$

The same process applied to the Lobachevskian plane leads to the result

$$dA = \frac{k^3 d\eta d\xi}{(k^2 - \xi^2 - \eta^2)^{\frac{3}{2}}}. \quad . \quad . \quad . \quad . \quad . \quad . \qquad (4)$$

Eq. (3) may be applied to find the area of the circle $\xi^2 + \eta^2 = k^2 \tan^2 \frac{a}{k}$ in the Riemannian geometry. We have*

$$A = 4k^3 \int_0^{k \tan \frac{a}{k}} \int_0^{\sqrt{k^2 \tan^2 \frac{a}{k} - \eta^2}} \frac{d\eta d\xi}{(k^2 + \eta^2 + \xi^2)^{\frac{3}{2}}} = 4\pi k^2 \sin^2 \frac{a}{2k}.$$

Similarly the area of the circle $\xi^2 + \eta^2 = k^2 \tanh^2 \frac{a}{k}$ in the Lobachevskian geometry is found to be

$$A = 4\pi k^2 \sinh^2 \frac{a}{2k} = \pi k^2 \left(e^{\frac{a}{2k}} - e^{-\frac{a}{2k}} \right)^2.$$

43. We have noticed in sec. 32 that the formulas for the non-Euclidean trigonometry include those of the Euclidean trigonometry as a limiting case when $k = \infty$. A similar remark applies to the non-Euclidean analytic geometry. We note that as $k = \infty$

$$\lim\ k \sin \frac{a}{k} = \lim\ k \tan \frac{a}{k} = \lim\ k \sinh \frac{a}{k} = \lim\ k \tanh \frac{a}{k} = a$$

and $$\lim\ k \cos \frac{a}{k} = \lim\ k\ \cosh \frac{a}{k} = 1.$$

---

* The calculation is facilitated by changing the variables in the integral,

$$A = k^3 \int\int \frac{d\eta d\xi}{(k^2 + \xi^2 + \eta^2)^{\frac{3}{2}}}$$

to polar coordinates, by the methods of the calculus for such a problem. (See *Hedrick's* translation of *Goursat's* Mathematical Analysis, p. 266.)

We have, in the Riemannian geometry,

$$A = \int\int k \sin \frac{r}{k} dr d\theta,$$

and similarly in the Lobachevskian geometry,

$$A = \int\int k \sinh \frac{r}{k} dr d\theta.$$

The coordinates (ξ, η) of either the Riemannian of Lobachevskian geometry become in the limit the coordinates (x, y) of the Euclidean geometry, and the formulas of secs. 40–42 reduce either to the identity $1=1$ or to the corresponding Euclidean formula.

For example, Eq. (4) sec. 40 or sec. 41, gives at first sight $1=1$, but if we expand in powers of $\frac{1}{k^2}$ and consider the terms of lower order it is easy to obtain the formula

$$P_1P_2=\sqrt{(\xi_1-\xi_2)^2+(\eta_1-\eta_2)^2}.$$

On the other hand, Eq. (5), sec. 40 or sec. 41, gives at once

$$\cos\phi=\frac{a_1a_2+b_1b_2}{\sqrt{a_1{}^2+b_1{}^2}\sqrt{a_2{}^2+b_2{}^2}}.$$

It appears that the Riemannian and Lobachevskian geometries will differ, unappreciably from the Euclidean geometry, in their practical applications, provided k is very large. Therein lies the impossibility of determining by experience which of the three geometries is physically true.

X. REPRESENTATION OF THE LOBACHEVSKIAN GEOMETRY ON A EUCLIDEAN PLANE

44. Let P (ξ, η) be any point on a Lobachevskian plane, (r, θ) its polar coordinates, where r is always positive. Then (secs. 36, 41)

$$\left.\begin{aligned} \xi&=k\tanh\frac{r}{k}\cos\theta,\\ \eta&=k\tanh\frac{r}{k}\sin\theta,\\ \xi^2+\eta^2&=k^2\tanh^2\frac{r}{k}<k^2. \end{aligned}\right\}\quad\cdots\cdots\quad(1)$$

We may now interpret (ξ, η) as ordinary Cartesian coordinates upon a Euclidean plane, i.e.; a plane on which the Euclidean geometry is assumed to hold. Then to P on the Lobachevskian plane corresponds a point P' on the Euclidean plane and P' lies inside the circle $\xi^2+\eta^2=k^2$, called the **fundamental circle.**

Conversely, let (ξ, η) be the coordinates of any point on the Euclidean plane. Solving Eqs. (1), we have

$$\cos\theta=\frac{\xi}{\sqrt{\xi^2+\eta^2}},$$

$$\sin\theta=\frac{\eta}{\sqrt{\xi^2+\eta^2}},$$

$$r=\frac{k}{2}\log\frac{k+\sqrt{\xi^2+\eta^2}}{k-\sqrt{\xi^2+\eta^2}}.$$

Hence θ is uniquely determined and is always real and r is uniquely determined and is real, infinite, or imaginary, according as $\xi^2+\eta^2$ is less than, equal to, or greater than, k^2.

We have thus a relation between the Lobachevskian and Euclidean planes by which a point on the Lobachevskian plane corresponds to one and only one point in the interior of the fundamental circle on the Euclidean plane, and conversely. The points of the fundamental circle correspond to points at infinity on the Lobachevskian plane, while points outside the circle have no corresponding points on the Lobachevskian plane.

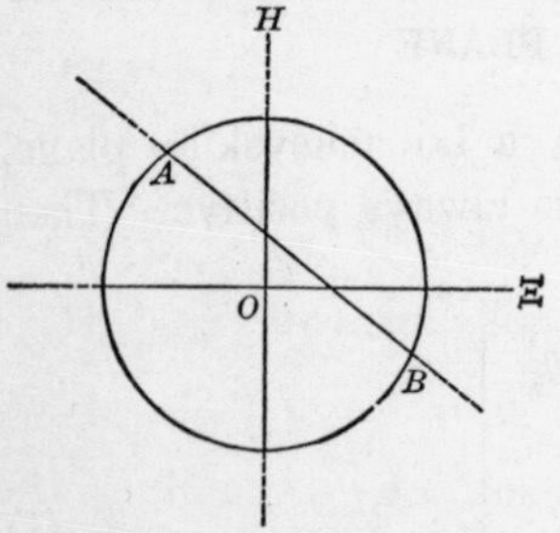

FIG. 35.

45. Consider now a straight line on the Euclidean plane (Fig. 35) with the equation

$$a\xi+b\eta+c=0.$$

Only that portion of AB which is within the fundamental circle will correspond to a line on the Lobachevskian plane, the points A and B corresponding to the points at infinity on the Lobachevskian plane.

Hence, unless the line AB meets the fundamental conic in two real points it will have no Lobachevskian counterpart.

The criterion that $a\xi+b\eta+c=0$ should meet $\xi^2+\eta^2=k^2$ in two real points is that

$$k^2(a^2+b^2)-c^2>0.$$

We thus find again the condition of sec. 41.

46. The distinction between intersecting, non-intersecting, and parallel lines is very clear in the representation we are considering. For if AB (Fig. 36) is any straight line on the Euclidean plane and P any point, the lines through P which intersect AB within the fundamental circle correspond to lines intersecting AB on the Lobachevskian plane, while the lines through P intersecting AB outside the circle correspond to lines on the Lobachevskian plane which do not meet AB.

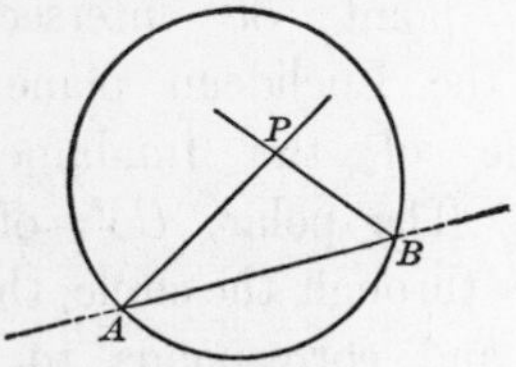

FIG. 36.

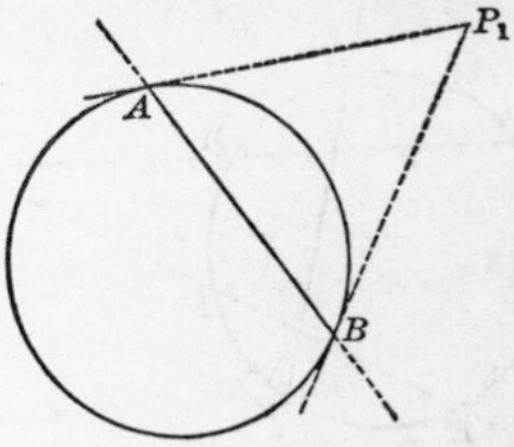

FIG. 37.

Between these two types of lines are the lines PA and PB which intersect AB on the fundamental circle and correspond to the Lobachevskian parallels.

47. Two straight lines

$$a_1\xi+b_1\eta+c_1=0 \quad \ldots\ldots\quad (1)$$

$$a_2\xi+b_2\eta+c_2=0 \quad \ldots\ldots\quad (2)$$

on the Lobachevskian plane are perpendicular, when (sec. 41)

$$k^2(a_1a_2+b_1b_2)-c_1c_2=0 \quad \ldots\ldots\quad (3)$$

The geometric meaning of this condition is readily given. Note first that if $P_1(\xi_1, \eta_1)$ (Fig. 37) is a point on the Euclidean plane, its polar AB with respect to the fundamental circle is

$$\xi_1\xi+\eta_1\eta-k^2=0.$$

This is the line

$$a_1\xi+b_1\eta+c_1=0$$

if $\xi_1 = -\frac{a_1k^2}{c_1}$, $\eta_1 = -\frac{b_1k^2}{c_1}$. That is, the point $\left(-\frac{a_1k^2}{c_1}, -\frac{b_1k^2}{c_1}\right)$ is the pole of the line Eq. (1), and similarly $\left(-\frac{a_2k^2}{c_2}, -\frac{b_2k^2}{c_2}\right)$ is the pole of the line Eq. (2). The condition Eq. (3) expresses the fact that the pole of Eq. (1) is on Eq. (2) and the pole of Eq. (2) on Eq. (1). Hence the following theorem:

Two lines on the Lobachevskian plane are perpendicular when each of the corresponding lines on the Euclidean plane passes through the pole of the other.

This leads to a shorter proof of the proposition of sec. 9 that two non-intersecting straight lines have a common perpendicular. For let LM and EF (Fig. 38) be two such lines. Their point of intersection P on the Euclidean plane lies outside of the fundamental circle. The polar, UV, of P, passes through the circle, therefore, and corresponds to the common perpendicular to LM and EF.

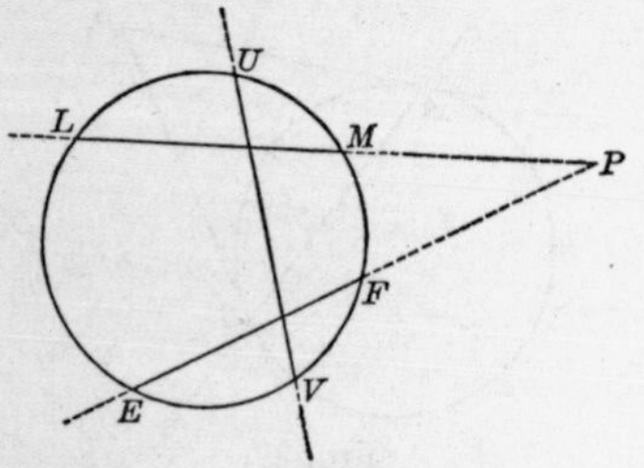

FIG. 38.

48. We shall now proceed to find the meaning on the Euclidean plane of the expression for a Lobachevskian distance (sec. 41, Eq. (4)). For convenience, place

$$P_1P_2 = d, \qquad k^2 - \xi_1^2 - \eta_1^2 = f_{11},$$
$$k^2 - \xi_2^2 - \eta_2^2 = f_{22}, \qquad k^2 - \xi_1\xi_2 - \eta_1\eta_2 = f_{12}.$$

Then Eq. (4), sec. 41, becomes

$$\frac{e^{\frac{d}{k}} + e^{-\frac{d}{k}}}{2} = \frac{f_{12}}{\sqrt{f_{11}}\sqrt{f_{22}}},$$

whence

$$\left.\begin{aligned} d &= k \log \frac{f_{12} \pm \sqrt{f_{12}^2 - f_{11}f_{22}}}{\sqrt{f_{11}}\sqrt{f_{22}}} \\ &= \pm\frac{k}{2} \log \frac{f_{12} + \sqrt{f_{12}^2 - f_{11}f_{22}}}{f_{12} - \sqrt{f_{12}^2 - f_{11}f_{22}}}. \end{aligned}\right\} \quad . \quad . \quad . \quad . \quad (1)$$

Now on the Euclidean plane, let P_1 and P_2 (Fig. 39) be the two points (ξ_1, η_1) and (ξ_2, η_2) respectively, and R and Q the points in which the line P_1P_2 meets the fundamental circle. Let P (ξ_1, η) be any point on P_1P such that

$$\frac{P_1P}{PP_2}=\lambda,$$

where λ is a Euclidean distance. Then

$$\xi=\frac{\xi_1+\lambda\xi_2}{1+\lambda}, \qquad \eta=\frac{\eta_1+\lambda\eta_2}{1+\lambda}.$$

Substituting these values in the equation of the fundamental circle,

$$\xi^2+\eta^2-k^2=0,$$

we shall have the values of λ corresponding to the points Q and R; namely

$$\lambda_1=\frac{P_1Q}{QP_2}=\frac{f_{12}+\sqrt{f_{12}^2-f_{11}f_{22}}}{\sqrt{f_{22}}},$$

$$\lambda_2=\frac{P_1R}{RP_2}=\frac{f_{12}-\sqrt{f_{12}^2-f_{11}f_{22}}}{\sqrt{f_{22}}}.$$

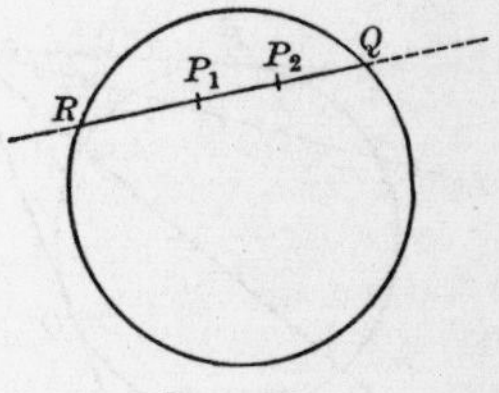

FIG. 39.

Eq. (1) then becomes

$$d=\pm\frac{k}{2}\log\frac{\lambda_1}{\lambda_2}=\pm\frac{k}{2}\log\frac{P_1Q}{QP_2}\cdot\frac{P_1R}{RP_2}.$$

The Lobachevskian distance between two points is $\frac{k}{2}$ *times the logarithm of the anharmonic ratio of the two given points and the two points of intersection of the fundamental circle and the line through the two given points.*

49. An analogous definition may be given to the Lobachevskian measure of angle. Place, for convenience,

$$k^2(a_1^2+b_1^2)-c_1^2=u_{11}, \qquad k^2(a_2^2+b_2^2)-c_2^2=u_{22},$$

$$k^2(a_1a_2+b_1b_2)-c_1c_2=u_{12}.$$

Then, from Eq. (5), sec. 41, we have

$$\phi = \pm\frac{i}{2}\log\frac{u_{12}+\sqrt{u_{12}^2-u_{11}u_{22}}}{u_{12}-\sqrt{u_{12}^2-u_{11}u_{22}}}.$$

Now consider the two lines AL, and AL_2 (Fig. 40) with the equations,

$$a_1\xi + b_1\eta + c_1 = 0,$$
$$a_2\xi + b_2\eta + c_2 = 0.$$

Any line through their point of intersection A has the equation

$$(a_1+\lambda a_2)\xi + (b_1+\lambda b_2)\eta + (c_1+\lambda c_2) = 0$$

and this line will be one of the tangent lines AR and AQ, if

$$k^2(a_1+\lambda a_2)^2 + k^2(b_1+\lambda b_2)^2 - (c_1+\lambda c_2)^2 = 0,$$

i.e., if λ has either of the values

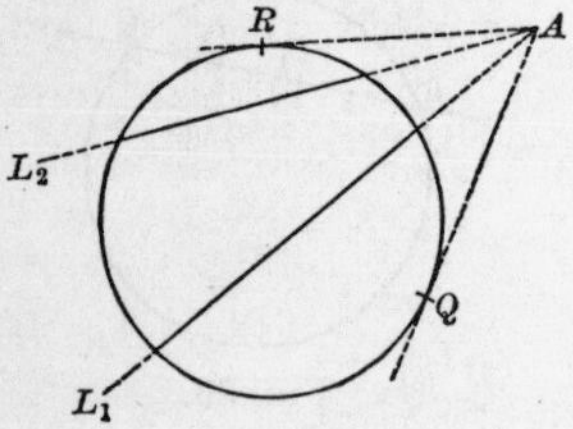

FIG. 40.

$$\lambda_1 = \frac{u_{12}+\sqrt{u_{12}^2-u_{11}u_{22}}}{\sqrt{u_{22}}},$$

$$\lambda_2 = \frac{u_{12}-\sqrt{u_{12}^2-u_{11}u_{22}}}{\sqrt{u_{22}}}.$$

Hence

$$\phi = \pm\frac{i}{2}\log\frac{\lambda_1}{\lambda_2}.$$

But $\frac{\lambda_1}{\lambda_2}$ is the anharmonic ratio of the four lines AL_1, AL_2, AR, and AQ. If A lies outside of the fundamental circle, λ_1 and λ_2 are real, and ϕ is imaginary. If A lies on the fundamental conic, $\lambda_1 = \lambda_2$, and $\phi = 0$. If A lies inside the fundamental conic, λ_1 and λ_2 are conjugate imaginary, and ϕ is real.

The Lobachevskian measure of angle between two lines is $\frac{i}{2}$ *times the anharmonic ratio of the two given lines and the two tangents to the fundamental circle from the point of intersection of the two given lines.*

50. The study of the circle on the Lobachevskian plane by means of its representation on the Euclidean plane leads to interesting results. We obtain the general equation of the circle by letting (ξ_1, η_1) in Eq. (4), sec. 41, be the fixed coordinates of the centre and letting $\xi_2=\xi$, $\eta_2=\eta$ be the variable coordinates of any point on the circle. The equation is then of the form

$$(\xi_1\xi+\eta_1\eta-k^2)^2=c(\xi^2+\eta^2-k^2), \quad . \quad . \quad . \quad . \quad . \quad (1)$$

where c is a constant.

This is the equation of a conic on the Euclidean plane. Coordinates which satisfy this equation and that of the fundamental circle

$$\xi^2+\eta^2-k^2=0$$

satisfy also the equation

$$\xi_1\xi+\eta_1\eta-k^2=0,$$

which is that of the polar of (ξ_1, η_1). Since the polynominal $\xi_1\xi+\eta_1\eta-k^2$ appears to the second power in Eq. (1) it follows that Eq. (1) is the equation of a conic which is tangent to the fundamental circle at the points where the latter is cut by the polar of (ξ_1, η_1).

There are therefore three cases to consider according as (ξ_1, η_1) lies outside, on, or inside the fundamental circle.

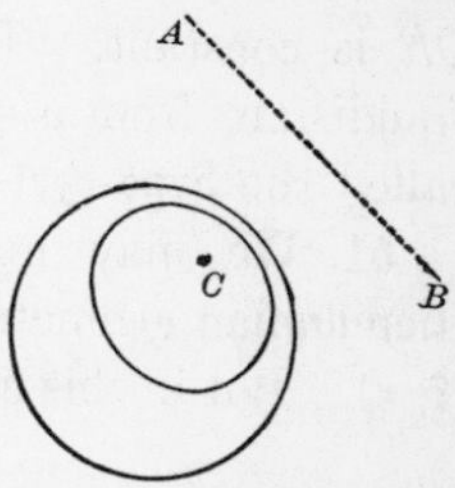

FIG. 41.

(1) When C (ξ_1, η_1) is inside the fundamental circle, the polar AB of C does not cut the circle in real points and hence the conic (1) lies entirely in the circle (Fig. 41). This corresponds to the ordinary circle on the Lobachevskian plane.

(2) Whence $C(\xi_1, \eta_1)$ lies on the fundamental circle, the polar of C is the tangent to the circle at the point (ξ_1, η_1). The conic (1) is then tangent to the circle at the same point (Fig. 42). This corresponds on the Lobachevskian plane to the curve approached by a circle as its centre receded to infinity and its radius becomes infinite. This curve is called a limit

curve or horicycle. Its revolution about one of its infinite radii generates the *limit-surface* mentioned in sec. 25.

(3) When $C(\xi_1, \eta_1)$ is outside the fundamental circle, the polar C cuts the fundamental circle in two points A and B (Fig. 43). The conic (1) is therefore tangent to the fundamental conic, and corresponds on the Lobachevskian plane to a real circle with imaginary centre and radius. The straight line AB is a special case of such a circle.

Draw any line CR through C, intersecting AB in Q. This represents on the Lobachevskian plane a line perpendicular to AB (sec. 47). Now in the Lobachevskian measurement

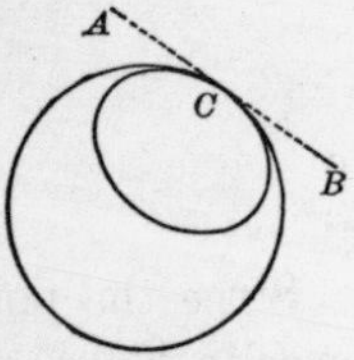

FIG. 42.

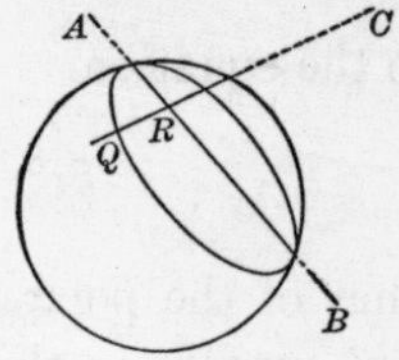

FIG. 43.

CR and CQ are constant for all positions of Q on AB. Then QR is constant. That is the locus of Q has all its points equidistant from a straight line AB. This curve is sometimes called the **hypo-cycle.**

51. We may make, of course, a representation of the Riemannian geometry on the Euclidean plane with coordinates (ξ, η). But in this case the fundamental circle has the equation

$$\xi^2 + \eta^2 + k^2 = 0$$

and is imaginary. The geometric properties are therefore not visible to the eye.

XI. RELATION BETWEEN PROJECTIVE AND NON-EUCLIDEAN GEOMETRY

52. We have obtained in secs. 48, 49 a special case of the system of measurement first given by *Cayley* and recognized by *Klein* as leading to the non-Euclidean geometries. The general principles can now be quickly stated.

Let us take, on a plane for which the Euclidean geometry holds, $x_1:x_2:x_3$ as homogeneous point coordinates and assume a *fundamental conic* with the equation

$$a_{11}x^2_1+a_{22}x_2^2+a_{33}x_3^2+2a_{12}x_1x_2+2a_{23}x_2x_3+2a_{31}x_3x_1=0$$

or, more compactly,

$$\Sigma a_{ik}x_ix_k=0. \quad (a_{ik}=a_{ki}). \quad . \quad . \quad . \quad . \quad . \quad (1)$$

Let the tangential equation of the same conic be

$$\Sigma A_{ik}\alpha_i\alpha_k=0, \quad (A_{ik}=A_{ki}), \quad . \quad . \quad . \quad . \quad . \quad (2)$$

i.e., let Eq. (2) be the condition that the straight line $\alpha_1x_1+\alpha_2x_2+\alpha_3x_3=0$ should be tangent to the conic of Eq. (1). For convenience, let us place

$$f_{xx}=\Sigma a_{ik}x_ix_k, \quad f_{yy}=\Sigma a_{ik}y_iy_k, \quad f_{xy}=\Sigma a_{ik}x_iy_k.$$

and

$$u_{\alpha\alpha}=\Sigma A_{ik}\alpha_i\alpha_k, \quad u_{\beta\beta}=\Sigma A_{ik}\beta_i\beta_k, \quad u_{\alpha\beta}=\Sigma A_{ik}\alpha_i\beta_k.$$

If P_1 and P_2 are two points on the plane, and Q and R are the points which the line P_1P_2 meets the fundamental conic, and $[P_1P_2QR]$ is the anharmonic ratio of the four points P_1P_2QR, then the Cayleyan projective measure of the distance P_1P_2 is defined by the equation

$$P_1P_2=M\log[P_1P_2QR],$$

where M is a constant.

Similarly, if AL, and AL_2 are two lines intersecting at A, and AR and AQ are the two tangents from A to the fundamental conic, and $[L_1L_2QR]$ is the anharmonic ratio of these four lines, then the Cayleyan projective measure of the angle ϕ between AL_1 and AL_2 is given by the equation

$$\phi = M_1 \log [L_1 L_2 Q R],$$

where M_1 is a constant.

The analytic expression of these measures is found as in secs. 48, 49.

If $x_1 : x_2 : x_3$ are the coordinates of P_1, $y_1 : y_2 : y_3$ the coordinates of P_2, and λ_1, λ_2 the roots of

$$f_{xx} + 2\lambda f_{xy} + \lambda^2 f_{yy} = 0,$$

then

$$\left.\begin{aligned} P_1P_2 &= M \log \frac{\lambda_1}{\lambda_2} \\ &= M \log \frac{f_{xy} + \sqrt{f_{xy}^2 - f_{xx}f_{yy}}}{f_{xy} - \sqrt{f_{xy}^2 - f_{xx}f_{yy}}} \\ &= 2M \log \frac{f_{xy} + \sqrt{f_{xy}^2 - f_{xx}f_{yy}}}{\sqrt{f_{xx}}\sqrt{f_{yy}}} \end{aligned}\right\} \quad . \quad . \quad . \quad . \quad (3)$$

By an easy calculation, we may deduce from this

$$\tfrac{1}{2}\left(e^{\frac{P_1P_2}{2M}} + e^{-\frac{P_1P_2}{2M}}\right) = \frac{f_{xy}}{\sqrt{f_{xx}}\sqrt{f_{yy}}}. \quad . \quad . \quad . \quad . \quad (4)$$

Also if $\alpha_1 x_1 + \alpha_2 x_2 + \alpha_3 x_3 = 0$ is the equation of AL_1, $\beta_1 x_1 + \beta_2 x_2 + \beta_3 x_3 = 0$ the equation of AL_2, and μ_1, μ_2 the roots of the equation

$$u_{\alpha\alpha} + 2\mu u_{\alpha\beta} + \mu^2 u_{\beta\beta} = 0$$

then

$$\left.\begin{aligned} \phi &= M_1 \log \frac{\mu_1}{\mu_2} \\ &= M_1 \log \frac{u_{\alpha\beta} + \sqrt{u_{\alpha\beta}^2 - u_{\alpha\alpha}u_{\beta\beta}}}{u_{\alpha\beta} - \sqrt{u_{\alpha\beta}^2 - u_{\alpha\alpha}u_{\beta\beta}}} \\ &= 2M_1 \log \frac{u_{\alpha\beta} + \sqrt{u_{\alpha\beta}^2 - u_{\alpha\alpha}u_{\beta\beta}}}{\sqrt{u_{\alpha\alpha}}\sqrt{u_{\beta\beta}}} \end{aligned}\right\} \quad . \quad . \quad . \quad (5)$$

whence

$$\tfrac{1}{2}\left(e^{\frac{\phi}{2M_1}}+e^{-\frac{\phi}{2M_1}}\right)=\frac{u_{\alpha\beta}}{\sqrt{u_{\alpha\alpha}}\sqrt{u_{\beta\beta}}}. \quad . \quad . \quad . \quad . \quad (6)$$

We have now to consider three cases according to the nature of the fundamental conic.

53. Case I. Let the fundamental conic be a real, non-degenerate conic; i.e., either an ellipse, hyperbola, or parabola.

If the points P_1 and P_2 are inside the conic, $[P_1P_2QR]$ is real and positive. Hence if the distance P_1P_2 is real we must take M a real constant, for example, $\frac{k}{2}$.

If A is inside the conic, the tangents AR and AQ are imaginary, and μ_1 and μ_2 are conjugate imaginary. Let $\mu=\rho e^{\theta i}$, then $\mu_2=\rho e^{-\theta i}$ and $\log\frac{\mu_1}{\mu_2}=2\theta i$. Hence if ϕ is to be real we must take M_1 pure imaginary. When AL_1 coincides with AL_2 we have

$$\phi=M_1\log 1=0 \text{ or } 2\,M_1 n\pi i,$$

where n is an integer. If then we so chose the unit of angle that the measure of a right angle shall be $\frac{\pi}{2}$, we must place $M_1=\frac{i}{2}$.

We are thus led to the same formulas as in secs. 48, 49, except that they are referred to a general conic instead of a circle.

The Lobachevskian geometry is easily built up on this foundation.

54. Case II. Let the fundamental conic be imaginary, i.e., let there be no real values of $x_1:x_2:x_3$ satisfying Eq. (1), sec. 52. Then λ_1 and λ_2 are conjugate imaginary, as are also μ_1 and μ_2. Hence to obtain real distance and angle we must take M and M_1 pure imaginary. As in sec. 53, we place $M_1=\frac{i}{2}$ and will place $M=\frac{ik}{2}$. We have then from Eqs. (4) and (6), sec. 52,

$$\cos\frac{P_1P_2}{k}=\frac{f_{xy}}{\sqrt{f_{xx}}\sqrt{f_{yy}}},$$

$$\cos\phi=\frac{u_{\alpha\beta}}{\sqrt{u_{\alpha\alpha}}\sqrt{u_{\alpha\beta}}},$$

which are analogous to those of the Riemannian geometry (sec. 40).

Since $\cos \frac{P_1P_2}{k}$ is never infinite, all straight lines are finite in length.

Two straight lines always intersect, since two linear equations have always a solution, which cannot represent a point at infinity.

The Riemannian geometry is easily built up from these foundations.

55. Case III. Let the fundamental conic degenerate. This may happen in two ways: either the point Eq. (1), sec. 52, may represent two straight lines; or the tangential Eq. (2), sec. 52, may represent two points. The latter is the most interesting case, especially when the tangential equation becomes

$$\alpha_1^2+\alpha_2^2=0, \quad \dots \dots \dots \quad (1)$$

which is satisfied by the coefficients of all straight lines which pass through one of the two points $x_1:x_2:x_3=1:\pm i:0$. If $x_3=0$ represents the line at infinity, these points are the **circular points at infinity.** Through each point of the plane go two straight lines satisfying Eq. (1), namely the **minimum lines.**

The formula for angle is readily found. In fact, we have at once from Eq. (6), sec. 52, with $M_1=\frac{i}{2}$,

$$\cos \phi=\frac{\alpha_1\beta_1+\alpha_2\beta_2}{\sqrt{\alpha_1^2+\alpha_2^2}\sqrt{\beta_1^2+\beta_2^2}}.$$

But this is the Euclidean formula for the angle between the two lines

$$\alpha_1 x+\alpha_2 y+\alpha_3=0,$$
$$\beta_1 x+\beta_2 y+\beta_3=0,$$

where we have placed $x=\frac{x_1}{x_3}$, $y=\frac{x_2}{x_3}$.

Hence: *The Euclidean angle between two lines is equal to $\frac{i}{2}$ times the logarithm of the anharmonic ratio of the two lines and the two minimum lines through their point of intersection.*

To obtain the Euclidean formula for distance from the general formula, sec. 52, is not so simple a matter, but it may be done as follows:

Let us take in place of Eq. (1) the equation

$$\alpha_1^2+\alpha_2^2+\varepsilon\alpha_3^2=0, \quad . \quad . \quad . \quad . \quad . \quad . \quad (2)$$

which goes over into Eq. (1) when $\varepsilon=0$. The corresponding point equation is

$$\varepsilon(x_1^2+x^2_2)+x_3^2=0. \quad . \quad . \quad . \quad . \quad . \quad . \quad (3)$$

From Eq. (4), sec. 52, we have if we place $M=\frac{k}{2}$,

$$\cosh\frac{P_1P_2}{k}=\frac{\varepsilon(x_1y_1+x_2y_2)+x_3y_3}{\sqrt{\varepsilon(x_1^2+x_2^2)+x_3^2}\sqrt{\varepsilon(y_1^2+y_2^2)+y_3^2}}.$$

We wish to show that this approaches as a limit the Euclidean formula as $\varepsilon\doteq 0$ and $k=\infty$. For that purpose, replace cosh $\frac{P_1P_2}{k}$ by its approximate value $1+\left(\frac{P_1P_2}{k}\right)^2$ and calculate P_1P_2.

There results

$$P_1P_2=ik\sqrt{\varepsilon}\frac{\sqrt{(x_1y_3-x_3y_1)^2+(x_2y_3-x_3y_2)^2+\varepsilon(x_2y_1-x_2y_3)^2}}{\sqrt{\varepsilon(x_1^2+x_2^2)+x_3^2}\sqrt{\varepsilon(y_1+y_2^2)+y_3^2}}.$$

Now let $\varepsilon\doteq 0$ and $k=\infty$, in such a way that $ik\sqrt{\varepsilon}\doteq 1$. We have in the limit

$$P_1P_2=\frac{\sqrt{(x_1y_3-x_3y_1)^2+(x_2y_3-x_3y_2)^2}}{\sqrt{x_3^2}\sqrt{y_3^2}}.$$

Finally, let us employ non-homogeneous coordinates by placing

$$x=\frac{x_1}{x_3}, \quad y=\frac{x_2}{x_3},$$

$$x'=\frac{y_1}{y_3}, \quad y'=\frac{y_2}{y_3}.$$

We have, then, the usual Cartesian formula

$$P_1P_2=\sqrt{(x-x')^2+(y-y')^2}.$$

Hence:

The Euclidean measure of distance is a limiting case of the Cayleyan projective measurement.

XII. THE ELEMENT OF ARC

56. We have found (secs. 40, 41) that in both the Riemannian and the Lobachevskian geometries the element of arc, ds, is the square root of a homogeneous quadratic function of the differentials of the coordinates which we have used. This is also true of the Euclidean geometry, where in rectangular Cartesian coordinates $ds=\sqrt{dx^2+dy^2}$.

Conversely, following the method first employed by *Riemann*, we may ask if these are all the types of geometries in which the element of arc is thus expressed. More precisely, the problem is as follows: Let it be assumed that a point on the plane may be determined by means of two coordinates x_1 and x_2, and that the distance between two infinitely near points (x_1, x_2) and (x_1+dx_1, x_2+dx_2) may be given by an equation of the form

$$ds=\sqrt{a_{11}dx_1^2+2a_{12}dx_1dx_2+a_{22}dx_2^2},$$

where a_{11}, a_{12}, a_{22} are functions of x_1 and x_2. It is required to discuss the geometry which results.

An adequate discussion of this question would be altogether too long for this place.*

We shall simply say that the straight line is then defined as the shortest distance between two points, its equation being the relation between x_1 and x_2 which makes the integral

$$s=\int\sqrt{a_{11}dx_1^2+2a_{12}dx_1dx_2+a_{22}dx_2^2},$$

taking between constant limits, a minimum.

---

* Consult *Woods*, "Space of Constant Curvature," Annals of Mathematics, 2d series, Vol. VIII, 1901–2; *Coolidge*, The Elements of Non-Euclidean Geometry, Chapter XIX.

It results finally that it is possible to replace (x_1, x_2) by polar coordinates (r, θ), whereby ds takes one of the forms

$$ds = \sqrt{dr^2 + r^2 d\theta^2},$$

$$ds = \sqrt{dr^2 + k^2 \sin^2 \frac{r}{k}\, d\theta^2},$$

$$ds = \sqrt{dr^2 + k^2 \sinh^2 \frac{r}{k}\, d\theta^2},$$

where k is a constant.

But there are the three forms which belong to the Euclidean, the Riemannian, and the Lobachevskian geometries respectively. We have thus the interesting result that no new type of geometry results from the new point of view. This statement, however, requires one modification. The present discussion, since it starts with the infinitely small and proceeds by the methods of the calculus, has to do only with a restricted portion of the plane. No hypothesis is made as to the behavior of straight lines when indefinitely extended, such as enters into the parallel postulates. A geometry, in fact, which agrees with the Euclidean, Riemannian, or Lobachevskian geometry respectively, in a restricted portion of the plane, may present new features when the total extent of the plane is considered. Into this subject we cannot go.*

---

* Consult *Woods*, "Forms of Non-Euclidean Space," in Boston Colloquium Lectures on Mathematics, New York, 1905.

IV

THE FUNDAMENTAL PROPOSITIONS OF ALGEBRA

By Edward V. Huntington

CONTENTS

APPENDIX

IV

THE FUNDAMENTAL PROPOSITIONS OF ALGEBRA

By Edward V. Huntington

I. INTRODUCTION

1. Purpose of the article. The main object of this article is to present, in as simple a form as possible, the results of some of the modern inquiries into the logical foundations of algebra; but the article is so arranged that readers who desire merely to increase their store of information about algebraic facts, without going into the discussion of logical foundations, may find, in Part IV, a *systematic introduction to the algebra of complex quantities,* which may be read independently of the rest of the article.

There has been much discussion of late years over the place which logical rigor should occupy in the teaching of elementary mathematics. Some have contended that the power to understand a logically rigorous demonstration is itself the most important result to be aimed at in mathematical study. Others have attached greater importance to the use of mathematics as a practical art, and have felt that too much insistence on logical rigor serves only to deaden the pupil's interest, and thus to destroy all the value the study might have, either as a practical art or as a training in logic.

It is not the purpose of the present article to discuss these pedagogical questions. It is intended merely to put before the reader a clear statement, in some detail, of what is actually involved in a strictly logical treatment of algebra, leaving to the teachers themselves the question as to how far logical rigor can be pressed in the classroom.*

2. The science of algebra vs. the science of geometry. It is a curious fact that the one striking example of rigorous mathematical reasoning with which everyone is familiar is taken from geometry rather than from algebra. *Euclid's* Elements have stood for 2000 years as the supreme illustration of the mathematical manner of reasoning. Axiom, theorem; hypothesis, conclusion; proposition, demonstration, corollary; the defence of every statement by reference to a previously established truth—all the apparatus and method of mathematical reasoning call up at once in our minds a text-book in geometry, never a text-book in algebra. Even the external form of our books contributes to this result. The current treatises on algebra are not divided into Book I, Book II, etc., as are those in geometry; their theorems are not numbered in consecutive order; little distinction is made between explanation and proof; .nothing is done to suggest the strict logical sequence of propositions which is so constantly emphasized in every book on geometry.

Until recent years, elementary algebra has been largely a miscellaneous collection of rules for the manipulation of algebraic expressions, and is not at all the developed science that elementary geometry has long since become. In fact, if it were not for the study of plane geometry in our schools, it is doubtful whether our school children would ever derive, from their study of algebra alone, any clear notion of what is meant by a mathematical demonstration.

This fact is the more remarkable, because, on account of the simpler nature of the concepts with which it deals, algebra is better suited than geometry to serve as an illustration of what is essentially involved in mathematical reasoning. In geometry, the very concreteness and familiarity of the subject-matter is apt to obscure the logical structure of the science, while

---

* Reference may here be made to a forthcoming book by John Wesley Young, entitled "Lectures on Fundamental Concepts of Algebra and Geometry," 1911.

in algebra, the more abstract character of the content of the theorems makes it easier to fix the attention on their formal logical relations.

The present article is intended as an introduction to the *science* of algebra as distinguished from the art of manipulating algebraic expressions. In what proportions the science and the art should be mingled in practical teaching is a question with which this article, as already stated, does not propose to deal.

3. The various types of algebra. Irrational and imaginary quantities. It should be mentioned at once that there is, strictly speaking, no one science of algebra, but rather a collection of closely related sciences, all of which are commonly grouped together under the general name of algebra.

For example, we have the algebra of positive integers; the algebra of all integers (positive, negative, and zero); the algebra of positive rationals; the algebra of all rationals; the algebra of all real quantities (rational and irrational, positive, negative, and zero); and, finally, the algebra which in a certain sense includes all these others, and is in many respects simpler than any of them, the algebra of complex quantities.

In these various algebras, many theorems are, in form, identical; but many other theorems are true in one algebra and false in another. For example, the theorem,

$$\text{If } a^3 = b^3, \text{ then } a = b,$$

is true in the algebra of real quantities, and not true in the algebra of complex quantities. Again, the theorem that "Every quantity has at least one cube root," is true in the algebra of all complex or all real quantities, but is false in the algebra of rational quantities or the algebra of integers.

The distinction between the various types of algebra is directly connected with the problem of the so-called "irrational" and "imaginary" quantities.

Much of the difficulty which perplexes every thoughtful student at the time when irrational and imaginary quantities are first introduced, is due to the failure to recognize the fact that he is really leaving one system of algebra, and passing to another and different system, and that the theorems established in the first system cannot be expected (without further proof) to hold in the second.

It is small wonder that a boy is confused and perplexed when he is told on one page that "the square of every number is positive, and hence $\sqrt{-1}$ cannot exist," and on the next page that "the $\sqrt{-1}$ really is a number, and obeys all the laws of algebra." The fact is, of course, that the $\sqrt{-1}$ occurs only in the algebra of complex quantities—a quite different algebra from the algebra of real quantities which the boy has so far studied; and it is simply not true to state that a quantity which belongs in one of these algebras obeys all the laws which are valid in the other.

Again, the pupil is often told that we "must" introduce the number $\sqrt{-1}$ "because" the equation $x^2 = -1$ must needs, in the nature of things, have a root. But why do we not say, with equal reason, that we "must" introduce the number infinity, "because" the equation $5/x=0$ must needs have a root? If we say that $\sqrt{-1}$ is "a number that obeys all laws of algebra," why do we not say that ∞, the existence of which may be claimed on the ground of precisely similar necessity, is also a "number that obeys all the laws of algebra"? Inconsistencies like this, while they do not trouble the average pupil, do present serious perplexities to those who are more critically inclined. It is not clear why a "must" that is so imperative in one case should be so ignored in a precisely similar case. The fact is, of course, that the alleged necessity carries no compulsion with it in either case; it is merely the expression of a *desire* for a simpler algebra, in which *every* equation shall have a root; the fact that the algebra of complex quantities comes nearer than any of the other algebras to fulfilling this desire is a matter for observation, not a consequence of logical necessity. And yet what pupil in our high schools has ever had a concrete example of complex algebra presented to him upon which he could make this observation? *

In regard to this whole problem of the introduction of irrational and complex quantities into elementary algebra, the method of successive "extension of the number-concept," which was historically the method by which these quantities were discovered, seems to be of very questionable value as a method of instruction at the present day. The very terms that have come down to us—*surd* (meaning "absurd"), *irrational*, *imaginary*—show the doubts about the legitimacy of these new quantities which were occasioned by this method of introducing them. In the light of the modern science of algebra, these doubts simply do not occur; the whole point of view in regard to algebraic quantities has changed; the old terminology itself is retained only out of respect for the past.

---

* Compare the trenchant remarks on this subject by *C. F. Gauss* in his famous Doctor's Dissertation, 1799. Reprinted in *Ostwald's* Klassiker der exacten Wissenschaften, under the title: Beweise für die Zerlegung ganzer algebraischer Functionen in reelle Factoren ersten und zweiten Grades.

After clear ideas have once been reached on these subjects, one is forced to raise the question whether it is necessary to perplex all our pupils of to-day with the same vagueness and obscurity through which the earlier pioneers had to struggle. Is it necessary to turn out hundreds of pupils, as we do, from our courses in algebra, with the conviction hopelessly fixed in their minds that some of the things with which algebra deals are, in all truth, "absurd" and "imaginary"?

In the opinion of the present writer, if the irrational and imaginary quantities are to be introduced into elementary work at all, the method which is most satisfactory from the strictly scientific point of view, is also by far the simplest and most satisfactory from the point of view of the elementary student. This opinion it is hoped will be borne out by the sequel. (See especially secs. 36, 38, 39, 42, and remarks in secs. 26, 28, 29 and 30.)

4. Plan of the article. The space at our disposal does not permit the separate development of the several types of algebra, in the order in which, beginning with the algebra of the positive integers, these types would naturally be presented to the pupil. We shall confine ourselves chiefly to the *algebra of complex quantities*, which is the most inclusive and the most interesting type. In IV a geometrical example of this type of algebra is given (without the use of trigonometry) and in V the abstract theory of the algebra is developed, that is, *the precise conditions are laid down which any system must satisfy in order to be equivalent to the algebra in question* (sec. 30). In sec. 35 several examples of "pseudo-algebras" are given, that is, systems that satisfy most, but not all, of the conditions of sec. 30; for it is only by a study of what the algebra is *not* that we can fully understand what it *is*.

II and III are preliminary to the main discussion. In II a number of geometrical facts are observed, of which use will be made in IV. III shows how this collection of geometrical facts can be reduced to an abstract science, and serves to illustrate, in this very simple case, all the steps of the reasoning which will be used in the general case in V.

The chief points in the article which may be unfamiliar to many readers are the following: The analysis of the fundamental concepts which occur in algebra; the notion of the "equivalence," or "isomorphism," of two algebraic systems with respect to these fundamental concepts; the notion of the "sufficiency" of a selected set of fundamental propositions to determine uniquely a particular type of algebra; and the method of establishing the "consistency" and "independence" of the propositions of such a set.

II. THE ADDITION OF ANGLES AND THE MULTIPLICATION OF DISTANCES

5. The addition of angles. We begin with a preliminary discussion of the very simple and familiar process of the addition of angles.

By an **angle,** as in all higher mathematics, we mean an amount of rotation of a line about a fixed point O, in a plane. Such a rotation may be counter-clockwise or clockwise, and of any amount; as, $+250°$, $-780°$, etc.

To clarify our ideas about rotations of more than 360°, it will be well to adopt *Riemann's* famous device, and think of the plane about the point O as made up of numerous distinct sheets, joined together after the fashion of a spiral staircase; a moving radius rotating about the point O winds around from one sheet to the next as if it were following the thread of a screw. Two angles like 360° and 720° are thus kept distinct; for although the terminal lines of these angles point in the same direction, they lie in different sheets of the *Riemann* surface.

If two angles α and β are given, a third angle γ may be derived from them by the following familiar process: starting with a given initial line as the zero angle, perform the rotation indicated by α; then continuing from the terminal line of α, perform a rotation equal in amount and direction to β; the final position thus reached is the terminal line of the required angle γ. This angle γ is called the **sum** of the given angles α and β (with respect to the chosen zero) and is denoted by $\alpha+\beta$.

6. Concerning the addition of angles, as thus defined, the reader may easily verify the following familiar statements:

(*a*) If α and β are any two angles (whether equal or unequal), then their sum, $\alpha+\beta$, is an angle uniquely determined by α and β (with respect to the chosen zero-angle).

(*b*) $\alpha+\beta=\beta+\alpha$. (Commutative law for addition.)

(*c*) If α, β, γ are any three angles, $(\alpha+\beta)+\gamma=\alpha+(\beta+\gamma)$. (Associative law for addition.)

(*d*) If $\alpha+\beta=\alpha+\beta'$, then $\beta=\beta'$. ("Law of cancellation" for addition.)

If we introduce, for abbreviation, the notation, $2\alpha=\alpha+\alpha$, $3\alpha=\alpha+\alpha+\alpha, \ldots, n\alpha=\alpha+\alpha+\cdot\cdot\cdot+\alpha$ to n terms, where n is any positive integer, we have further:

(*e*) If $n\alpha=n\beta$, then $\alpha=\beta$.

The angle $n\alpha$ is called the **nth multiple** of the angle α.

Three other facts of somewhat different character ("existence theorems") are the following:

(*f*) There is one and only one angle x such that $x+x=x$; this angle x is the *zero* angle, and is denoted by **0**.

(*g*) Every angle α determines uniquely an angle α' such that $\alpha+\alpha'=\mathbf{0}$. This angle α' is called the **opposite of** α and is denoted by $-\alpha$.

(*h*) For every angle α and every positive integer n, there is an angle y, uniquely determined by α and n, such that $ny=\alpha$. This angle y is called the nth **submultiple of** α, denoted by α/n. For example, we have $\alpha/2$, $\alpha/3$, etc.

7. Among the many further facts which might be mentioned, the following are the most important for our present purpose:

(*i*) If **0** is the zero angle, then for every angle α, $\alpha+\mathbf{0}=\alpha$.

(*j*) If α and β are any given angles, there is always an angle x, uniquely determined by α and β, such that $\alpha=\beta+x$; this angle x is called the **remainder,** α **minus** β, and is denoted by $\alpha-\beta$, and the process by which it is obtained is called **subtraction.** The angle $\alpha-\beta$ is the same as the angle $\alpha+(-\beta)$. Hence, to *subtract* an angle β, means to *add the opposite of* β.

(*k*) If m and n are any positive integers, the angle $m(\alpha/n)$ is equal to the angle $(m\alpha)/n$, so that either may be denoted by $(m/n)\alpha$.

All these statements, (*a*)–(*k*), may be regarded as the direct result of observation. There is no necessary logical order among them; any one may be obtained without reference to the others directly from the figure, as the reader may readily verify.

8. First step toward the science of this process. Selection of axioms. Now this miscellaneous collection of facts about angles does not constitute a *science*. In order to reduce it to a science, the first step is to do what *Euclid* did in geometry, namely, *to select a small number of the given facts as axioms, and then to show that all other facts can be deduced from these axioms by the methods of formal logic.*

As a convenient choice of axioms for the science of the addition of angles, we may take the propositions (*a*)–(*h*) in sec. 6; from these axioms the other propositions, (*i*), (*j*), (*k*), etc., can be deduced as theorems, without further reference to the definition.

For example, the proof of theorem (*i*) is as follows: By (*f*), $\mathbf{O}+\mathbf{O}=\mathbf{O}$, hence, by (*a*), $\alpha+(\mathbf{O}+\mathbf{O})=\alpha+\mathbf{O}$, whence, by (*c*), $(\alpha+\mathbf{O})+\mathbf{O}=\alpha+\mathbf{O}$, whence, by (*b*), $\mathbf{O}+(\alpha+\mathbf{O})=\mathbf{O}+\alpha$; therefore, by (*d*), $\alpha+\mathbf{O}=\alpha$, which was to be proved.

Similarly, the proof for (*j*) is as follows: By (*f*) and (*g*), there is an angle $-\beta$ such that $\beta+(-\beta)=\mathbf{O}$. Let $x=\alpha+(-\beta)$, which is known to be an angle, by (*a*). Then, by the use of (*b*), (*c*), (*g*), and (*b*), and theorem (*i*),

$$\beta+x=\beta+[\alpha+(-\beta)]=\beta+[(-\beta)+\alpha]=[\beta+(\ \ \beta)]+\alpha=\mathbf{O}+\alpha=\alpha+\mathbf{O}=\alpha;$$

that is, the angle $\alpha+(-\beta)$ is an angle which, when added to β, produces α, as was to be proved. That this angle is uniquely determined by α and β follows at once from (*d*).

The proof of (*k*) may be illustrated by a numerical case. Let $x=3(\alpha/2)$ and $y=(3\alpha)/2$; then by (*a*) and (*c*),

$$\begin{aligned}2x&=[3(\alpha/2)]+[3(\alpha/2)]=[\alpha/2+\alpha/2+\alpha/2]+[\alpha/2+\alpha/2+\alpha/2]\\&=[\alpha/2+\alpha/2]+[\alpha/2+\alpha/2]+[\alpha/2+\alpha/2]=[2(\alpha/2)]+[2(\alpha/2)]+[2(\alpha/2)]\\&=3[2(\alpha/2)]\\&=3[\alpha],\text{ by the definition of }\alpha/2.\end{aligned}$$

But also, $2y=2[(3\alpha)/2]=(3\alpha)$, by the same definition. Therefore, $2x=2y$, whence $x=y$, by (*e*). The general case for m and n is proved in a similar way.

It must not be supposed that proofs like these, in which every step is carefully justified by reference to one or other of the axioms, are necessary to convince us that the statements in question are true; indeed, in this particular case, the theorems proved are quite as obvious as the axioms on which the proof is based; all of them may be obtained independently, by direct observation of the figure.

The fact is that a mathematical demonstration, strictly speaking, is not concerned with the *truth* of the proposition at all; it is concerned merely with the *logical relation* that exists between the given proposition and certain other propositions called the axioms—in other words, all that a mathematical demonstration tells us is that *if* the axioms are true, *then* the theorem in question will also be true—provided, of course, that our deductive reasoning is sound.

Provided that our deductive reasoning is sound—there is the difficulty. How can we be sure that each step of the deduction is logically justified? How can we be sure that no assumption is tacitly used in the proof which was not explicitly stated in the axioms? Even *Euclid* did not escape this danger; he often used, for example, assumptions about the motion of a rigid body which he did not include in his axioms. In fact, it is only in recent years that a really complete list of axioms for geometry has been laid down.* How can we be sure that similar errors will not creep into our reasoning in algebra?

The answer to this question involves a further refinement of the scientific method, which will be discussed in Part III.

9. The multiplication of distances. The system studied in the preceding sections on the addition of angles is an example of the type of algebra called the "algebra of all real quantities" as far as the operation of addition is concerned.

We now consider a second operation, to be called multiplication, this operation being performed not on angles, but on geometric lengths, or distances.

Suppose two distances a and b are given; and then, having chosen a given distance u as a "unit distance," find a distance x by the construction shown in Figure 1, in which b is at right angles to u and a, and the oblique lines are parallel.

* See Monograph I.

This distance x is called the **product** of the given distances a and b (with respect to the chosen unit) and is denoted by $a \times b$, or $a \cdot b$, or simply ab. The process by which this product is obtained is called **multiplication.**

From this definition it follows that if $x = a \times b$, *the area of the rectangle whose sides are x and u is equal to the area of the rectangle whose sides are a and b.*

To see that the two rectangles, $OCDU$ and $OBEA$, are equivalent, note that the part $OBQU$ is common to both; further, the lines PQ, QR, CS, and TA are all equal to BU (being portions of parallels inter-

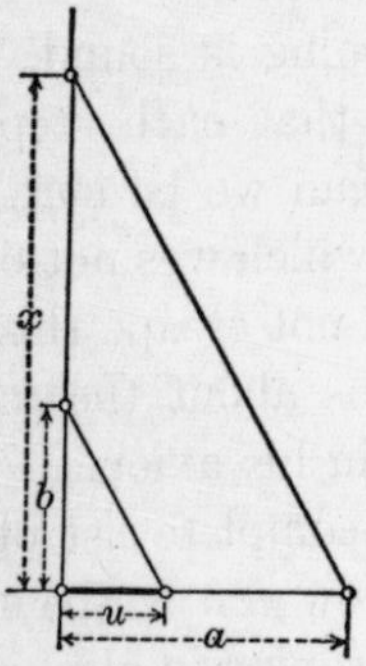

FIG. 1.

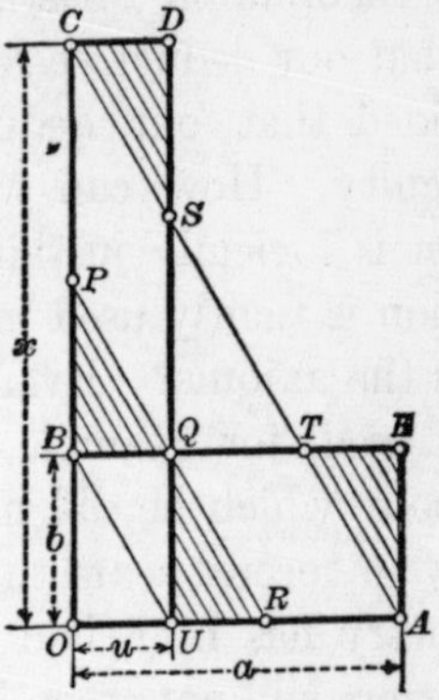

FIG. 2.

cepted between parallels), so that the triangles BPQ and DCS in one rectangle are equal to the triangles UQR and ETA in the other; and, finally, the parallelograms $CSQP$ in one rectangle and $QTAR$ in the other are equivalent (having equal bases PQ and QR and equal altitudes).*

10. Concerning the multiplication of distances, as thus defined, the reader may readily verify the following statements:

(*a*) If a and b are any two distances (whether equal or unequal) then their product, $a \times b$, is a distance uniquely determined by a and b (with respect to the chosen unit distance).

---

* It will be noticed that this proof does not assume the theorem that the area of a rectangle is equal to its base times its altitude, nor any theorems on ratio and proportion.

(*b*) $a\times b=b\times a$. (Commutative law for multiplication.)

(*c*) If a, b, c are any three distances, then

$$(a\times b)\times c=a\times(b\times c).$$

(Associative law for multiplication.)

To see that this is true, let $a\times b=x$ and $b\times c=y$, and then $x\times c=z$ and $a\times y=z'$, so that we have

$$(a\times b)\times c=x\times c=z \quad \text{and} \quad a\times(b\times c)=a\times y=z'.$$

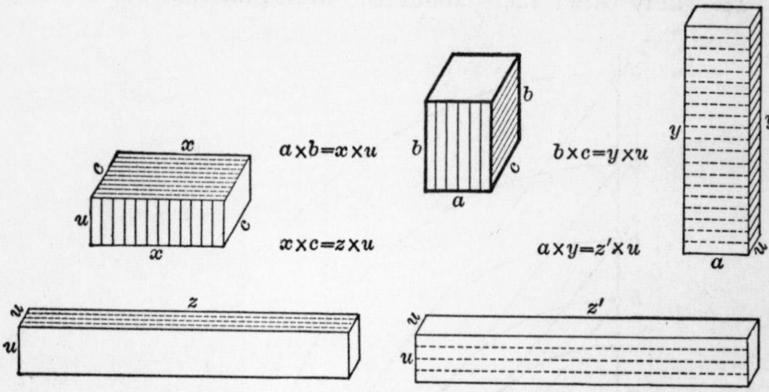

FIG. 3.

Then show that the parallelopiped whose edges are z, u, u and the parallelopiped whose edges are z', u, u both have the same volume as the parallelopiped whose edges are a, b, c. Therefore $z=z'$.

(*d*) If $a\times b=a\times b'$, then $b=b'$. ("Law of cancellation" for multiplication.)

If we introduce, for abbreviation, the notation $a^2=a\times a$, $a^3=a\times a\times a$, . . ., $a^n=a\times a\times\cdot\cdot\cdot\times a$ to n factors, where n is any positive integer, we have further (see Figure 4):

(*e*) If $a^n=b^n$, then $a=b$.

The distance a^n is called the **nth power** of the distance a.

Three other facts of somewhat different character ("existence theorems") are the following:

(*f*) There is one and only one distance x such that $x\times x=x$. This distance x is the **unit distance,** and is denoted by $\mathbf{1}$.

(*g*) Every distance a determines uniquely a distance a' such that $a\times a'=\mathbf{1}$. This distance a' is called the **reciprocal of** a

and is denoted by a^{-1} or $1/a$. For example, if a is five times **1** then a^{-1} is one-fifth of **1**, etc.

(*h*) For every distance a and every positive integer n, there is a distance y, uniquely determined by a and n, such that $y^n = a$. This distance y is called the **nth root of** a, denoted by $a^{1/n}$ or $\sqrt[n]{a}$. For example, if a is a length nine times as long as **1**, then $\sqrt{a}$, or $a^{\frac{1}{2}}$, will be a length three times as long as **1**, etc.

11. Many other facts about the multiplication of distances

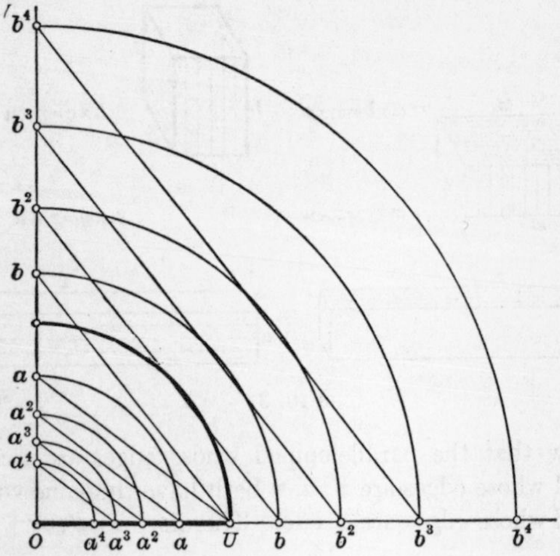

FIG. 4.

might be mentioned, of which the following will suffice for our present purpose:

(*i*) If **1** is the unit distance, then for every distance a, $a \times \mathbf{1} = a$.

(*j*) If a and b are any given distances, there is always a distance x, uniquely determined by a and b, such that $a = b \times x$; this distance x is called the **quotient,** a **divided by** b, and is denoted by a/b; and the process by which it is obtained is called **division.** For example, if $a = 10(\mathbf{1})$ and $b = 5(\mathbf{1})$, then $a/b = 2(\mathbf{1})$; etc.

The distance a/b is the same as the distance $a \times (b^{-1})$

Hence, to *divide* by the distance b means to **multiply by the reciprocal of** b.

(k) If m and n are any positive integers, the distance $(a^{1/n})^m$ is equal to the distance $(a^m)^{1/n}$, so that either may be denoted by $a^{m/n}$.

All these statements, (a)–(k), about the multiplication of distances, like the statements (a)–(k) in secs. 6–7 about the addition of angles, may be regarded as the direct result of observation—any one of them being obtainable immediately, without reference to the others.

12. First step toward the science of this process. In order to reduce this miscellaneous collection of facts to a science, we may take as the axioms of the science the propositions (a)–(h) in sec. 10, and proceed exactly as in sec. 8; the steps of the reasoning are precisely parallel, and need not be repeated here.

The system here studied is an example of the type of algebra called "the algebra of positive reals," as far as the operation of multiplication is concerned.

We now turn to the problem (already referred to in sec. 8) of how to make more rigorous the science of these two systems.

III. THE ABSTRACT THEORY OF THESE OPERATIONS

13. Parallelism between these two operations. The parallelism between the two systems just described is too striking to have escaped attention. The propositions (a)–(h) in sec. 6 are, as far as their *form* is concerned, identical with the propositions (a)–(h) in sec. 10. The meaning and content of the two sets of propositions are of course very different; the first set concerns the addition of angles, while the second set concerns the multiplication of distances; but their form is the same, since all the propositions of the second set can be obtained at once from those of the first by replacing "angle" by "distance," "sum" by "product," "zero" by "unit," "opposite" by "reciprocal," "subtraction" by "division," etc. This duality between the two sets of propositions will of course extend through all the propositions that are deducible from them by the methods of formal logic; from every proposition concerning the addition (or subtraction) of angles, a corresponding proposition concerning the multiplication (or division) of distances can at once be obtained by merely changing the interpretation of the symbols, without changing the form of the statement.

14. Postulates for an abstract science to include them both. This duality at once suggests the possibility of developing a general theory which shall include both these theories as special cases. To do this, we proceed as follows: Consider a general *class of things or "elements" denoted by A, B, C, etc.*, without specifying whether these things are to be angles (α, β, γ, etc.) or distances (a, b, c, etc.), and a general *rule of combination denoted by* $\circ$, without specifying whether this rule of combination is to be addition ($+$) or multiplication ($\times$);* and *impose upon these symbols the following conditions:*

(a) *If A and B are elements of the class, then* $A\circ B$ (*read:* "*A with B*") *is an element of the class, uniquely determined by A and B.*

(b) $A\circ B = B\circ A$.† (Commutative law.)

(c) $(A\circ B)\circ C = A\circ(B\circ C)$. (Associative law.)

(d) *If* $A\circ B = A\circ B'$, *then* $B = B'$. ("Law of cancellation.")

(e) *If* $A^{[n]} = B^{[n]}$, then $A = B$.

Here $A^{[n]}$ means $A\circ A\circ\cdots\circ A$, to n elements, where n is a positive integer.

(f) *There is an element X such that* $X\circ X = X$.

[It can be shown from the preceding conditions that there cannot be more than one such element. For, suppose these were two such elements, X and Y, such that $X\circ X = X$ and $Y\circ Y = Y$; then, by (*a*), $(X\circ X)\circ Y = X\circ(Y\circ Y)$, whence, by (*c*), $X\circ(X\circ Y) = X\circ(Y\circ Y)$, whence, by (*d*), $X\circ Y = Y\circ Y$; therefore, by (*b*), $Y\circ X = Y\circ Y$, whence, by (*d*), $X = Y$.]

---

* A system composed of a class K and a rule of combination $\circ$ we shall speak of as a "system (K, $\circ$)."

† The equality sign, $=$, is used to indicate that the two expressions between which it stands are interchangeable in any proposition of the theory. If desired, the laws of operation with this symbol may be formally stated as follows: (1) $A = A$; (2) if $A = B$ then $B = A$; (3) if $A = B$ and $B = C$, then $A = C$.

(*g*) *If X is the unique element such that $X \circ X = X$, then for every element A there is an element A' such that $A \circ A' = X$.*

[It follows from (*d*) that this element A' is uniquely determined by A.]

(*h*) *For every element A and every positive integer n, there is an element Y such that $Y^{[n]} = A$, where $Y^{[n]}$ means $Y \circ Y \circ \cdots \circ Y$ to n elements.*

[It follows from (*e*) that this element Y is uniquely determined by A and n.]

15. Consistency of the postulates. From these eight conditions, or "postulates," as we shall call them, a long list of theorems can be deduced; for example:

(*i*) If X is the unique element such that $X \circ X = X$, then for every element A,

$$A \circ X = A;$$

moreover, *any system which satisfies all these conditions* (*a*)–(*h*) *will satisfy also all the theorems derived therefrom.*

But the first question to be asked about such a set of conditions or "postulates," is this: Are they *consistent* demands? In other words, does any system exist which satisfies all the conditions? In this case the answer is, of course, affirmative; for, if the class $A, B, C, \ldots$ is the class of *angles*, and the rule of combination $\circ$ is the rule of *addition*, then all the conditions are satisfied, as we saw in sec. 6; the elements X, A', and Y, whose existence is demanded in (*f*), (*g*), and (*h*), are the "zero angle," the "opposite of A," and the "nth submultiple of A," of that system. Again, if the class $A, B, C \ldots$ is the class of *distances*, and the rule of combination $\circ$ is the rule of *multiplication*, then also all the conditions are satisfied, as we saw in sec. 10; the elements X, A', and Y now being called the "unit distance," the "reciprocal of A," and the "nth root of A." Indeed, the system of angles, under addition, and the system of distances, under multiplication, are only two examples out of many which satisfy all these eight conditions, so that we may be well assured that the conditions are consistent.

These eight postulates, (*a*)–(*h*), *may therefore be taken as the fundamental propositions of an abstract science, which will exhibit, in skeleton form, the logical structure of a large class of systems, of which the systems described in Part II are examples.*

This is the refinement of the scientific method, to which reference was made in sec. 8. The great advantages of the method are: first, that the essential properties of a whole class of systems are epitomized in one abstract theory; and secondly, that the liability to error in deducing one theorem from another is vastly reduced by the abstract form of statement, which includes everything that is essential and nothing that is accidental.

For example, in the proof of theorem (*i*) in sec. 8, it was an "accident" that the symbols "α" and "**O**" represented angles, and the symbol "+" addition; the essential thing was that these symbols obeyed the formal laws laid down in propositions (*a*)–(*h*).

Further, if any system, consisting of a class of elements *A*, *B*, *C*, . . . and a rule of combination $\circ$, is laid before us, we have only to assure ourselves that this system satisfies the eight postulates of our abstract science, in order to be convinced that this system will also satisfy all the derived theorems, which form the body of the science.

16. On the uses of an abstract science. From this discussion it will be evident that the main interest of an abstract science centers about the logical relations between abstract propositions, rather than about the applicability of these propositions to concrete things. But many important mathematical theories have been developed as "abstract sciences," from an apparently quite arbitrary set of postulates, which have later proved to be powerful tools in applied mathematics, when important practical systems that satisfied all the postulates of these particular theories unexpectedly presented themselves.

The case of the algebra of complex quantities, the study of which will form the main part of the present article, is precisely a case in point. This algebra was developed, historically, from the purest of purely "mathematical" motives—to satisfy a scientific curiosity as to what conclusions could be drawn from certain assumed hypotheses, with no thought of application to electrical engineering or any other branch of practical science; and yet when the electrical engineers, long after, began to develop the theory of alternating currents, they found that the fundamental conditions of their problem were formally identical with the fundamental postulates of the abstract science of this algebra; consequently the whole highly developed mathematical theory, with all its ramifications, became at once an invaluable tool, ready to hand, for the work of this most practical of practical sciences.

17. Examples of systems that do not satisfy these postulates. Concerning the set of postulates (*a*)–(*h*) of sec. 14, it will be instructive to give here a few examples of systems which do *not* satisfy all of these postulates; for it is only by understanding what a thing is not that we can fully understand what it is. For this purpose, we shall exhibit eight systems, each of which satisfies all but one of the eight postulates.

EXAMPLE (*a*). Let the class $A, B, C, \ldots$ be the class of all angles between $-10°$ and $+10°$, and let $A \circ B$ be $A+B$.

This system fails to satisfy postulate (*a*), since $7° \circ 8° = 15°$, for instance, is not in the class. All the other postulates are satisfied.

EXAMPLE (*b*). Let the class be the class of positive integral numbers; and let the rule of combination be such that $A \circ B = B$. For example, $7 \circ 8 = 8$, $15 \circ 3 = 3$, etc.

This system clearly fails to satisfy the commutative law, postulate (*b*); but all the other postulates are satisfied. Thus, in postulate (*f*), any element X will have the required property $X \circ X = X$; since this element X is not uniquely determined, postulate (*g*) has nothing further to demand; this postulate is, therefore, as we say, satisfied "vacuously." * To show that postulate (*h*) is satisfied, take $Y = A$.

EXAMPLE (*c*). Class: all angles; rule of combination: $A \circ B = (A+B)/3$.

Here the associative law, (*c*), is not satisfied, since, for example,

$$(3° \circ 6°) \circ 12° = 3° \circ 12° = 5°, \quad \text{while} \quad 3° \circ (6° \circ 12°) = 3° \circ 6° = 3°.$$

All the other postulates are satisfied. Thus, in (*f*), take X = the zero angle; in (*g*), take $A' = -A$; in (*h*), notice first that

$$A^{[2]} = \frac{2}{3}A, \quad A^{[3]} = \left(\frac{1}{3} + \frac{2}{3^2}\right)A, \quad A^{[4]} = \left(\frac{1}{3} + \frac{1}{3^2} + \frac{2}{3^3}\right)A,$$

* It is not surprising that X is not uniquely determined in this system, since postulate (*b*) was one of the postulates required for the proof of uniqueness given above.

so that in general, by the formula for the sum of a geometric series,

$$A^{[n]}=\frac{3^{n-1}+1}{2\times 3^{n-1}}A;$$

hence, if we take

$$Y=\frac{2\times 3^{n-1}}{3^{n-1}+1}A,$$

postulate (*h*) will be satisfied.

EXAMPLE (*d*). Class: all angles; rule of combination: if A is distinct from B, $A\circ B=$ the zero angle; but $A\circ A=A$.

This system fails to satisfy the "law of cancellation," but satisfies all the other postulates. Postulate (*g*) is satisfied "vacuously," since there is no uniquely determined element X to which this condition could refer.

EXAMPLE (*e*). Class: all angles; congruent angles being regarded as equal;* rule of combination: $A\circ B=$ that angle in the first revolution which is congruent to $A+B$.

Here (*e*) is not satisfied, since, for example, $60°^{[2]}=60°\circ 60°=120°$, and also $240°^{[2]}=240°\circ 240°=120°$, while 60° and 240° are not equal angles. All the other postulates are satisfied.

EXAMPLE (*f*). Class: all positive distances; rule of combination: $A\circ B=$ the hypotenuse of a right triangle of which A and B are the legs.

Here (*f*) is not satisfied, since the hypotenuse of a right triangle is never equal to a leg. All the other postulates are satisfied, postulate (*g*) "vacuously."

EXAMPLE (*g*). Class: all positive angles and the zero angle; rule of combination: $\circ=+$.

This system clearly does not satisfy postulate (*g*), since if $A=10°$, for example, the opposite of A is not in the class. All the other postulates are satisfied.

EXAMPLE (*h*). Class: all integral numbers, positive, negative, and zero; rule of combination: $\circ=+$, where $+$ means the ordinary "+" of arithmetic.

* Congruent angles are those that differ only by a multiple of 360°.

This system fails on postulate (*h*), since, for example, there is no integral number y such that $y+y+y=5$. It clearly satisfies all the other postulates.

18. Independence of the postulates. These examples enable us to answer a second question concerning the set of postulates (*a*)–(*h*) in sec. 14. We have already inquired whether these postulates are consistent (sec. 15); we may now ask, Are they *independent?* That is, are none of them merely consequences of the rest? Or, in other words, is the set of postulates *free from redundancies?*

The examples just cited show that in this case the postulates *are* all independent; for, if postulate (*a*), for example, were a consequence of the other seven postulates, then every system which satisfied the other seven would also satisfy (*a*); but this is not the case, as is shown by the example cited; therefore postulate (*a*) is not a consequence of the other seven postulates. Similarly, each one of the eight postulates is shown to be independent of the rest.

In this connection it may be noticed that the postulates (*a*)–(*h*) in sec. 14 are often simpler statements than the propositions (*a*)–(*h*) in sec. 6 or sec. 10. For example, (*f*) in sec. 6 is really a double statement: (1) there is at least one angle x such that $x+x=x$, and (2) there is not more than one such angle; in sec. 14 we see that only the first part of this statement need be assumed as postulate (*f*), since the second part of the statement is a consequence of (*a*), (*b*), (*c*), and (*d*).

The problem of reducing every postulate to its simplest form is one of the most fascinating problems in this kind of work; if we "weaken" the statement too much, we shall not be able to deduce what we wish to from it; while if we do not weaken it enough, we shall have difficulty in proving it independent. It would, of course, not be desirable to carry this reduction too far in elementary teaching; for the farther back we drive our postulates, the longer is the logical journey we must travel in deducing from these postulates the later and more interesting propositions of the science.

19. On the sufficiency of the postulates to determine a single type of system. We turn, finally, to a third question concerning the postulates (*a*)–(*h*) in sec. 14. We have been dealing with systems consisting of a class, say K, and a rule of combination, $\circ$; and among these systems $(K, \circ)$ we have found some that satisfy the conditions laid down in this set of postulates, and some that do not. Now the question to be raised is this: *Are all the systems $(K, \circ)$ that satisfy these postulates essentially of the same type?* By systems of the same type we mean systems which are "isomorphic" with respect to the class K and the rule of combination $\circ$; two systems $(K, \circ)$ and $(K', \circ')$ being called isomorphic if the elements of the class K can be paired off (put into "one-to-one correspondence" with) the elements of the class K' in such a way that whenever A and B in the class K correspond to A' and B' in the class K', then $A \circ B$ in K will correspond to $A' \circ' B'$ in K'.

As an example, we have the system of angles, with the rule of combination addition (sec. 5), and the system of distances, with the rule of combination multiplication (sec. 9); these two systems are isomorphic; for, if we take any angle α, not $\mathbf{O}$, and any distance a, not $\mathbf{1}$, and pair off the angles with the distances in the manner suggested by the following scheme:

$$\begin{array}{ccccccccccccc} \ldots & -3\alpha & -2\alpha & -\alpha & \mathbf{O} & \frac{1}{2}\alpha & \alpha & \frac{3}{2}\alpha & 2\alpha & 3\alpha & 4\alpha & \ldots \\ \ldots & a^{-3} & a^{-2} & a^{-1} & \mathbf{1} & a^{\frac{1}{2}} & a & a^{\frac{3}{2}} & a^2 & a^3 & a^4 & \ldots \end{array}$$

then the conditions for isomorphism are easily seen to be satisfied.*

These two systems are therefore of the same type.

It is easy, however, to find systems that satisfy all the postulates (a)–(h) and are *not* isomorphic with either of the systems just considered. For example, consider the system in which the class K is the class of all "rational" angles (that is, the class of all angles expressible in the form $\pm\frac{m}{n}1°$, where m and n are positive integers), and in which the rule of combination $\circ$ is the ordinary rule of addition. This system, like the system of *all* angles considered above, satisfies all the postulates, as is readily verified; but the two systems are not isomorphic; for if we attempted to set up an isomorphism between them, we should necessarily pair off first the zeros of the two systems together, and then the rational fractions of 1° in one system with the rational fractions of some angle α_1 in the other; whereupon the one system would be

---

* Incidentally we notice that this isomorphism may be set up in an infinite number of ways, since the angle α and the distance a may be chosen at pleasure.

already exhausted, while the other would still contain an infinite number of unpaired elements (compare sec. 28).

The answer to our third question is therefore, in this case, in the negative; all the systems that satisfy the postulates (*a*)–(*h*) of sec. 14 are *not* of the same type. To distinguish between the various types of systems that satisfy these postulates, further conditions would have to be added.

These facts may be expressed by saying that the postulates in question, while they are *consistent* (sec. 15), and *independent* (sec. 18), are *not* "*sufficient*," that is, not sufficient to determine any single type of system $(K, \circ)$.*

20. Note on the terms "axiom" and "postulate." We have now introduced to the reader, in connection with the very simple systems studied in Part II, all the fundamental ideas which we shall need to use in the main part of the article. Before leaving this preliminary work, however, it may be well to say a word in regard to a disputed question of terminology; namely, the question of the proper use of the term "axiom."

Some authors, particularly in Germany, have called any

---

* The postulates for general algebra, which are given below in sec. 30, will be found to have all three of the properties of consistency, independence, and sufficiency. A "sufficient" set of postulates is also called "categorical," this term having been introduced by *Veblen* in 1904. (*O. Veblen*, A System of Axioms for Geometry, Trans. Am. Math. Soc., Vol. V, p. 346.) The term "sufficient" was first used by *E. V. Huntington* in 1902 (A Complete Set of Postulates for the Theory of Absolute Continuous Magnitude, Trans. Am. Math. Soc., Vol. III, p. 264). For a criticism of these terms, see *L. Couturat*, Les Principes des Mathématiques, p. 169.

The earliest example of a "sufficient" or "categorical" set of postulates is a set of five postulates for the algebra of positive integers given by *G. Peano* in 1889. (See Bull. Am. Math. Soc., ser. 2, Vol. IX, p. 41, 1902.) In this connection compare also two papers by *A. Padoa*, (1) Essai d'une théorie algébrique des nombres entiers, précédé d'une introduction logique à une théorie déductive quelconque; Bibliothèque du Congrès international de Philosophie, Paris, 1900, Vol. III, pp. 309-365; and (2) Un nouveau système irréductible des postulats pour l'algèbre, Compte rendu du deuxième Congrès international des Mathématiciens, Paris, 1900, pp. 249–256; and a short note by *D. Hilbert*, Ueber den Zahlbegriff, Jahresber. der deutschen Mathematiker-Vereinigung, Vol. VIII, 1900, pp. 157–168.

set of conditions adopted as the basis of an abstract science, like the conditions (*a*)–(*h*) of sec. 14, a set of *axioms* for that science. In the opinion of the present writer, however, the term axiom should be applied only to statements of *fact*, like the propositions of sec. 6 or sec. 10, never to statements of *conditions to be satisfied*, like the propositions of sec. 14.

The propositions of sec. 6 or sec. 10 are properly called axioms, because they are obviously true statements about certain definite operations on angles or distances. The propositions of sec. 14, on the other hand, are of quite different character. We have called them "postulates," from the Latin *postulo*, because they are "demands" or conditions which a given system may or may not happen to satisfy. They are logically analogous to demands or conditions set up in other fields of activity; for example, just as any man who satisfies the conditions set up for admission to the army is entitled to belong to that particular class of men, so any system (K, $\circ$) that satisfies the conditions set up in sec. 14 is entitled to belong to a certain class of systems. No one would think of calling the conditions for admission to the army "axioms"; and there is no more reason for calling the conditions of sec. 14 by that name.

Indeed if the word "axiom" is preserved in its well-established meaning, the recognition of the distinction between axiom and postulate, if properly understood, may well serve to mark the transition from the older to the more modern point of view in regard to the nature of abstract mathematical reasoning.*

In regard to the term "postulate," there seems to be little choice between "postulate," "assumption," "primitive proposition," all of which are in good use. Strictly speaking, these postulates, and all the theorems deducible from them, are not propositions at all, but rather what *Bertrand Russell* † has called "propositional functions," which become propositions (true or false) only after particular values are assigned to the variable symbols K and $\circ$.

---

*Compare *M. Bôcher's* St. Louis Address, 1904, Bull. Amer. Math. Soc., Vol. XI, pp. 115–135, especially the first footnote on p. 129. Also *J. W. A. Young*, The Teaching of Mathematics, pp. 193–201.

† The Principles of Mathematics, Vol. I, 1903; or *L. Couturat*, Les Principes des Mathématiques.

IV. GEOMETRICAL EXAMPLE OF THE ALGEBRA OF COMPLEX QUANTITIES: THE SYSTEM OF POINTS IN A PLANE

21. Points in a plane; "real" and "imaginary" points.* As a first concrete example of the algebra of complex quantities, consider the class of all points that lie in a plane in which two points, O and U, are fixed.

These points are divided into "**real**" points and "**imaginary**" points. The "real" points are all the points that lie on the line through O and U, this line being called **the axis of reals**; the "imaginary" points are all the remaining points of the plane.† A "real" point is called **positive** or **negative** according as it lies on that half of the real axis which contains U, or on the other half. The point O itself is called the **zero point** (see below) and is neither positive nor negative.

An **imaginary** point is called a **pure imaginary** if it lies on a line through O perpendicular to the axis of reals.

The position of any point a in the plane is determined when we know: (1) the *distance* of a from O (the distance OU being taken as the unit of measurement); and (2) the *angle* which the line Oa makes with the axis OU. Two points are "equal," that is, coincident, when and only when their "distances" are equal and their "angles" equal or congruent.

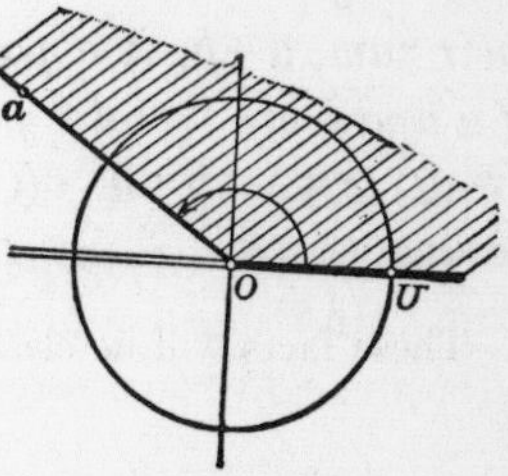

FIG. 5.

The notation $(5, \angle 120°)$, for example, is used to denote a point whose "distance" is 5 times OU, and whose "angle" is $120°$.

---

* The system of points in the plane was first studied by *C. Wessel*, in 1799, and by *Argand*, in 1806.

† The terms "real" and "imaginary" are unfortunate legacies from the eighteenth century, which have become firmly fixed in mathematical literature; the so-called imaginary points are of course no more imaginary, in the ordinary sense of the word, than any other points of the plane.

All the points whose distances equal OU are called **points on the " unit circle."**

Among these points in the plane, we now proceed to define certain rules of combination which we shall call " addition " and " multiplication."

22. Addition of points in the plane. If two points a and b are given, a third point x may be derived from them by the following process: Starting from O, perform the journey from O to a; then continuing from a, perform a journey equal to length and direction to the journey from O to b; the point finally reached is the required point x.*

The point x thus determined is called the **sum** of the given points a and b, (with respect to the chosen point O) and is denoted by $a+b$.

The + sign here used must of course not be confused with the + sign of arithmetic, because the a and b here denote not numbers, but points.

23. Concerning the addition of points in the plane, as thus defined, the reader may easily verify the following statements:

(1) *If a and b are any two points (equal or unequal) then their sum, $a+b$, is a point, uniquely determined by a and b; and if a and b are " real " points, then $a+b$ is also " real."*

(2) $a+b=b+a$. (Commutative law for addition.)

(3) $(a+b)+c=a+(b+c)$. (Associative law for addition.)

These facts will be clear from the accompanying figures.

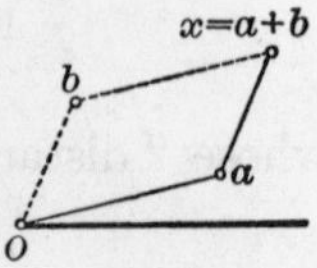

FIG. 6.

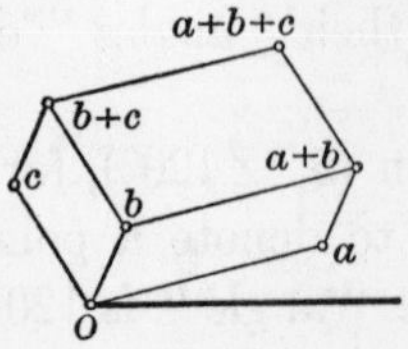

FIG. 7.

(4) *If $a+b=a+b'$, then $b=b'$.* (" Law of cancellation " for addition.)

---

* In the cases in which a and b are not in line with O, the point X may also be described as the fourth vertex of a parallelogram whose sides are Oa and Ob.

(5) *If $na=nb$, then $a=b$. Here n is any positive integer, and na means $a+a+\cdots+a$, to n terms.* The point na is called the **nth multiple of a**.

If a is not O, the series of points a, $2a$, $3a$, . . . will lie beyond a on the straight line through O and a. Obviously, if a is a real point, na will also be real, and positive or negative, according as a is positive or negative.

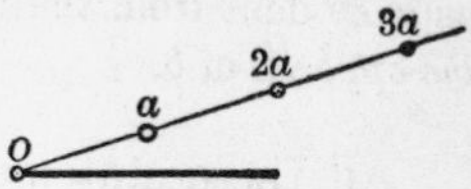

FIG. 8.

(6) *There is a unique point z such that $z+z=z$.* This point z is called the **zero point** of the system, and is denoted by **O**.

This point **O** is the point O of the figure. Obviously, from the definition, if a is any point, $a+\mathbf{O}=a$.

(7) *Every point a determines uniquely a point a' such that $a+a'=\mathbf{O}$.* This point a' is called the **opposite** of a, and is denoted by $-a$; *and if a is any real point, $-a$ will also be real.*

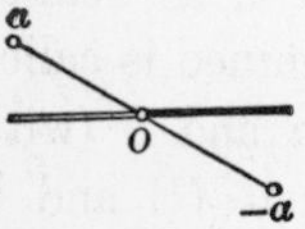

FIG. 9.

The point $-a$ is the point symmetrical to a with respect to O.

(8) *If a point a and a positive integer n are given, there is always a point x such that $nx=a$.* This point x is called the **nth submultiple of a,** and is denoted by a/n; and if a is real, a/n will also be real.

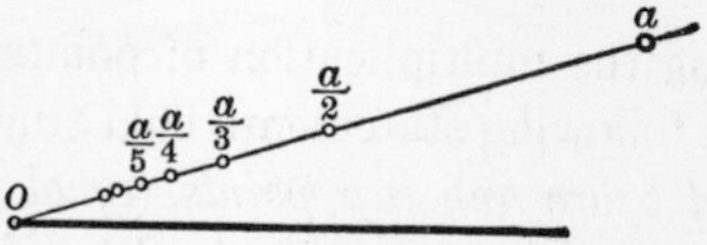

FIG. 10.

If a is not **O**, the series of points a, $a/2$, $a/3$, . . . will lie on the straight line between a and **O**, the series becoming more and more crowded as it approaches the point **O**. Obviously, if $a=\mathbf{O}$, $\mathbf{O}/n=\mathbf{O}$. Further, if m and n are any positive integers, $m(a/n)=(ma)/n$; this point is denoted by $(m/n)a$.

(9) *If a and b are any two points, there is always a point x such that $a=b+x$.* This point x, which is uniquely determined

by a and b, is called the **remainder, a minus b,** and is denoted by $a-b$; and if a and b are real, then $a-b$ is also real.

To construct this point $a-b$, notice that it is the same as $a+(-b)$, as is evident from the figure; hence, to *subtract* a point b means to *add the opposite* of b.

All these statements concerning the addition of points are exactly analogous to the statements in sec. 6 and sec. 7 concerning the addition of angles.

24. Multiplication of points in the plane. We now define a second operation upon these points.

If a and b are any two points in the plane, a third point x may be derived from them by the following process: find the "angle" of x by taking the *sum of the angles* of a and b, as defined in sec. 5; find the "distance" of x, by taking the *product of the distances* of a and b, as defined in sec. 9. The point x thus determined is called the **product** of the given points a and b (with respect to the fixed points O and U) and is denoted by $a \times b$, or $a \cdot b$, or simply ab.

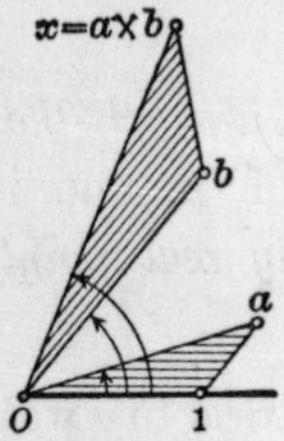

FIG. 11.

For example, if $a=(2, \angle 10°)$ and $b=(3, \angle 15°)$, then $a \times b=(6, \angle 25°)$. Here again the $\times$ sign must not be confused with the $\times$ of arithmetic, since the letters a and b here denote, not numbers, but points in the plane.

25. Concerning the multiplication of points in the plane, as thus defined, the following statements hold true:

(10) *If a and b are any two points (equal or unequal) then their product $a \times b$ is a point uniquely determined by a and b; and if a and b are real, then $a \times b$ is also real.*

In particular, if a and b are both positive, or both negative, $a \times b$ will be positive; but if one factor is positive and the other negative, then the product, as obtained by the rule, will be negative.

(11) $a \times b=b \times a$. (Commutative law for multiplication.)

(12) $(a \times b) \times c=a \times (b \times c)$. (Associative law for multiplication.)

The truth of these statements (11) and (12) is evident from the fact that the addition of angles and the multiplication of distances are themselves commutative and associative (secs. 6, 10).

(13) *If* $a\times b=a\times b'$, *and* a *is not* **0**, *then* $b=b'$. ("Restricted law of cancellation" for multiplication.)

(14) $a\times(b+c)=(a\times b)+(a\times c)$. (Distributive law of multiplication with respect to addition.)

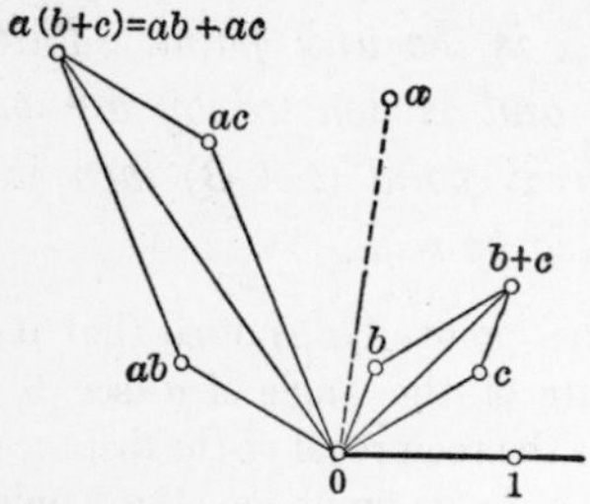

FIG. 12.

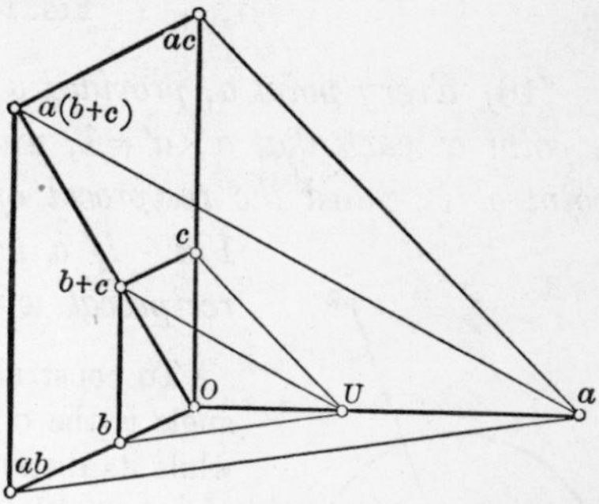

FIG. 13.

To see that this distributive law holds, let each of the points b, c, and $b+c$ be multiplied by a, as in Fig. 12; it is required to show that the point $a(b+c)$ is the sum of the points ab and ac. To show this, place the quadrilateral O, ab, ac, $a(b+c)$, together with the parallelogram O, b, c, $(b+c)$, in a plane perpendicular to the line OU, in the manner shown in Fig. 13, and lay off the distance Oa along that line. By the definition of the multiplication of distances, the lines U-c and a-ac, in Fig. 13, are parallel, as are also the lines U-$(b+c)$ and a-$a(b+c)$; therefore the planes a-ac-$a(b+c)$ and U-c-$(b+c)$ are parallel, and hence the lines ac-$a(b+c)$ and c-$(b+c)$, in which these planes intersect the given plane, are parallel. Hence ac-$a(b+c)$ is parallel to O-ab; and similarly, ab-$a(b+c)$ is parallel to O-ac. Therefore the quadrilateral in question is a parallelogram, and the point $a(b+c)$ is the sum of the points ab and ac, as required.*

(15) *There is a unique point* u, *distinct from* **0**, *such that* $u\times u=u$; *this point* u *is called the* **unit point** *of the system, and is denoted by* **1**.

* The truth of the distributive law may also be inferred directly from Fig. 12, from the properties of similar triangles; but the proof given above has the advantage of not involving the theory of ratio and proportion, or the "incommensurable case.'

This point u is the point U of the figure; that is, the point $(1, \angle 0^\circ)$. Obviously, from the definition of multiplication, if a is any point, $a \times \mathbf{1} = a$.

The successive multiples of the point $\mathbf{1}$ [sec. 23, (5)] are denoted, for brevity, as follows: $\mathbf{1}+\mathbf{1}=2(\mathbf{1})=\mathbf{2}$; $\mathbf{1}+\mathbf{1}+\mathbf{1}=3(\mathbf{1})=\mathbf{3}$; etc.

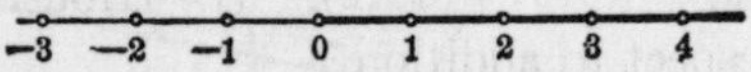

FIG. 14.

(16) *Every point a, provided a is not $\mathbf{0}$, determines uniquely a point a' such that $a \times a' = \mathbf{1}$, where $\mathbf{1}$ is the unit point. This point a' is called the reciprocal of a, and is denoted by a^{-1} or $1/a$. If a is a real point (not $\mathbf{0}$) then its reciprocal will also be real.*

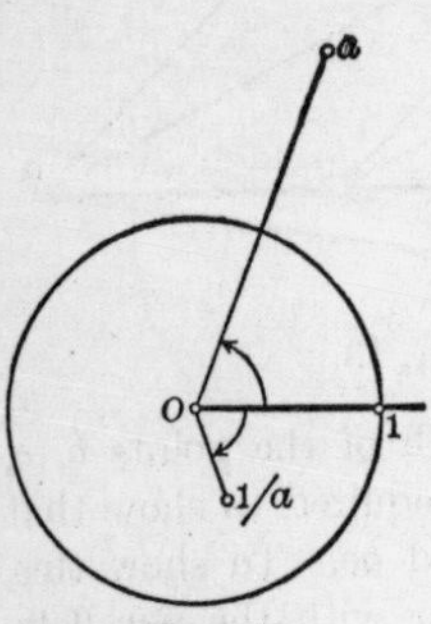

FIG. 15.

To construct the point $1/a$, notice that its angle is the opposite of the angle of a (sec. 6), while its distance is the reciprocal of the distance of a (sec. 10). If a is a point on the "unit circle" (sec. 21), then $1/a$ will also be on the unit circle; while if a is inside the circle, $1/a$ will be outside, and the nearer a approaches the point $\mathbf{0}$, the farther off will $1/a$ recede.

(17) *If a and b are any points, and b not $\mathbf{0}$, then there is always a point x such that $a = b \times x$. This point x, which is uniquely determined by a and b, is called the* **quotient, a divided by b**, *and is denoted by a/b. Moreover, if a and b are real (and b not $\mathbf{0}$) then a/b will also be real.*

To construct this point a/b, notice that its angle must be the angle of a minus the angle of b (sec. 7), while its distance must be the distance of a divided by the distance of b (sec. 11).

In particular, $\mathbf{1}/\mathbf{1} = \mathbf{1}$, and $(m\mathbf{1})/(n\mathbf{1}) = (m/n)\mathbf{1}$, where m and n are any positive integers [sec. 23, (8)]. Hence, if we

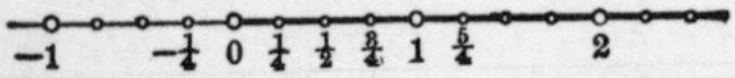

FIG. 16.

denote $m\mathbf{1}$ and $n\mathbf{1}$ by $\mathbf{m}$ and $\mathbf{n}$ [sec. 25, (15)] then $\mathbf{m}/\mathbf{n} = (m/n)\mathbf{1}$. For example, $\mathbf{2}/\mathbf{3} = (2/3)\mathbf{1}$. Notice here that $\mathbf{2}$ and $\mathbf{3}$ are points, whose quotient must be found by the rules for the division of points, while 2 and 3 are numbers, indicating how often a certain operation is to be repeated.

(18) *If a is any point, and* **O** *is the zero point, then* $a \times \mathbf{O} = \mathbf{O}$; *and if a product* $a \times b = \mathbf{O}$, *then at least one of the factors a and b must be* **O**.

In view of these propositions, (1)–(18), we notice in passing that the *system of points in the plane is a system in which addition, subtraction, multiplication, and division (except division by zero) are always possible; and the same is true of the system composed of the "real" points alone.*

(19) *The notation* a^n, *where n is any positive integer, means* $a \times a \times a \times \cdots \times a$ *to n factors; and the point* a^n *is called the* **nth power of the point a.** In particular, a^2 is called the **square** and a^3 the **cube** of the point *a*. Obviously, from the definition of multiplication, $\mathbf{1}^n = \mathbf{1}$, and $\mathbf{O}^n = \mathbf{O}$.

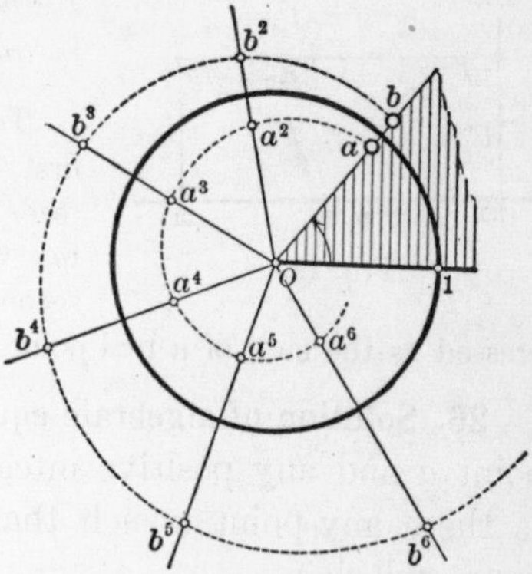

FIG. 17.

To construct the point a^n, notice that the angle of a^n is the *n*th multiple of the angle of *a* (sec. 6); while the distance of a^n is the *n*th power of the distance of *a* (sec. 10). If the point *a* lies on the unit circle, then a^n will also lie on this circle; if the point *a* lies outside the circle, then the series of powers, $a, a^2, a^3, \ldots$ will lie outside the circle, on a spiral curve which recedes farther and farther from it; if the point *a* lies inside the circle, the series $a, a^2, a^3, \ldots$ will lie inside the circle, on a spiral which again recedes farther and farther from the circle, coiling up around the point **O**.

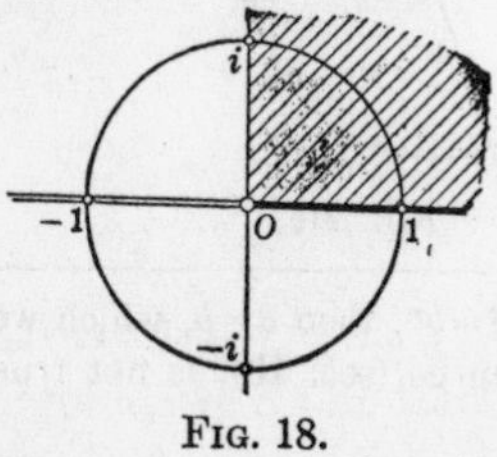

FIG. 18.

Of special interest are the powers of **i**, where **i** denotes the point (1, ∠90°). Referring to the figure, and applying the rule for the multiplication of points, we see that the successive powers of the point **i** repeat in cycles of four:

$$\mathbf{i}=\mathbf{i},\ \mathbf{i}^2=-\mathbf{1},\ \mathbf{i}^3=-\mathbf{i},\ \mathbf{i}^4=\mathbf{1},$$
$$\mathbf{i}^5=\mathbf{i},\ \mathbf{i}^6=-\mathbf{1},\ \mathbf{i}^7=-\mathbf{i},\ \mathbf{i}^8=\mathbf{1}, \text{ etc.}$$

A similar fact is true of the point $-\mathbf{i}$, that is, the point $(1, \angle 270°)$. Hence,

(20) *There are two points x such that $x^2 = -\mathbf{1}$, where $-\mathbf{1}$ is the opposite of the unit point* **1**. *These two points are called the* **imaginary units** *of the system, and are denoted by* i *and* $-$i.

It will be noticed that multiplying any point by **i** has the effect of rotating the point through 90° about O; while multiplying it by $-\mathbf{1}$ rotates it through twice that angle, or 180°.

(21) *If a is any point, there are always two " real " points, x and y, such that $a = x + \text{i}y$, where* i *is one of the " imaginary units."*

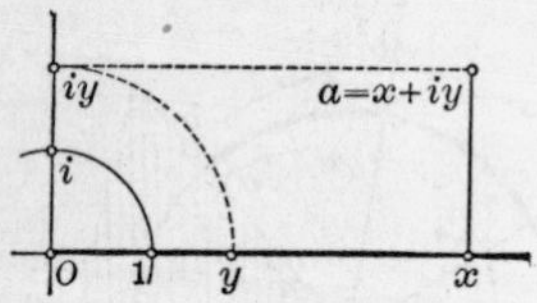

FIG. 19.

To see this, we have only to observe, first, that any "pure imaginary" point (sec. 21) can be expressed in the form iy, where y is some real point, and, second, that any point a can be expressed as the sum of a real point and a pure imaginary.

26. Solution of algebraic equations. Suppose now that any point a and any positive integer n are given; and let us ask, Is there any point x such that $x^n = a$? An inspection of the figure will show:

(22) *If n is any positive integer, and a is any point not* **O**, *there will be n distinct points x such that $x^n = a$; each of these points is called* **an nth root of** *a.*

Thus, every point a, except **O**, has two square roots, three cube roots, four fourth roots, and so on.*

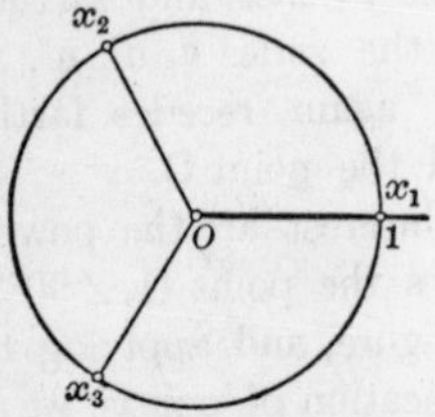

FIG. 20.

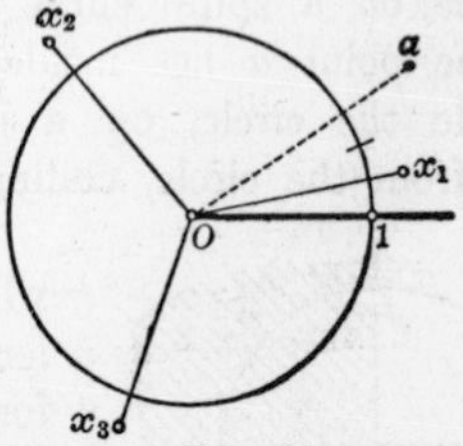

FIG. 21.

* It will be noticed that the proposition: If $a^n = b^n$, then $a = b$, which we found to be true when a and b represented distances (sec. 10), is not true when a and b represent points in the plane.

To construct these points, notice first that if $a=\mathbf{1}$, the nth roots of $\mathbf{1}$ are points on the "unit circle," and divide that circle into n equal parts, beginning with the point $\mathbf{1}$; for, any one of these points, when raised to the nth power according to the rule, will produce the point $\mathbf{1}$. In general, the nth roots of any point a will lie on a circle whose radius is the nth root of the "distance" of a (sec. 10), and will divide this circle into n equal parts, beginning with the point whose "angle" is the nth submultiple of a (sec. 6). If any one of the nth roots is given, the rest can be obtained from it by multiplying by the nth roots of the point $\mathbf{1}$. The notation $a^{1/n}$, or $\sqrt[n]{a}$, is used to denote that particular nth root of a which has the smallest (positive) angle. Thus, $\mathbf{i}=\sqrt{-\mathbf{1}}$, and $-\mathbf{i}=-\sqrt{-\mathbf{1}}$.

If we confine ourselves to *real* points, the statement of the situation is more complicated. Thus, if a is real, and n is an *odd* number, *one* of the nth roots of a will be real, and will be positive or negative according as a is positive or negative. If a is a positive real, and n is *even*, *two* of the nth roots of a will be real, one positive and one negative; but if a is a negative real, and n is *even*, *none* of the nth roots of a will be real.

More generally, suppose we have any *algebraic equation of the nth degree* in x, that is, any equation of the form

$$p_0x^n+p_1x^{n-1}+p_2x^{n-2}+\cdots+p_{n-1}x+p_n=\mathbf{0},$$

where n is a given positive integer, and $p_0, p_1, p_2, \ldots, p_n$ are any given points, provided p_0 is not zero; and let us inquire whether there is any value of x which will satisfy this equation. If there is such a point x, it is called a **root** of the equation.

The facts in the case are these:

(23) *Every algebraic equation of the nth degree:*

$$p_0x^n+p_1x^{n-1}+p_2x^{n-2}+\cdots+p_{n-1}x+p_n=\mathbf{0}$$

can be written as the product of n linear factors:

$$p_0(x-x_1)(x-x_2)\cdots(x-x_n)=\mathbf{0},$$

*where the points $x_1, x_2, \ldots, x_n$ are fixed points depending on the coefficients $p_0, p_1, \ldots, p_n$; each of these points $x_1, x_2, \ldots, x_n$ is a root of the equation, and there are no other roots.**

* Since the n factors $x-x_1, x-x_2, \ldots, x-x_n$ are not necessarily distinct from one another, the number of distinct roots may be any number from

The fact thus stated may be directly verified in the case of equations of the first, second, third, and fourth degrees (called **linear, quadratic, cubic,** and **biquadratic** equations, respectively).

For example, the linear equation $ax+b=0$ (a not zero), has the root $x=-b/a$; and the quadratic equation $ax^2+bx+c=0$ has the roots $x_1=(-b+\sqrt{b^2-4ac})/(2a)$ and $x_2=(-b-\sqrt{b^2-4ac})/(2a)$; and similar solutions can be obtained for equations of the third and fourth degrees.*

The proof for the general case of an equation of the nth degree is more complicated, and will be given in Appendix II.

It is important to notice that the fact just stated concerning the number of roots of an algebraic equation—or, what comes to the same thing, the number of linear factors—is true only when we take into consideration all the points of the plane. If we confined ourselves to the points on the real axis, the corresponding statement would be much more complicated.

For example, the statement that "every quadratic equation $ax^2+bx+c=0$ has two (real or coincident) roots" is a true statement only when we are dealing with the complete system of all the points in the plane (or with some equivalent system). If we are dealing with the real points alone, we must say: "a quadratic equation $ax^2+bx+c=0$ has *two* roots, or *one* root, or *no* root, according as b^2-4ac is positive, zero, or negative." To state, as is often done, that in case b^2-4ac is negative, the two roots still "exist" but have now "become imaginary" is thoroughly mischievous. The simple fact is, that if we are dealing with the real points alone, and b^2-4ac is negative, then there is *no* real point such that $ax^2+bx+c=0$. No juggling with words will alter this fact; and no talk of "imaginary points" can possibly have any definite meaning for the student until he has become acquainted with some actual system in which such points occur.

We now turn to a third property of the system of points in the plane, namely, the relation of order among the points on the axis of reals.

---

1 to n, inclusive; for the sake of brevity, however, it is customary and convenient to say that *an equation of the nth degree always has n roots,* understanding that in special cases some or all of these roots may be coincident.

* See Monograph V.

27. The relation of order among the real points. From the description of the so-called "real" points in sec. 21, it is obvious, in the first place, that

(24) *The real points form a subclass within the class of all the points of the plane. In particular, the points* **O** *and* **1** *are real points.*

Within this subclass of real points, if the point a precedes the point b as we progress along the axis of reals in the direction OU, then we write

$$a < b$$

(read: "a **algebraically less than** b," or, better, "a **precedes** b"). The same situation may also be expressed by writing $b > a$ (read: "b algebraically greater than a," or "b follows a.")

Concerning this relation of serial order among the points on the axis of reals, the following statements are evident:*

(25) *If a and b are real points, and a not equal to b, then either $a < b$ or $b < a$.*

(26) *If $a < b$, then a is not equal to b.*

(27) *If $a < b$ and $b < c$, then $a < c$.* (Law of transitivity.)

(28) *If a, x, and y are real points, and $x < y$, then $a + x < a + y$.*

(29) *If $a > O$ and $b > O$, then $a \times b > O$.*

If $a > O$, then a is a positive real point, and if $a < O$, a negative real point (sec. 21). Hence the statement just made can be expressed by saying that if a and b are positive, their product $a \times b$ will also be positive.

(30) *If $a < b$, there are always real points x such that $a < x$ and $x < b$.* Such points x are said to lie **between** the points a and b.

A further fact, which is not so obvious, but which may be accepted as a geometric axiom, is the following:

(31) (*Dedekind's principle.*) *If M is any (non-empty) subclass of real points, and if all the points of M precede a given*

---

* For a detailed elementary study of the relation of serial order, see *E. V. Huntington*, The Continuum as a Type of Order, reprinted from the Annals of Mathematics, 1905 (Publication Office of Harvard University).

point c, then there will be a uniquely determined point x, called the **upper limit of M**, *having the following properties:*

First, every point in M precedes, or at most equals, x;

Second, if x′ is any real point such that x′ < x, then there is at least one point of M that follows x′.

FIG. 22.

In other words, if a subclass of real points has *any* "upper bound," it will have a "*least* upper bound," or "upper limit."

Similarly, a subclass of real points that has any lower bound, will have a "greatest lower bound," or "lower limit."

This fact is of great importance in connection with the so-called irrational points, as explained in the next section.

Finally, we have what is known as the *Principle of Archimedes:*

(32) *If a and b are any positive points, and a is "less than" b, it is always possible to find some multiple of a which is "greater than" b.*

This fact is of great importance in the theory of measurement.

28. Classification of real points. Among the real points the points **1**, **2**, **3**, . . . [sec. 25, (15)] are called the **positive integral points**, and the points **−1**, **−2**, **−3**, . . . the **negative integral points**; all these, together with the point **0**, form the subclass of **"all integral points."**

All real points which can be expressed in the form $\pm\mathbf{m}/\mathbf{n}$, where **m** and **n** are any positive integral points [sec. 25, (17)] together with the point **0**, are called the **rational** points. The rational points which are not integral are called **fractional;** the fractional points lie between the integral points.

All real points which are not rational are called **irrational.**

That not all the real points are "rational" can be made clear by the following familiar reasoning: Consider the diagonal, *D*, of a square whose side is the unit distance, *u*; this length *D* cannot be expressed as a rational fraction of *u*; for, if $D = (m/n)u$, where *m* and *n* are positive integers, then, since the area of the square on *D* is equal to twice the area of the square on u, we should have $m^2/n^2 = 2$, and this numerical relation cannot be satisfied by any integers m and n*. Hence, if we take a point x on the real axis so that its distance from **O** is equal to D, then this point x cannot be expressed in the form $(m/n)\mathbf{1}$, and is therefore an irrational point.

From sec. 27, (31) it is clear that every irrational point a can be regarded as the limit of an infinite sequence of rational points, a_1, a_2, a_3 .... Of special importance are the sequences of the form illustrated by the following example:

$$a_0 = \mathbf{6};\ a_1 = \mathbf{4/10};\ a_2 = \mathbf{0/10^2};\ a_3 = \mathbf{3/10^3};\ a_4 = \mathbf{1/10^4};\ \ldots,$$

where each numerator is one of the points **0, 1, 2, 3, ... 9** [see sec. 25, (15)], and each denominator is a power of the point **10**. A sequence of this form is called a **decimal fraction,** and is denoted, for brevity, as follows (taking the same example):

$$\mathbf{6};\ \mathbf{6.4};\ \mathbf{6.40};\ \mathbf{6.403};\ \mathbf{6.4031};\ldots$$

These points are the first terms of the sequence that would be obtained if we attempted to approximate toward the point $\sqrt{\mathbf{41}}$ by a sequence of rational points in the decimal form; in fact, the algorithm for "extracting the square root" of the *point* **41** is exactly analogous to the familiar algorithm for extracting the square root of the *number* 41 in arithmetic; but it should be clearly understood that when we are dealing with the system of points, the point $\sqrt{\mathbf{41}}$, like all the other irrational or rational points, is already given, from the start, in the system of points, while if we are dealing with the system of numbers, and have developed that system as far as the rational numbers, there is *no* rational number whose square is the number 41, and hence there is *no* rational number which could be denoted by $\sqrt{41}$. Before we can speak of the "number" $\sqrt{41}$ as the limit of a sequence of rational numbers, we must first define what we mean by "irrational numbers"—that is, we must point out what the objects are that we agree to call by that name, and how these objects can be "introduced" into our "number system." The ingenious manner in which this "enlargement of the number concept" has been accomplished is explained in

* For, if $m^2/n^2 = 2$, then $m^2 = 2n^2$; in this equation, the left-hand side contains the factor 2 an even number of times, if at all, while the right-hand side contains the factor 2 either once or some other odd number of times. The equation is therefore impossible, since a whole number can be factored in only one way.

Appendix I; but throughout the body of the article we are dealing only with the geometrical system of points.

29. First step toward the science of this algebra. Selection of axioms. These 32 propositions, in secs. 23–27, might well be taken as a set of axioms for the science of algebra (compare sec. 8); they are not all "simple statements," and they are not all independent, as will be shown in the more rigorous analysis given in Part V; but they are so chosen that all the theorems which form the main body of the science can be deduced from them without undue labor.

In particular, the question of the irrational and imaginary quantities becomes, as we have just seen, not a question of "introducing" newly devised elements into the system, but merely a question of classification of elements that are already known to exist in the given system.

V. THE ABSTRACT THEORY OF THE ALGEBRA OF COMPLEX QUANTITIES

30. A complete set of postulates for the algebra of complex quantities.* The system of points in the plane, studied in Part IV, is the best known and most easily understood example of the type of algebra called the algebra of complex quantities. Other examples will be given in sec. 33, and in Appendix I. We now proceed to analyze what is logically essential in this system.

The fundamental notions of the system are: the class of points in general; the class of "real" points; the operations of addition and multiplication; and the relation of order. Abstractly considered, therefore, the **fundamental notions** in terms of which all the propositions of the algebra can be stated, are the following:

(1) A class of elements, a, b, c . . ., which we may denote by K;

* The set of postulates here given is substantially the same as that first published by the writer in Trans. Amer. Math. Soc., Vol. VI, 1905, pp. 209–229.

(2) A class of elements which we may denote by C;

(3) A rule of combination, which we may denote by $\oplus$;

(4) A rule of combination, which we may denote by $\odot$;

(5) A relation, which we may denote by $\circledcirc$.

Any system involving these fundamental notions we shall speak of as a "system $(K, C, \oplus, \odot, \circledcirc)$."

We now impose on these symbols the conditions expressed in **postulates** 1–27, below; the object being to show that every system $(K, C, \oplus, \odot, \circledcirc)$ which satisfies these twenty-seven postulates is of the same "type" as the system of points in the plane.

POSTULATE 1. If a and b are elements of K, then $a \oplus b$ is an element of K, called the **sum** of the elements a and b.

POSTULATE 2. $a \oplus b = b \oplus a$.

POSTULATE 3. $(a \oplus b) \oplus c = a \oplus (b \oplus c)$.

POSTULATE 4. If $a \oplus b = a \oplus b'$, then $b = b'$.

POSTULATE 5. There is an element z in K such that $z \oplus z = z$.

DEFINITION. If there is only one such element z, this unique element is called the **zero** element of the system.

POSTULATE 6. For every element a in K there is an element a' in K, such that $a \oplus a' = z$, where z is the zero element.*

DEFINITION. If this element a' is uniquely determined by a, it is called the **opposite of a**, and is denoted by $-a$.

Any system $(K, \oplus)$ *that satisfies these postulates* 1–6 *is called an* **Abelian group** *with respect to the operation* $\oplus$.†

POSTULATE 7. If a and b are elements of K, then $a \odot b$ is an element of K, called the **product** of the elements a and b.

POSTULATE 8. $a \odot b = b \odot a$.

POSTULATE 9. $(a \odot b) \odot c = a \odot (b \odot c)$.

POSTULATE 10. If $a \odot b = a \odot b'$, and a is not zero, then $b = b'$.

POSTULATE 11. $a \odot (b \oplus c) = (a \odot b) \oplus (a \odot c)$.

---

* If there is no zero element in the system, postulate 6 becomes meaningless—demands nothing. We say then that every system that contains no zero element satisfies this postulate "vacuously." A similar remark applies to several of the other postulates.

† For bibliographical references to definitions of "groups" and "fields," see Trans. Amer. Math. Soc., Vol. VI, 1905, p. 181.

Postulate 12. There is an element u in K, different from zero, such that $u \odot u = u$.

Definition. If there is only one such element u, this unique element is called the **unit** element of the system.

Postulate 13. For every element a in K, provided a is not zero, there is an element a' in K, such that $a \odot a' = u$, where u is the unit-element.

Definition. If this element a' is uniquely determined by a, it is called the **reciprocal of a,** and is denoted by $1/a$, or a^{-1} (provided a is not zero).

Any system $(K, \oplus, \odot)$ *that satisfies these postulates* 1–13 *is called a* **field** *with respect to the operations* $\oplus$ *and* $\odot$.*

The following postulates concern the class C and the relation $\otimes$:

Postulate 14. If a and b are elements of C, and a not equal to b, then either $a \otimes b$ or else $b \otimes a$.

Postulate 15. If $a \otimes b$, then a is not equal to b.

Postulate 16. If $a \otimes b$ and $b \otimes c$, then $a \otimes c$.

These three postulates, 14–16, *make the class C an "ordered" class, with respect to the relation* $\otimes$.

Postulate 17. (Dedekind's postulate.) If M is any (non-empty) subclass in C, and if there is an element c in C such that $a \otimes c$ for every element a in M, then there is an element x in C having the following properties with regard to the subclass M: (1) if a belongs to M, then $a \otimes x$, or at most, $a = x$; (2) if x' is any element of C such that $x' \otimes x$, then there is at least one element a in M such that $x' \otimes a$.

Definition. If this element x is uniquely determined by the subclass M, it is called the **upper limit** of M.

The following two postulates serve to connect the relation $\otimes$ with the operations $\oplus$ and $\odot$.

Postulate 18. Within the class C, if $x \otimes y$, then $a \oplus x \otimes a \oplus y$. †

Postulate 19. Within the class C, if $z \otimes a$ and $z \otimes b$, where z is the zero element, then $z \otimes a \odot b$.

* For bibliographical references to definitions of "groups" and "fields" see Trans. Amer. Math. Soc., Vol. VI, 1905, p. 181.

† Provided $a \oplus x$ is not equal to $a \oplus y$.

If, in these last six postulates, we replace " C " by " K," the postulates 1–19, *as thus altered, form a complete set of postulates for the subalgebra of all real quantities* (compare sec. 37).

The following postulates concern the class C and the operations $\oplus$ and $\odot$:

POSTULATE 20. If a is an element of C, then a is an element of K.

POSTULATE 21. The class C contains at least two elements.

POSTULATE 22. If a and b belong to C, and have a sum $a\oplus b$, then $a\oplus b$ also belongs to C.

POSTULATE 23. If a belongs to C, and has an opposite, $-a$, then $-a$ also belongs to C.

POSTULATE 24. If a and b belong to C, and have a product, $a\odot b$, then $a\odot b$ also belongs to C.

POSTULATE 25. If a belongs to C, and has a reciprocal, $1/a$, then $1/a$ also belongs to C.

These six postulates, 20–25, *together with postulates* 1–13, *make the class C, like the class K, a " field " with respect to $\oplus$ and $\odot$.*

POSTULATE 26. If K is a " field " there is an element j in K such that $j\odot j = -u$, where $-u$ is the opposite of the unit element.

DEFINITION. If there are two (and only two) such elements, j and $-j$, either of them may be called the **" imaginary unit "** of the system.

POSTULATE 27. If K and C are " fields " and K contains an " imaginary unit " j, then for every element a in K there are elements x and y in C, such that $x\oplus(j\odot y) = a$.

These postulates, 1–27, *form a complete set of postulates for the algebra of complex quantities.*

From these twenty-seven postulates all the theorems of the algebra of complex quantities can be deduced.

In particular, it is easily proved that every system that satisfies these postulates will have a unique zero-element and a unique unit-element; also, every element a will determine a unique opposite, $-a$, and (except when a is zero) a unique reciprocal, $1/a$; the pair of imaginary units j and $-j$ is uniquely determined; and every subclass of the kind described in Dedekind's postulate will have a unique upper limit.

To avoid any possible misunderstanding, it may be well to state again that these postulates are not by any means intended for use in elementary instruction. Such a set of postulates exhibits, in skeleton form, the logical structure of a particular type of algebra; but an interest in the logical structure of a science naturally does not arise in a student's mind until the facts of that science have long been familiar to him.

It must not be supposed, moreover, that the set of postulates here given is the only possible set of postulates for the algebra in question; or that the fundamental notions here mentioned are the ones that are necessarily adopted. On the contrary, a wide range of choice is possible; but any set of symbols selected as the fundamental notions for the algebra must be definable in terms of the fundamental notions here given, and any set of postulates selected as the fundamental propositions of the algebra must be deducible from the postulates here given.*

In the actual development of the algebra from these postulates, when only one system is contemplated, we of course omit the circles around the signs $\oplus$, $\odot$, and $\otimes$, and replace z, u, and j by the more familiar **0**, **1**, and **i**; but when we are comparing several systems, or testing a given system to see whether it satisfies the postulates, then the more general notation is essential, if we would avoid hopeless confusion.

31. Consistency of the postulates. To establish the consistency of these twenty-seven postulates, we must exhibit at least one actual system (K, C, $\oplus$, $\odot$, $\otimes$) that satisfies them all (compare sec. 15).

The simplest system of this kind is the system studied in Part III; namely:

$K=$ the class of all points in the plane (sec. 21);
$\oplus = +$, as defined in sec. 22;
$\odot = \times$, as defined in sec. 24;
$C=$ the class of all points on the axis of reals (sec. 21);
$\otimes = <$, as defined in sec. 27.

---

* Considerations of this kind were first emphasized by the Italians, as *Peano, Padoa, Pieri, Burali-Forti*, etc., their work dating from about 1890.

That this system satisfies all the postulates of sec. 30 is evident from the facts enumerated in Part IV. Here $z=\mathbf{0}$, $u=\mathbf{1}$, and $j=\mathbf{i}$.

Other such systems, built up out of purely arithmetical material, without recourse to geometric intuitions, will be mentioned in Appendix I. Any one of these systems shows that the postulates are consistent.

Still other, and very instructive examples are given in sec. 33.

32. Sufficiency of the postulates. Further, the twenty-seven postulates of sec. 30 are *sufficient* to determine a definite type among the systems ($K, C, \oplus, \odot, \otimes$); that is, any two systems ($K, C, \oplus, \odot, \otimes$) that satisfy all these postulates will be "isomorphic" with respect to K, C, $\oplus$, $\odot$, and $\otimes$ (sec. 19).

To prove this, suppose two systems ($K, C, \oplus, \odot, \otimes$) and ($K', C', \oplus', \odot', \otimes'$) are given. First, pair the elements z and u of class K with the elements z' and u' of class K'; then pair all the rational real elements of K with the corresponding rational real elements of K'; and, further, pair the irrational real elements of K with the irrational real elements of K' by pairing the limit of every sequence of rationals in K with the limit of the corresponding sequence of rationals in K'. In this way a one-to-one correspondence is established between the subclasses C and C'. Next, taking one of the elements $\pm\sqrt{-u}$ in K as j, and one of the elements $\pm\sqrt{-u'}$ in K' as j', pair these elements j and j'; and finally pair every element $x\oplus j\odot y$ in K with the corresponding element $x'\oplus' j'\odot' y'$ in K', thus completing the one-to-one correspondence between the two classes. It is then easy to see that the correspondence is of such a nature that if a and b in K correspond to a' and b' in K', then $a\oplus b$ will correspond to $a'\oplus' b'$ and $a\odot b$ to $a'\odot' b'$; and, furthermore, if $a\otimes b$, then $a'\otimes' b'$. The isomorphism between the two systems is thus established.

It may be noticed that the isomorphism between the two systems can be set up in two ways, according to which of the elements $\pm\sqrt{-u}$ we take as j. It is a curious fact that there is no way of distinguishing between j and $-j$ by any statement that can be expressed in terms of the symbols K, C, $\oplus$, $\odot$, and $\otimes$; that is, any true statement involving j and expressible in terms of these symbols alone, will remain a true statement when j is replaced by $-j$.

All the systems that satisfy these twenty-seven postulates are therefore identical as far as properties statable in terms of K, C,

$\oplus$, $\odot$, and $\otimes$ are concerned: that is, every proposition statable in terms of these symbols alone will either be true for all such systems, or else be false for all of them.

33. Examples of isomorphic systems. The following examples of isomorphic systems will be instructive; in each case the symbols $+$, $\times$, and $<$ are to be understood in the sense defined in IV.

(*a*) K = class of all points in the complex plane; $a \oplus b = a + b$; $a \odot b = 5(a \times b)$; C = class of all points on the axis of reals; $\otimes = <$.

Here $z = \mathbf{0}$, $u = \mathbf{1/5}$, $j = \mathbf{i/5}$.

(*b*) K = class of all points in the complex plane; $a \oplus b = (a \times b)/(a+b)$, except that $a \oplus b = a + b$ whenever a or b or $a+b$ is zero; $a \odot b = a \times b$; C = class of all points on the axis of reals; $(a \otimes b) = (a < b)$, except that when a and b are both positive or both negative, $(a \otimes b) = (a > b)$.

Here $z = \mathbf{0}$, $u = \mathbf{1}$, $j = \mathbf{i}$.

(*c*) K = class of all points in the complex plane; $a \oplus b = a + b + \mathbf{1}$; $a \odot b = a \times b + a + b$; C = class of all points on the axis of reals; $\otimes = <$.

Here $z = -\mathbf{1}$, $u = \mathbf{0}$, $-u = -\mathbf{2}$, and $j = \mathbf{i} - \mathbf{1}$.

Each of these systems satisfies all the twenty-seven postulates of sec. 30, and hence is strictly isomorphic with the system described in IV*. It will be noticed that the ordinary meaning of addition is preserved in Example (*a*), and the ordinary meaning of multiplication in Example (*b*). Other examples are given in Appendix I.

34. Independence of the postulates. Finally the twenty-seven postulates of sec. 30 are all *independent;* that is, no one of them can be deduced from the remaining twenty-six.

To prove this, we must exhibit, in the case of each postulate, a system (K, C, $\oplus$, $\odot$, $\otimes$) which satisfies all the other postulates, but not the one in question (compare sec. 18). A complete list of such "pseudo-algebras" is given in the Transactions of the American Mathematical Society, Vol. VI, 1905, pp. 227–229; a few examples from this list are given in the next paragraph, the most interesting one being the example for Postulate 18.

35. Selected examples of systems that satisfy all but one of the postulates.

EXAMPLE FOR 1. Let K be a class consisting of five elements, **0**,

---

* Each of these systems is obtained from the ordinary complex plane by a projective transformation.

1, **−1**, **i**, **−i**, and C a class consisting of three of these elements, namely, **0**, **1**, **−1**, and let $\oplus$, $\odot$, and $\otimes$ mean the ordinary $+$, $\times$, and $<$.

This system does not satisfy Postulate 1, since, for example, the element $\mathbf{1}\oplus\mathbf{1}=\mathbf{2}$ does not belong to the class. All the other postulates are satisfied.

EXAMPLE FOR 3. K=all complex quantities; C=all real quantities; $a\oplus b=(a+b)/3$; $\odot=\times$; $\otimes=<$.

This system does not satisfy the associative law for addition (compare Example (*c*), sec. 17). All the other postulates are satisfied.

EXAMPLE FOR 4. The same as for 3, except that $\oplus$ is now defined so that $a\oplus b=\mathbf{0}$ for all values of a and b.

In this system, postulate 4, the "law of cancellation" for addition, is clearly not satisfied. There is a zero element $z=\mathbf{0}$, and a unit element $u=\mathbf{1}$; and Postulate 6 is satisfied. Since $a+a'=\mathbf{0}$, whatever the value of a', we cannot speak of "the opposite of a," since this element a' is not uniquely determined. Hence postulates like 26 and 27, which presuppose the existence of an opposite, are satisfied "vacuously."

EXAMPLE FOR 8. K=all complex quantities; C=all real quantities; $\oplus=+$; $a\odot b=b$; $\otimes=<$.

This system clearly does not satisfy the commutative law for multiplication. All the other postulates are satisfied. (The system does not contain a unique unit element, and therefore all the postulates which presuppose such an element are satisfied "vacuously.")

EXAMPLE FOR 11. The usual system of complex quantities, except that $\odot$ is so defined that $a\odot b=a+b-1$.

Here $z=\mathbf{0}$, $u=\mathbf{1}$; since the distributive law is not satisfied, the system is not a "field," and Postulates 26 and 27 demand nothing. All the other postulates are satisfied.

EXAMPLE FOR 12. K=the class of all complex quantities $x+\mathrm{i}y$, in which x and y are *even integers* (positive, negative, or zero); C=all the elements of this class which are real; $\oplus$, $\odot$, and $\otimes$ defined as the ordinary $+$, $\times$, and $<$.

This system contains no unit element, but satisfies all the other conditions.

EXAMPLE FOR 16. K=all complex quantities; C=all real quantities; $\oplus=+$, $\odot=\times$; but $\otimes$ interpreted to mean "not equal to."

This system satisfies all the postulates except the law of transitivity; for, with the meaning given to $\otimes$, we may have $a\otimes b$ and $b\otimes c$, and yet not $a\otimes c$.

EXAMPLE FOR 17. The ordinary system of complex quantities, $x+\mathrm{i}y$, with x and y restricted to *rational* values (positive, negative, or zero).

EXAMPLE FOR 18. K = a class of nine objects, let us say nine umbrellas, marked with the labels 0, 1, 2, 3, 4, 5, 6, 7, 8; C = the subclass composed of umbrellas 0, 1, and 2, with $\otimes = <$; $\oplus$ and $\odot$ defined according to the following tables:*

$\oplus$	0	1	2	3	4	5	6	7	8
0	0	1	2	3	4	5	6	7	8
1	1	2	0	4	5	3	7	8	6
2	2	0	1	5	3	4	8	6	7
3	3	4	5	6	7	8	0	1	2
4	4	5	3	7	8	6	1	2	0
5	5	3	4	8	6	7	2	0	1
6	6	7	8	0	1	2	3	4	5
7	7	8	6	1	2	0	4	5	3
8	8	6	7	2	0	1	5	3	4

$\odot$	0	1	2	3	4	5	6	7	8
0	0	0	0	0	0	0	0	0	0
1	0	1	2	3	4	5	6	7	8
2	0	2	1	6	8	7	3	5	4
3	0	3	6	4	7	1	8	2	5
4	0	4	8	7	2	3	5	6	1
5	0	5	7	1	3	8	2	4	6
6	0	6	3	8	5	2	4	1	7
7	0	7	5	2	6	4	1	8	3
8	0	8	4	5	1	6	7	3	2

For example, $3 \oplus 7 = 1$; $3 \odot 7 = 2$.

This remarkable system does not satisfy Postulate 18, as we see by taking $a = 1$, and $x = 1$, $y = 2$. All the other postulates can be shown to be satisfied, although the labor of a direct verification of the associative and distributive laws would be large. The zero element of the system is $z = 0$, the unit element is $u = 1$, and the imaginary units are 4 and 8. To show that Postulate 27 is satisfied, take $\mathrm{i} = 4$, and build all the elements of the form $x + \mathrm{i}y$, where x and y belong to C; this set of elements will be seen to exhaust the given class K.

This system is a good example of the strange "pseudo-algebras" which would have to be admitted if we left out even one of the twenty-seven conditions imposed by the postulates.

EXAMPLE FOR 20. K = all complex quantities $x + \mathrm{i}y$, where x and y are restricted to rational values (positive, negative, or zero); C = all real quantities; $\oplus$, $\odot$, and $\otimes$ meaning the ordinary $+$, $\times$, and $<$.

This system satisfies all the postulates except the 20th.

EXAMPLE FOR 24. K = all complex quantities, with $\oplus = +$, and $\odot = \times$; C = all pure imaginaries (sec. 21), with $\otimes$ defined so that $\mathrm{i}x \otimes \mathrm{i}y$ whenever $x < y$.

Here the product of two elements of C will not (in general) belong to C, but all the other postulates are satisfied (19 and 27 vacuously).

EXAMPLE FOR 26. K = all real quantities, C = all real quantities, $\oplus = +$, $\odot = \times$, $\otimes = <$.

This system contains no "imaginary units."

* Advanced students will recognize this system as a Galois Field of order 3^2.

Example for 27. The system employed to show the independence of Postulate 27 is a rather complicated one, as follows: K = the class of all algebraic expressions T of the form,

$$T = A_m t^m + A_{m+1} t^{m+1} + A_{m+2} t^{m+2} + \ldots,$$

where t is a parameter, and m any integer (positive, negative, or zero), while the A's are ordinary complex quantities. The operations $\oplus$ and $\odot$ are defined as the ordinary $+$ and $\times$ for such (finite or infinite) expressions. The class C is the class of all those elements T in which all the coefficients are zero except A_0, and A_0 is real; that is, C = the class of real quantities. Within this class C, $\otimes$ is defined as the ordinary $<$.

This system satisfies all the postulates except Postulate 27. It is larger than the system of ordinary complex quantities, and contains that system just as the system of ordinary complex quantities contains the system of real quantities. Postulate 27 is therefore a *restrictive* condition.

36. What is algebra? We are now in a position to answer the question, "What *is* the algebra of complex quantities?" The answer is, the algebra of complex quantities is the scientific study of that particular type of "system ($K, C, \oplus, \odot, \otimes$)" which satisfies the twenty-seven postulates of sec. 30; any system ($K, C, \oplus, \odot, \otimes$) that satisfies these twenty-seven conditions may be taken as a representative example of the algebra, and all the propositions which are logically deducible from these twenty-seven postulates are the propositions which form the body of the science.

The system of points in a plane, described at length in Part IV, is the simplest representative example of this algebra, and is the *only* example which could possibly be used to advantage in elementary instruction (compare Appendix I, especially sec. 42).

Again, if one asks, "What *is* an imaginary quantity?" the answer is this: If any system ($K, C, \oplus, \odot, \otimes$) that satisfies the twenty-seven laws of complex algebra is given, then any element of K, not belonging to the subclass C, is called an "imaginary" element of that system.

The question "What is an irrational quantity?" may be answered in a similar way.

A striking peculiarity of the set of postulates adopted in sec. 30 is that *none of the postulates presupposes any knowledge of arithmetic, not even the notion of counting.**

37. A complete set of postulates for the subalgebra of real quantities. A complete set of postulates for the algebra of all real quantities may be obtained from the list in sec. 30 as follows: *Omit postulates* 20–27; *abandon the distinction between the classes K and C, and make postulates* 14–19 *apply to the whole class K.*

The resulting set of nineteen postulates, 1–19, will be *consistent, sufficient,* and *independent;* and *any system* ($K, \oplus, \odot, \otimes$) *which satisfies them all will be an example of the type of algebra called the algebra of all real quantities.*†

Complete sets of postulates for other subalgebras, as the algebra of positive integers, the algebra of all integers, the algebra of all rationals, etc., are given in another paper by the writer.‡

38. On the value of complex algebra in problems concerning real quantities. As already pointed out, the rules of operation in any of the subalgebras are more complicated, that is, more subject to exceptions, than are the rules of operation in the general algebra of complex quantities. On this account, it is usually worth while to employ the algebra of complex quantities even in cases where the data of the problem, and the required answer, are all real quantities. For example, if it is required to find a *real* value of x that satisfies a given equation $ax^2+bx+c=0$, the simplest plan is first to find *all* the values of x that satisfy the equation, and then to pick out those, if any, that are real. Similarly, if the problem calls for a positive value (or an integral value) of x, we do not confine ourselves

* This must not be understood to imply that the postulates of sec. 30 would therefore form a suitable introduction to algebra for beginners; compare the remark near the end of sec. 30.

† For bibliographical references, see Trans. Amer. Math. Soc., Vol. III, 1902, p. 265.

‡ The Fundamental Laws of Addition and Multiplication in Elementary Algebra, reprinted from the Annals of Mathematics, 1906. (Publication Office of Harvard University).

to the algebra of positive quantities (or the algebra of integral quantities) but proceed at once to operate in the realm of all complex quantities, and then select those results that satisfy the given conditions.

It is chiefly for reasons of this sort, if at all, that the algebra of complex quantities should be taught in the secondary schools; for elementary practical problems in which this type of algebra is directly applicable are not of frequent occurrence.

APPENDIX I. OTHER EXAMPLES OF THE ALGEBRA OF COMPLEX QUANTITIES

39. Arithmetical systems. In the latter half of the nineteenth century a large amount of effort was expended in devising definitions of the irrational and imaginary quantities which should rest on a purely arithmetical basis, independent of any geometrical intuitions. The problem, as we should now state it, was this: To construct, *out of purely arithmetical material,* systems that satisfy the postulates 1–27 of sec. 30, and are therefore isomorphic with the system of points in the plane.

The only use made of such systems is in the proof of the consistency of the postulates—a non-geometric system being, from certain points of view, more satisfactory for this purpose than a geometric one; but after the consistency of the postulates is once established, these arithmetical systems need not be again referred to, and from the elementary pedagogical point of view, they seem to have no value whatever.

Since, however, many of the newer text-books are inclined to lay great stress on this matter, a brief account of one of these arithmetical systems will here be given. The system is built up by successive steps from the system of natural numbers, 1, 2, 3, . . .; and we shall assume that the rules for adding and multiplying these numbers are known.

40. System based on Dedekind's "cuts." The best known of these arithmetical systems is one based on a very ingenious idea published by *R. Dedekind* in his "Stetigkeit und irrationale Zahlen," in 1872. The steps by which the system is constructed are as follows:

(*a*) *Positive rationals, R.* Consider first a class R composed of all possible *pairs of numbers,* m/n. (By "number" we mean, throughout this section, a natural number, 1, 2, 3, . . .) Two such pairs, m/n and m'/n', are called **equal** if the numbers mn' and $m'n$ are the same; the pair $(mn'+m'n)/(nn')$ is called the **sum,** and the pair $(mm')/(nn')$ the **product,** of the pairs m/n and m'/n'; * and the pair m/n is said to

* The product of two equal pairs is called the "square" of that pair.

precede, or be **less than** the pair m'/n' if the number mn' is less than the number $m'n$.

If two number pairs are denoted by a and b, their sum and product, as just defined, may be denoted by $a+b$ and $a \times b$; and the notation $b<a$ may be used to denote that b "precedes" a. Further, if $b<a$, there is always a pair x, such that $b+x=a$; this pair x is called the **remainder** a minus b, and is denoted by $a-b$.

The system R thus defined is an example of the type of algebra called the algebra of positive rational quantities.

(*b*) *Positive reals, Q.* In the series R thus defined, there is an infinity of ways in which the whole series of number pairs can be divided into two parts, U and V, such that every pair in the class U "precedes" every pair in the class V. Every such *method of division* in the series R is called a **cut** (U, V). For example, the following set of instructions: Assign to U every pair whose square "precedes" 2/1, and to V every pair whose square "follows" 2/1—is a "cut."

If there is a pair m/n which is either the last pair in U or else the first pair in V, then this pair m/n is called the **generating element** of the cut, and the cut is called a **rational cut;** but for most cuts, no such pair will exist.

We now consider a class Q composed of all possible "cuts" in the series R. Two cuts (U, V) and (U', V') are called **equal** if the classes U and V are the same as the classes U' and V' respectively. A cut (X, Y) is called the **sum** (or **product**) of the cuts (U, V) and (U', V') if the class X contains every pair which is the sum (or product) of a pair in U and a pair in U', while the class Y contains every pair which is the sum (or product) of a pair in V and a pair in V'. A cut (U, V) is said to **precede** a cut (U', V'), if there is any pair in the class V which precedes a pair in the class U'. If A and B are two cuts, then $A+B$ means their sum, and $A \times B$ their product, as just defined, and $B<A$ means that B precedes A.

Further, if A and B represent two cuts, and B precedes A, then there is always a cut x, which, when added to B, according to the rule, will produce A: this cut x is called the **remainder, A minus B,** and is denoted by $A-B$.

The system Q thus defined is an example of the algebra of positive real quantities. It is a system in which Dedekind's principle can be shown to hold; but the proof requires very close reasoning.*

(*c*) *All reals, q.* Next, we consider a still more complicated class, q, made up of three kinds of elements: (1) All symbols of the form ^{+}A, where A is any element of the class Q, and $^{+}$ is a distinguishing mark, read "positive"; (2) all symbols of the form ^{-}A, where A is any element

* See *Weber* and *Wellstein,* Elementar-Mathematik, Vol. I, sec. 23.

of the class Q, and $^-$ is a distinguishing mark, read "negative"; (3) an extra symbol, 0, called zero.

Within this class q, "**sums,**" "**products,**" and the relation of "**precedence**" are defined by the following formulas, in which $A, B, \ldots,$ denote elements of the class Q, and $A+B$, $A-B$, $A\times B$, and $A<B$ have the meanings already defined for that class:

$$^+A \oplus {}^+B = {}^+(A+B), \qquad A \oplus {}^-B = {}^-(A+B);$$

$$^+A \oplus {}^-B = {}^-B \oplus {}^+A = {}^+(A-B) \text{ if } B<A, \text{ and } = {}^-(B-A) \text{ if } A<B;$$

$$^+A \oplus 0 = 0 \oplus {}^+A = {}^+A, \quad {}^-A \oplus 0 = 0 \oplus {}^-A = {}^-A, \quad {}^+A \oplus {}^-A = {}^-A \oplus {}^+A = 0;$$

$$^+A \odot {}^+B = {}^+(A\times B), \ {}^-A \odot {}^-B = {}^+(A\times B), \ {}^+A \odot {}^-B = {}^-B \odot {}^+A = {}^-(A\times B);$$

$$^+A \odot 0 = 0 \odot {}^+A = 0, \qquad {}^-A \odot 0 = 0 \odot {}^-A = 0;$$

$$^+A \otimes {}^+B \text{ when } A<B, \ {}^-A \otimes {}^-B \text{ when } B<A; \ {}^-A \otimes {}^+B; \ {}^-A \otimes 0, \ 0 \otimes {}^+A.$$

These definitions being once established, the circles may be dropped from the symbols $\oplus$, $\odot$, and $\otimes$.

Further, if α and β are any elements of q (whether $\alpha<\beta$ or $\beta<\alpha$), there will always be an element x in q such that $\alpha=\beta+x$; this element x is called the **remainder,** α **minus** β, and is denoted by $\alpha-\beta$.

The system q thus defined is an example of the algebra of all real quantities, for, like the system of points on the axis of reals, it can be shown to satisfy all the nineteen postulates of sec. 37; the labor of verification is in this case, however, very considerable, especially in case of Dedekind's postulate.

(*d*) Finally, we construct still another class, K, by taking as elements of K all possible *couples* of the form (α, β), where α and β are any elements of the class q—that is, any real quantities.

Two such couples (α, β) and (α', β') are called **equal** when $\alpha=\alpha'$ and $\beta=\beta'$.

The **sum** and **products** of two couples are defined by the following formulas, in which α and β denote any elements of the system of real quantities, q, and $\alpha+\beta$, $\alpha-\beta$, and $\alpha\times\beta$ have the meanings defined for that system:

$$(\alpha, \beta) \oplus (\alpha', \beta') = (\alpha+\alpha', \beta+\beta'),$$
$$(\alpha, \beta) \odot (\alpha', \beta') = (\alpha\alpha'-\beta\beta', \alpha\beta'+\alpha'\beta).$$

Within the class K, the couples of the form $(\alpha, 0)$, in which the second element is zero, form a subclass C, and within this subclass C a couple $(\alpha, 0)$ is said to **precede** a couple $(\alpha', 0)$ if α precedes α' in the system q.

The complete system K thus constructed can be shown to satisfy all the twenty-seven postulates of sec. 30, and is, therefore, like the system of points in the plane, an example of the algebra of complex quantities.

41. System based on Cantor's "regular sequences." Another system of the same general character can be built up by using "methods of forming infinite sequences" of a certain special kind in the series of rational quantities, instead of "methods of forming cuts" in that series. The definitions of "sums" and "products" in this system are of course quite different, in detail, from the definitions in the system just described; but the general plan by which the system is built up, and the highly abstruse nature of the concepts involved, are the same in both cases.

42. Comments on these arithmetical systems. It will be sufficiently obvious from the above descriptions that these arithmetical systems are wholly unsuitable for use in elementary instruction. And yet it is unfortunately customary to speak of the elements of such an arithmetical system as the genuine "algebraic quantities," and to regard the points in the plane as merely "geometrical representations" of them. As a matter of fact, *both the arithmetical and the geometrical systems are equally entitled to stand as representatives of the type of algebra in question*—the only genuine definition of the system being embodied in the *laws of operation* of the system, as expressed in a set of postulates like those in sec. 30.

And when we consider what the elements of the arithmetical system really are—"couples" of "methods of division" of a series of "pairs of numbers"—while the elements of the other systems are simply geometric points, it is easy to decide which of these systems is the more suitable concrete example to present to an elementary student.

Moreover, the complicated nature of these arithmetical systems is not lessened by calling them systems of *numbers*, in an extended sense of the term number.* It has become customary, during the latter part of the nineteenth century, to speak of all the objects described in sec. 40 or sec. 41 as "numbers," and to regard algebra as the study of these "number systems;" but in actual practice the original definitions of these so-called "numbers" drop entirely out of mind, and a "number system" comes to be thought of as *any* system of objects which can be put into one-to-one correspondence with the system of points in the plane. Indeed, too often a text-book will profess to "introduce" or "invent" a new "number" to correspond to some point, without vouchsafing any description whatever of the object so invented, beyond the statement that it does correspond to the point. If a "number" is

* To avoid confusion, at least in elementary work, it seems preferable to reserve the word "number" for its ordinary arithmetical use, and to call the other elements "quantities" as is done, for example, in Professor *Bôcher's* new book on "Higher Algebra." Thus the term "complex *quantity*" is surely less perplexing to a beginner than "complex *number*."

thus to have no properties that a "point" does not have, it would seem unnecessary to make the distinction in terminology; for the two systems become no longer parallel, but identical!

As a matter of fact, *all that is really essential in either the system of points or the system of numbers is the set of formal laws which govern the operations within these systems.*

APPENDIX II. PROOF THAT EVERY ALGEBRAIC EQUATION HAS A ROOT

43. We give here the proof, omitted in sec. 26, that every algebraic equation,

$$p_0x^n + p_1x^{n-1} + p_2x^{n-2} + \ldots + p_{n-1}x + p_n = 0,$$

has at least one root. Here n is any positive integer, and p_0, $p_1, p_2, \ldots p_n$ are any given points in the complex plane (p_0 not zero).

Numerous proofs of this important theorem have been given, the earliest rigorous demonstration being due to *Gauss* (1799). The proof here presented differs from those commonly given in the fact that no use is made of trigonometry, or of the method of separating a complex quantity into its real and pure imaginary parts.

Throughout the proof we shall use the notation $|a|$, due to *Weierstrass*, to denote the distance of the point a from the zero point. It is obvious from the definition of addition of points (sec. 22) that if $x = a + b + c + \cdots$, then the distance of x cannot exceed the sum of the distances of $a, b, c, \ldots$: that is,

$$|a + b + c + \cdots| \leq |a| + |b| + |c| + \cdots;$$

it is also obvious, by the definition of the subtraction of points, that $|a - b|$ will denote the distance between the two points a and b.

As a further matter of notation, we denote the left-hand side of the given equation by $f(x)$:

$$f(x) = p_0x^n + p_1x^{n-1} + p_2x^{n-2} + \cdots + p_{n-1}x + p_n,$$

the value of $f(x)$ when $x=a$ is then denoted by $f(a)$, and our problem is to show that there is at least one point $x=a$ such that $f(a)=0$. The function $f(x)$ is called a polynomial of the nth degree in x.

44. In order to simplify the proof, we first establish the following properties of the function $f(x)$.

(1) *Given, any distance R, we can find a distance G such that $|f(x)|<G$ whenever $|x|<R$.*

For, take $G>n\cdot|p|\cdot|S^n|$, where p is the most distant of the given points $p_0, p_1, \ldots, p_n$ and S is a point such that $|S|>R$ and also $>|\mathbf{1}|$. Then whenever $|x|<R$, we shall have $|x^k|<R^k<|S^k|\leqq|S^n|$, $(k=1, 2, \ldots, n)$, and therefore,

$$\begin{aligned}|f(x)| &= |p_0x^n+p_1x^{n-1}+\cdots+p_{n-1}x+p_n|\\ &\leqq |p_0x^n|+|p_1x^{n-1}|+\cdots+|p_{n-1}x|+|p_n|\\ &<|pS^n|+|pS^n|+\cdots+|pS^n|+|pS^n|\\ &<n\cdot|p|\cdot|S^n|,\end{aligned}$$

which is less than G, as required.

(2) *By taking $|x|$ sufficiently large, we can make $|f(x)|$ as large as we please.* That is, given any distance g, we can find a distance h such that $|f(x)|>g$ whenever $|x|>h$.

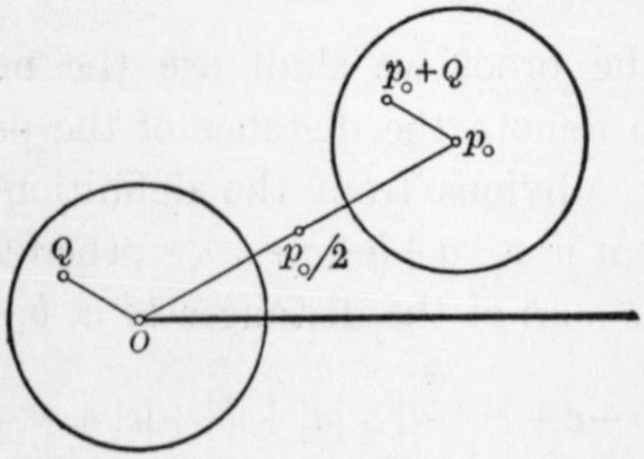

FIG. 23.

For, write $f(x)$ in the form $f(x)=x^n(p_0+Q)$, where

$$Q=\frac{p_1}{x}+\frac{p_2}{x^2}+\cdots+\frac{p_{n-1}}{x^{n-1}}+\frac{p_n}{x^n},$$

and take h larger than $|\mathbf{1}|$, and larger than each of the distances $(2g/|p_0|)^{1/n}$ and $(2n|p|)/|p_0|$, where p is the most distant of the given points $p_0, p_1, \ldots p_n$.

Then, whenever $|x| > h$,

$$\begin{aligned} |Q| &\leqq \frac{|p_1|}{|x|} + \frac{|p_2|}{|x^2|} + \cdots + \frac{|p_n|}{|x^n|} \\ &< \frac{|p|}{|h|} + \frac{|p|}{|h^2|} + \cdots + \frac{|p|}{|h^n|} \\ &< n\frac{|p|}{|h|} < n\frac{|p|}{(2n|p|)/|p_0|} \\ &< \frac{|p_0|}{2}, \end{aligned}$$

and therefore, as we may see from the figure, $|p_0 + Q| > \frac{|p_0|}{2}$.

Further, whenever, $|x| > h$, $\quad |x^n| > 2g/|p_0|$.

Hence, whenever $|x| > h$, $\quad |f(x)| = |x^n| \cdot |p_0 + Q| > g$, as required.

(3) *The polynomial $f(x)$, of the nth degree, may be written in the form*

$$f(x) = f(a) + (x-a)^k F(x),$$

*where a is any given point in the plane, and $F(x)$ is another polynomial, of the $(n-k)$th degree, and such that $F(a)$ is not zero.**

For, we have

$$f(x) = p_0 x^n + p_1 x^{n-1} + \cdots + p_{n-1}x + p_n,$$

and

$$f(a) = p_0 a^n + p_1 a^{n-1} + \cdots + p_{n-1}a + p_n,$$

whence, by subtraction,

$$f(x) - f(a) = p_0(x^n - a^n) + p_1(x^{n-1} - a^{n-1}) + \cdots + p_{n-1}(x-a).$$

Now $x^m - a^m$, where m is any positive integer, is always divisible by $x-a$; † hence $f(x)-f(a)$ contains the factor $x-a$ at least once, and may be written in the form $f(x)-f(a) = (x-a)F_1(x)$, where $F_1(x)$ is a polynomial of the $(n-1)$st degree. It may of course happen that it contains the factor $x-a$ more than once, but by dividing by $x-a$ as often as possible, say k times, we shall finally arrive at the equation $f(x)-f(a) = (x-a)^k F(x)$, where $F(x)$ is a polynomial, of degree $n-k$, that is not divisible by $x-a$. Moreover, this polynomial $F(x)$ will not become zero when $x=a$; for, as above, $F(x) - F(a) =$ an expression

* In case $k=n$, $F(x)$ reduces to a constant, not zero.

† Thus, $x^m - a^m = (x-a)(x^{m-1} + ax^{m-2} + a^2x^{m-3} + \cdots + a^{m-2}x + a^{m-1})$.

containing $x-a$ as a factor, and if $F(a)$ were zero, then $F(x)$ itself would contain $x-a$ as a factor, which is not the case.

(4) *The polynomial* $f(x)$ *is* **continuous** *at every point* $x=a$.

Roughly speaking, this means that a small change in the position of x will produce a correspondingly small change in the position of $f(x)$. More precisely, *given any radius* R *about the point* $f(a)$, *we can always find a radius* r *about the point* a, *such that whenever* $|x-a|<r$, $|f(x)-f(a)|<R$.

To show that this is true, write $f(x)$ in the form

$$f(x)=f(a)+(x-a)^kF(x),$$

as in (3), and draw a circle of radius $|\mathbf{1}|$ about the point a, and a more inclusive circle of radius $|a|+|\mathbf{1}|$ about the point $\mathbf{O}$. By (1), we can find a distance G such that $|F(x)|<G$ whenever x lies within the larger (and hence whenever x lies within the smaller) circle. If now we take $r<(R/G)^{1/k}$, and also $<|\mathbf{1}|$, then whenever $|x-a|<r$ we shall have

$$|f(x)-f(a)|=|(x-a)^k|\cdot|F(x)|<r^k\cdot G<(R/G)G=R,$$

as required.

(5) *If* $f(a)$ *is not zero, we can always choose* x *so that* $|f(x)|<|f(a)|$; *that is, so that the point* $f(x)$ *is nearer the zero point than* $f(a)$ *is.*

To see that this is true, we shall write $f(x)$ in the form

$$f(x)=f(a)+(x-a)^kF(x),$$

as in (3), and then show that x can be so chosen that the point $(x-a)^kF(x)$ will fall within the region shaded in the figure; that is, so that the *distance* of $(x-a)^kF(x)$ will be less than $|f(a)|$, while its *angle* will lie between $\theta+120°$ and $\theta+240°$, where θ is the angle of the point $f(a)$. When x is so chosen, the sum of the point $(x-a)^kF(x)$ and the fixed point $f(a)$ will then lie within the region bounded by the dotted line in the figure, and hence will be nearer to $\mathbf{O}$ than $f(a)$ is.

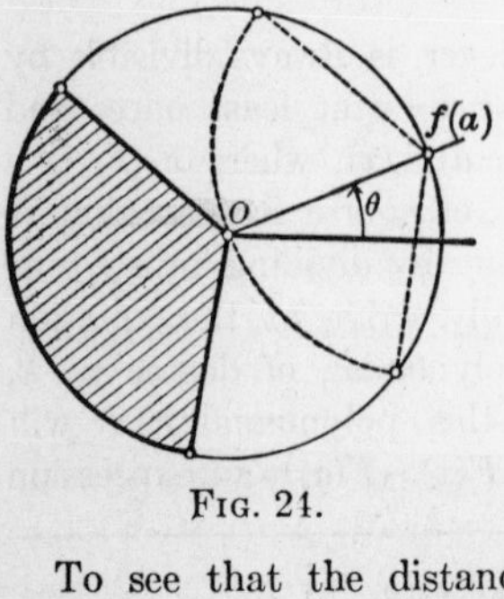

FIG. 21.

To see that the distance of $(x-a)^kF(x)$ can be made less than $|f(a)|$, we have merely to notice that the factor $|(x-a)^k|$ can be made as small as we please by taking x sufficiently near to a, while the other factor, $|F(x)|$, by (1), remains less than some finite quantity G.

To see that the angle of $(x-a)^k F(x)$ can be made to lie between $\theta+120°$ and $\theta+240°$, notice first that this angle is equal to $k\phi+\xi$, where ϕ is the angle of $x-a$ and ξ is the angle of $F(x)$. Now ξ, the angle of $F(x)$, can, by (4), be made to differ by as little as we please from α, the angle of $F(a)$, by taking x sufficiently near to a; in particular, if we take $|x-a|<r$, where r is sufficiently small, ξ will lie between, say, $\alpha-60°$ and $\alpha+60°$. Having thus chosen the *distance* of $x-a$, we can still vary ϕ, the *angle* of $x-a$, at pleasure, by moving x around the circumference of its small circle of radius $|x-a|$ about a. In particular, if we take $\phi=(\theta-\alpha+180°)/k$, then $k\phi+\alpha=\theta+180°$, and $k\phi+\xi$ will lie between $\theta+120°$ and $\theta+240°$, as required.

The following general property of points in the plane will also be useful.

(6) *If an infinite collection of points x all lie within a finite region of the plane, say within a square of side D, then there will be at least one point X, within or on the boundary of the square, having the following property: every circle, however small, drawn about X as a centre, includes an infinite number of points that belong to the collection.* Such a point X is called a **cluster point** for the given collection; but it may or may not itself belong to the collection.

To see that such a cluster point will always exist, we have merely to draw through each point of the collection lines parallel to the sides of the square, and consider the sets of points in which these lines cut two adjacent sides of the square. Each of these sets of points, by Dedekind's principle, [sec. 27, (31)], will have at least one limit point; and the point of intersection of lines drawn through these limit points, parallel to the sides of the square, will be the cluster point required.

(7) *If a collection of points $\{x\}$ is given, and the corresponding points $\{f(x)\}$ possess a cluster point Y, then there is at least one point x in the plane such that $f(X)=Y$.*

To prove this, pick out from the collection $\{f(x)\}$ an infinite sequence of points, $f(x_1)$, $f(x_2)$, . . . , having the following properties: (a) Each point of the sequence is nearer to Y than the preceding point is; and (b) every circle drawn about Y as a centre will contain an infinite number of points of the sequence. The corresponding points, x_1, $x_2, \ldots,$ will then all lie within a finite region of the plane, as we may see by (2), and they will, therefore, by (6), have at least one cluster point, X. This point X will have the required property, $f(X)=Y$.

For, suppose $f(X)$ were equal to Y', where Y' is different from Y. Then we could draw two non-overlapping circles of radii R and R', about the points Y and Y', respectively, and deduce a contradiction, as follows: In the first place, from the nature of the sequence $f(x_1)$, $f(x_2), \ldots,$ all the points of this sequence beyond a certain stage, say, $f(x_k)$, will lie within the circle R about the point Y. On the other hand, since $Y'=f(X)$, we can, by (4), draw a circle of radius r' about X so that whenever x lies within this circle r', $f(x)$ will lie within the circle R', and hence outside the circle R. Therefore none of the points of the sequence $x_1, x_2, \ldots,$ beyond the stage x_k can lie within the circle r', which contradicts the fact that X is a cluster point for this sequence.

45. The main proposition can now be established, as follows:

Suppose the proposition is false; that is, suppose that there is a distance c, not zero, such that $|f(x)|>c$ for every point x in the plane. Then, by Dedekind's principle, the possible values of $|f(x)|$ must have a lower limit, $b, \geqq c$, such that $|f(x)|$ is never less than b, but can be brought as near to b as we please by properly choosing x.

Two cases are now conceivable—either there is a point a such that $|f(a)|=b$, or else $|f(x)|>b$ for all values of x.

The first case is impossible, since, if there were a point a such that $|f(a)|=b$, then, by (5), there would be also a point x such that $|f(x)|<b$, which is contrary to the hypothesis that b is the lower limit of $|f(x)|$.

In the second case, $|f(x)|$ has the lower limit b, but never reaches it. If therefore we draw a circle of radius b about the point O, there will be an infinite number of points $f(x)$ in a finite region just outside this circle. It is easy to see, by (6), that this collection of points $f(x)$ will have a cluster point Y somewhere on the circumference of the circle of radius b; therefore, by (7), there is a point X for which $f(X)=Y$; but for this point $|f(X)|=b$, and the second case is therefore as impossible as the first.

Hence the supposition with which we started must be false, and the theorem that every algebraic equation has at least one root is thus established.

The general theorem in sec. 26 (23) follows without difficulty.

V

THE ALGEBRAIC EQUATION

By G. A. Miller

CONTENTS

V

THE ALGEBRAIC EQUATION

By G. A. Miller

I. GENERAL INTRODUCTION

1. Aim of the monograph. The present monograph aims to give a sketch of some of the most fundamental processes in which the algebraic equation occupies a central position, and thus to fix the attention more completely on the underlying thoughts and the historical setting than would be feasible in a short treatise on the theory of equations. The monograph is intended to supplement such treatises rather than to replace them. By means of the historic setting of many elementary facts it is hoped that parts of it may be useful also to those who have only such a knowledge of the equation as would naturally result from an elementary course in algebra.

2. How it should be read. The reader is advised not to insist on understanding every statement before proceeding to the next. To some readers such concepts as *domain of rationality, substitution group,* and *ρ-valued rational function* may be new, and our short account of them may not appear entirely satisfactory. A slight knowledge of such dominating concepts and of their applications is, however, much better than total ignorance, and if the present monograph leads to an intelligent search for knowledge along these important lines its perusal will not have been in vain.

3. Mathematics presupposed. To avoid prolixity it has seemed desirable to presuppose, in a few places, an elementary knowledge of determinants as well as a knowledge of the first derivative of a function of a single variable. As it seemed undesirable to presuppose an elementary knowledge of the *Galois* theory of equations some fundamental processes could not be sketched with the completeness that would be desirable. It is hoped, however, that the viewpoint which has been adopted will tend to prepare the way for this general theory; this is especially true of the methods used to solve the cubic and the biquadratic equations. While the common road to a knowledge of the equation leads through numerous problems, it is sometimes desirable to take a broad survey of the historic setting and of the underlying principles, and thus to gather new inspiration and a deeper insight. It is hoped that the present monograph may aid in taking such surveys.

4. Type of questions studied. Equations of the form $x^n=1$ play an important rôle in the general theory of equations. Since the fundamental properties of these equations are treated in Monograph No. VII, secs. 28, 29, they are not given in the present monograph. As the roots of the equation $x^n=\pm a$ may be obtained by multiplying those of $x^n=\pm 1$ by the arithmetic nth root of the positive number a, it results that the theory of the equations of the form $x^n=1$ is almost equivalent to that of equations with two coefficients not zero. For many purposes it is convenient to study equations from the standpoint of the number of coefficients which are supposed to differ from zero, especially when this number does not exceed 3, but in the present monograph the classification is made with respect to the degrees of the unknowns. The interesting properties which result from the assumption that the coefficients represent successively the various terms of sequences of numbers have been left untouched for want of space.

II. HISTORICAL SKETCH AND DEFINITIONS

5. Introduction. "An equation is the most serious and important thing in mathematics," says *Sir Oliver Lodge.** It is also one of the oldest mathematical concepts, since the fundamental operation of counting itself is based upon the idea of a kind of equality between the things counted. Even elementary algebraic equations are very old; for, such instances as "Heap, its one-seventh, its whole, it makes 19," and "Heap, its two-thirds, its one-half, its one-seventh, its whole, it makes 33," are found in the work of an Egyptian *Ahmes* written about 1700 B.C. It is evident from these and many similar instances that the ancient Egyptians used "heap" with the same significance as our more modern x, and that the given statements are respectively equivalent to the equations

$$\frac{x}{7}+x=19,$$

$$\frac{2x}{3}+\frac{x}{2}+\frac{x}{7}+x=33.$$

On fragments of papyri which have been deciphered more recently, but are probably older than the work of *Ahmes*, statements equivalent to the system of two simultaneous equations

$$x^2+y^2=100, \qquad y=\tfrac{3}{4}x,$$

have been found. Even special systems of n equations involving n unknowns were solved at an early date. A Greek named *Thymaridas* gave a rule for solving the following system:

$$x_1+x_2+x_3+\ldots+x_n=s,$$

$$x_1+x_2=a_1,\ x_1+x_3=a_2,\ \ldots\ x_1+x_n=a_{n-1}.$$

It is an interesting fact that the technical terms *given* (known) and *unknown* are involved in this ancient rule. A similar system was solved by a Hindu *Aryabhata* of the sixth century A.D, but the methods for solving general systems of

* Easy Mathematics, 1906, p. 127.

m equations in n unknowns are of comparatively recent origin. In general, the ancient mathematicians and those of the Middle Ages sought merely numerical values of the unknowns in a system of equations, but did not give the *expressions* representing the unknowns in terms of the *coefficients*.

6. Definitions. An equation of the form

$$a_1x_1+a_2x_2+a_3x_3+\ldots+a_nx_n=k,$$

where $a_1, a_2, \ldots, a_n, k$ are supposed to represent known numbers and $x_1, x_2, \ldots, x_n$ are unknowns, is called an equation of the **first degree,** or a **linear equation.** Equations which are true only on condition that the unknowns involved have particular values are called **conditional equations.** If an equation is true for every set of values that may be arbitrarily assigned to the unknowns, or if it is a true relation between known numbers only, the equation is called an **identical equation,** or briefly, an **identity.**

Thus $\qquad 2\cdot3+4\cdot7=34, \qquad 3m-2m=m$*

are identical equations, while

$$2x+3y=1, \qquad 5x-2y=12,$$

are *conditional* equations.

If it is assumed that a sequence of numbers may be assigned to the unknowns of an equation these unknowns are called **variables.** Whether the letters of an equation are to represent unknown constants or variables depends upon the point of view, but the difference between these concepts should be

---

* In an identical equation the symbol $=$ is frequently replaced by $\equiv$. This symbol was first used with the present meaning by *Riemann*, according to *Kronecker's* Vorlesungen über Zahlentheorie, 1901, p. 86. *Gauss* used it with a different meaning in the theory of congruences, such as $10\equiv3$ (mod. 7), (see Monograph No. VII), at an earlier date, 1801. Hence this symbol is now used to represent both something stronger and also something weaker than what is generally implied by the symbol $=$. As *Kronecker* observed the stronger meaning seems the more natural, as $\equiv$ would appear to imply something more than $=$, but the symbol is more extensively used with the weaker meaning.

carefully observed. By varying the meaning of the letters the equation reveals its full significance and usefulness.

An equation involving no unknowns with fractional exponents is said to be of the **nth degree** if it involves at least one term in which the sum of the exponents of the unknowns is n but no term in which the sum of these exponents exceeds n. If all the terms, which are not identically zero, of an equation are of the same degree it is said to be **homogeneous.** For instance, $x+y=0$, $x^2-xy+7y^2=0$ are homogeneous equations of the first and second degrees respectively.

In view of ancient geometric interpretations, equations of the second and the third degree are commonly called **quadratic** and **cubic** respectively. If an equation is reduced to an identity when known numbers are substituted for the unknowns, these numbers are called **roots** of the equation and the roots are said to **satisfy** the equation. The process of determining the roots is called a **solution** of the equation. If the unknowns of two or more equations are supposed to have the same values the equations are said to be **simultaneous** equations.

7. Fundamental problems. Two fundamental problems in the theory of equations are the solution of the general equation of the nth degree in one unknown and the solution of a system of m simultaneous equations in n unknowns. Although the former of these is a special case of the latter it is of such paramount importance and difficulty that it may be regarded as a fundamental problem in the theory of equations. Only very special cases of these problems were solved by the ancient and mediæval mathematicians, and both problems have furnished nuclei for extensive theories which are still in the process of development. An instance of the solution of special cases of the first is furnished by the "heap" problems of *Ahmes*, which were mentioned above. Among other instances are the following: the extraction of square roots, such as

$$\sqrt{\frac{25}{16}}=\frac{5}{4},\quad \sqrt{\frac{25}{4}}=\frac{5}{2}$$

found recently on an Egyptian papyrus now in the Berlin

Museum; the geometrical representation of roots of equations of small degrees by the early Greeks, including *Euclid*, and especially by the Arabs, the finding of one positive rational root of quadratic equations by *Diophantus*, and the recognition of the fact that at least some numerical quadratic equations have two roots by the Hindus and the Arabs.

Starting from such special cases as these, mathematicians have gradually been enabled to comprehend the fact that *every equation of degree n in one unknown has exactly n roots.* This elegant theorem is commonly known as the **fundamental theorem of algebra.*** In France it is also known as the **theorem of d'Alembert,†** since *d'Alembert* published a proof of it in 1746, which was supposed in his day to be rigorous. The first satisfactory proof was given by *Gauss* in 1799. The gradual progress toward this theorem through many centuries furnishes an impressive picture of the slow pace at which our rich mathematical inheritance was developed, and of the interesting history which surrounds the fundamental theorems.

The second fundamental problem mentioned above has also led to rich results in modern times. When restricted to the case in which the m simultaneous equations in n unknowns are linear, the problem has led to an important branch of mathematics known as *determinants*, and the theory of determinants, in turn, has thrown much light on this problem. The isolated simultaneous equations of the ancient Egyptians and of the ancient Greeks gave expression to needs of the human mind which have been largely satisfied, but which have fortunately led to a deeper sense of the need of still further developments and of hope that such developments will be forthcoming. In our brief treatment of the algebraic equation we shall devote most of our space to the consideration of equations involving only one unknown, since such equations form also the basis of the theory of a system of m simultaneous equations in n unknowns.

---

* For a proof of this theorem see Monograph No. IV, Appendix II.

† The noted Italian mathematician *S. Pincherle* also styles it the theorem of *d'Alembert* in his Lezioni di Algebra Complementare, 1909, p. 109.

8. Symbols. The ancient and mediæval mathematicians commonly wrote the word equals, or its equivalent, between the two members of an equation. This was, however, not universal, but a large number of different symbols have been used to indicate equality between the two members of an equation. Even *Ahmes* used a symbol (⋦) for such an equality, *Diophantus* used ι as an abbreviation of the word 'ἴσοι (equal) and the western Arabs made use of a symbol resembling a capital J for the same purpose. During the sixteenth century the symbol ∝, standing for the first two letters of *aequalis*, was extensively used. Our modern symbol = was introduced by *Record* in 1557 in his Whetstone of Witte, and the reason assigned for choosing this particular symbol was that "noe 2 thynges can be moare equalle" than two parallel lines. During the seventeenth century two parallel vertical lines were frequently used, especially in France, instead of =, since the latter was used to represent the absolute difference between two numbers. It was also a recognized abbreviation for the word *est* in mediæval manuscripts.

The most important things about an equation are the unknowns. In fact these characterize a conditional equation and the determination of the range of values of the unknowns is the main mission of the equation.* Among the various symbols that have been used for a single unknown none seems more expressive than the one employed by *Ahmes*, 1700 B.C.; for the term *heap* naturally implies that the number of the individuals is unknown. *Diophantus* represented the unknown by a final sigma, ς, and the Hindu, *Brahmagupta*, represented the first unknown by *yâvat tâvat*, and if more than one unknown were employed he used colors, black, blue, yellow, etc., to represent the second, third, fourth, etc., unknowns. *Alkarismi*, the noted Arab whose work gave rise to the term *algebra*, and whose name gave rise to the term *algorithm*, called the unknown the *thing* or the *root*, and these terms were in common

* These remarks are based upon an elementary point of view. From another point of view, it is equally true that the known coefficients completely dominate and determine the possible values of the unknowns.

use during the Middle Ages. In 1637 *Descartes* introduced the present custom of representing the unknowns by the last letters of the alphabet (x, y, z) and the knowns by the first letters (a, b, c, etc.).

9. Domain of rationality. One of the most useful modern concepts relating to the algebraic equations is that of the *domain of rationality*. If a symbol R, which obeys the ordinary laws of algebra, is combined with itself and the results of such combination, by addition, subtraction, multiplication and division (division by zero being always excluded) in every possible way, there results a certain totality of expressions, which evidently has the important property that no additional expression results from the combination of the expressions of the totality with respect to any of the four given operations. These operations are collectively called the **rational operations of algebra,** and the given totality is known as the **domain of rationality** constituted by R, and it is denoted by (R).* If R represents the number 1 and if we operate on this number and the resulting numbers in every possible way according to the rational operations of algebra, the resulting totality is composed of all the rational numbers. The same totality would have been obtained by letting R represent any other rational number besides 0. That is, $(1)\equiv(n)$, where n is any rational number except 0.

To understand the meaning of domain of rationality it is important to observe that it implies a totality which is closed as regards the rational operations of algebra. In this connection it is interesting to observe that the n nth roots of unity form a closed totality as regards multiplication and division but not as regards addition and subtraction. For instance, if we take the four fourth roots of unity 1, -1, i, $-i$ ($i\equiv\sqrt{-1}$) and combine them in every possible way by means of the operations of multiplication and division we obtain no additional number. Similarly, the set of eight numbers

$$-1,\ -2,\ 3,\ 4,\ \tfrac{1}{2},\ \tfrac{3}{2},\ \tfrac{2}{3},\ \tfrac{4}{3}$$

* See also Monograph No. VIII, sec. 4.

forms a closed totality as regards the operations of subtracting from 2 and dividing 2, as may easily be verified. Such closed totalities, involving either a finite or an infinite number of distinct elements, are of fundamental importance in various mathematical subjects. A totality of numbers which is closed as regards the two operations of addition and subtraction is known as a **number modulus.** The rational integers, for instance, form such a modulus, but they do not form a domain of rationality.*

In general, the domain of rationality (R) must include the domain of rational numbers, since it includes $\frac{R}{R}=1$. Hence the rational numbers of elementary arithmetic constitute the smallest possible domain of rationality,† and this domain is included in every other domain. The most general expression of the domain (R) may evidently be reduced to the form

$$\frac{a_0+a_1R+\ldots+a_nR^n}{b_0+b_1R+\ldots+b_mR^m},$$

where $a_0, a_1, \ldots, a_n$ and $b_0, b_1, \ldots, b_m$ are ordinary positive or negative integers. That is, *the domain of rationality* (R) *is composed of all the rational functions of* R *with integral coefficients.*

It is evident that the totality of the rational integral functions, i.e., all the functions of the form

$$a_0+a_1R+\ldots+a_nR^n$$

* Numerous examples of such finite closed totalities may be found in any book dealing with groups of finite order, such as *Burnside,* Theory of Groups, 1897; *Dickson's* Linear Groups, 1901; and *Cajori's* Introduction to the Modern Theory of Equations, 1904. A few very elementary examples are found in the article entitled "Groups of subtraction and division," *Quarterly Journal of Mathematics* Vol. XXXVII, 1906, p. 80. The totality of numbers lying on a line through the origin in the ordinary complex number plane clearly forms an infinite totality which is closed as regards addition and subtraction but not generally as regards multiplication and division. Hence this totality is also a number modulus. If it is closed as regards each of the four rational operations of algebra the line must be the totality of real numbers. Cf. *American Mathematical Monthly,* Vol. XV, 1908, p. 117.

† The trivial domain composed of 0 is excluded from our consideration.

where $a_0, a_1, \ldots, a_n$ have the same meaning as above, has the property that no additional function arises by combining any two of them (or any one with itself) by means of any of the three operations addition, subtraction, and multiplication. This totality is known as the **domain of integrity** constituted by R and it is denoted by $[R]$. When $R=1$ this domain reduces to the totality of the ordinary positive and negative integers, and $[R]$ is always included in (R). It was observed that (R) results when all the rational operations are successively performed upon R. This fact is generally expressed by saying that (R) is **generated** by R as regards the rational operations. On the contrary $[R]$, is not usually generated by R, as may be seen, for instance, when $R \equiv \sqrt{2}$. There is, however, an infinity of pairs of elements in $[R]$ which generate $[R]$ when they are combined with respect to the rational integral operations of algebra. The simplest of these pairs is R and 1.

The totality of rational functions, with rational coefficients, of the symbols $R_1, R_2, R_3, \ldots$ (where the number of symbols is finite or infinite) is called a **domain of rationality** and is denoted by $(R_1, R_2, R_3, \ldots)$. Each of the symbols $R_1, R_2, R_3, \ldots$ is called an **element of the domain.** Similarly, the integral domain $[R_1, R_2, R_3, \ldots]$ may be defined by replacing the expressions rational functions and rational coefficients in the preceding definition by integral functions and integral coefficients respectively. A rational integral function $f(x)$, of x, is said to be in the domain of rationality $(R_1, R_2, R_3, \ldots)$ if all its coefficients are in this domain; if all its coefficients are in the domain of integrity $[R_1, R_2, R_3, \ldots]$ the function is said to be in this domain. If $f(x)$ is the product of two rational integral functions in the same domain of rationality, $f(x)$ is said to be **reducible** in this domain. When this cannot be done in a given domain $f(x)$ is said to be **irreducible** in this domain.

Functions which are irreducible in one domain may be reducible in another. For instance, x^2+x-1 is irreducible in $(\sqrt{2})$ but it is reducible in $(\sqrt{5})$; on the other hand, x^2-2 is reducible in the former of these domains but not in the latter. Neither of these functions is reducible in the domain of rational numbers, although both of them are in this domain. From the fundamental theorem it results that every rational integral function of x whose degree exceeds one is reducible in some domain of rationality. If we consider rational integral functions in two or more variables it is not possible to prove a similar theorem. For instance, the function $xy-1$ is in the domain of rational numbers, but it can be proved that this function cannot be resolved into two factors whose coefficients are in any domain of rationality whatever. For further developments regarding the concepts of reducibility and domain of rationality, and extensive references to the literature on these subjects, we refer to tome I, volume 2 of the Encyclopédie des Sciences Mathématiques, p. 205. A clear introduction to the subject is given in *Dickson's* Theory of Algebraic Equations, 1903, and in *Cajori's* Introduction to the Modern Theory of Equations, 1904.

III. EQUATIONS WITH ONE UNKNOWN AND WITH LITERAL COEFFICIENTS

10. General statement. The ancient and the mediæval mathematicians knew only five algebraic operations, viz., addition, subtraction, multiplication, division, and the extraction of roots. These operations suffice to solve every equation of the form

$$f(x)=a_0x^n+a_1x^{n+1}+\ldots+a_n=0,$$

where a_0,* $a_1, \ldots, a_n$ are real or complex numbers and n is a positive integer, provided $n<5$; but they are not sufficient to solve this general equation when $n>4$. The first rigorous proof of this important theorem was published in 1824 by a Norwegian mathematician named *Abel*,† and the theorem

---

* Unless the contrary is stated it will be assumed that $a_0\neq 0$. When a_0 is real we may assume that it is positive, but when it is complex we cannot make this assumption, since the terms positive and negative cannot be directly applied to complex numbers.

† This proof appeared also in *Crelle's* Journal, Vol. I, 1826.

marks an important line of division between equations of the first four degrees and those of a higher degree. Numerous efforts to solve by means of these operations * the general equation of the fifth and higher degrees had preceded *Abel's* proof of the fact that such efforts were necessarily futile.

It should be emphasized that there is a vast difference between proving the *existence* of a root of $f(x)=0$ and *finding* this root. The existence of such a root is proved by the fundamental theorem of algebra, but the finding of methods to express such a root in terms of the coefficients $a_0, a_1, \ldots, a_n$ is a much more difficult problem when $n>4$. In 1858 the noted French mathematician *Hermite* found a method by means of which he could express a root of the general equation of the fifth degree in terms of certain functions known as elliptic functions. More recently it has been proved that a root of the general equation of degree n may be represented in terms of the coefficients by means of certain functions called Fuchsian.†

The very important theorem that $f(x)$ is divisible by $x-x_1$ whenever x_1 is a root of $f(x)=0$ was observed by *Descartes.* This theorem establishes two fundamental facts, viz., (1) that the finding of the roots of $f(x)=0$ is equivalent to resolving $f(x)$ into its linear factors, and (2) that the proof of the existence of one root of $f(x)=0$ proves the existence of n roots. Moreover, it is not difficult to prove this important theorem. The proof may be obtained as follows:

Let $$f(x)=a_0x^n+a_1x^{n-1}+\ldots+a_n. \quad . \quad . \quad . \quad . \quad (1)$$

Since x_1 is a root of $f(x)=0$, we have $f(x_1)=0$, or

$$0=a_0x_1{}^n+a_1x_1{}^{n-1}+\ldots+a_n \quad . \quad . \quad . \quad . \quad (2)$$

By subtracting (2) from (1) there results

$$f(x)=a_0(x^n-x_1{}^n)+a_1(x^{n-1}-x_1{}^{n-1})\ldots a_{n-1}(x-x_1).$$

* Solutions confined to the use of these operations are known as solutions by radicals.

† Cf. *Tropfke,* Geschichte der Elementar-Mathematik, Vol. I, 1902, p. 292.

As

$$x^l - x_1{}^l = (x - x_1)(x^{l-1} + x_1 x^{l-2} + \ldots + x_1{}^{l-1})$$

whenever l is any positive integer, it has thus been proved that

$$f(x) = (x - x_1)f_1(x)$$

where $f_1(x)$ is a rational integral function of x of degree $n-1$. In other words, $f(x)$ is divisible by $x - x_1$.

Since $f_1(x)$ is of the same general type as $f(x)$ we may apply to it the same kind of reasoning. In particular, if the general function of the form $f(x)$ has a root, $f_1(x)$ must also have a root (x_2) and hence it is divisible by $x - x_2$ with $f_2(x)$ as a quotient. As n is a finite positive integer, we must finally arrive at a linear quotient by repeating these operations and thus prove that

$$f(x) = a_0(x - x_1)(x - x_2) \ldots (x - x_n).$$

It should be emphasized that this process establishes the existence of these n linear factors only on the assumption that every such function as $f(x)$ has at least one root. The theorem just proved is evidently a special case of the theorem that if $f(x)$ is divided by $x - x_1$ the remainder is $f(x_1)$.

In 1629 *Girard* published an important work entitled Invention nouvelle en l'algèbre, in which he stated the theorem that $f(x) = 0$ has n roots and observed some general relations existing between the elementary symmetric functions of the roots and the coefficients of the equation. Special cases of these relations had been observed earlier by *Cardan* and *Vieta*. The more general relations can readily be deduced from the fact that

$$f(x) = a_0(x - x_1)(x - x_2) \ldots (x - x_n).$$

By multiplying the factors of the second member it is clear that the sum of the roots is $-a_1/a_0$, while the sum of the products of the different combinations of α roots is $(-1)^\alpha a_\alpha / a_0$, where $\alpha = 2, 3, \ldots, n$.

Girard even computed the values of the following symmetric functions of the roots

$$\sum_{i=1}^{i=n} x_i^2, \quad \sum_{i=1}^{i=n} x_i^3, \quad \sum_{i=1}^{i=n} x_i^4,$$

in terms of the ratios

$$\frac{a_1}{a_0}, \frac{a_2}{a_0}, \ldots, \frac{a_n}{a_0}$$

These ratios represent separately symmetric functions of the roots, as was observed in the preceding paragraph, and these interesting symmetric functions are technically known as **the elementary symmetric functions** of the n roots. They are respectively of degrees 1, 2, . . ., n. This work of *Girard* prepared the way for the beautiful theorem that *every integral symmetric function of* $x_1, x_2, \ldots, x_n$ *can be expressed in one and in only one way as an integral function of the elementary symmetric functions.* A proof of this theorem may be found, among other places, in *Dickson's* Algebraic Equations, 1903, p. 99. A number of fundamental properties of symmetric functions are developed also in *Burnside* and *Panton's* Theory of Equations.

11. Substitutions and substitution groups. A profound study of the algebraic equation involves not only a knowledge of the properties of symmetric functions, but also a knowledge of rational functions which are not symmetric. In his noted memoir entitled "Reflexions sur la résolution algébrique des équations," Nouveux mémoires de l'Académie Royale des Sciences de Berlin, 1770 and 1771, *Lagrange* made a thorough study of the known methods which had been employed to solve equations of higher degrees, reviewing the methods employed by *Cardan, Ferrari, Descartes, Tschirnhaus, Euler,* and *Bézont.* He observed that the solution of an algebraic equation depends upon the solution of a certain other equation, since known as the **resolvent,** and he showed that the roots of the various resolvents are *rational* functions of the roots of the given equation. This led to a recognition of the fundamental fact that the problem of the solution of equations depends upon the properties of rational functions of the roots.

The fertile point of view at which *Lagrange* had arrived in the extensive memoir noted in the preceding paragraph called for a comprehensive study of the properties of rational functions, especially as regards the number of values assumed by such functions when their n elements are permuted in every possible manner. This study led to the *theory of substitutions,* called "calcul des combinaisons" by *Lagrange,* which has proved to be a most powerful instrument to secure a deep insight into the nature and properties of an algebraic equation. Among those who share with *Lagrange* the honor of having discovered the fundamental importance of the theory substitutions along this line we mention especially *Ruffini, Abel, Galois,* and *Jordan.*

A study of the various forms which a rational function assumes when its elements or letters are permuted furnishes one of the most natural ways to secure a knowledge of the true meaning of substitutions and substitution groups. For instance, the historic function

$$x_1x_2+x_3x_4$$

is evidently left unchanged by replacing x_1 by x_2 and x_2 by x_1. This fact is more briefly expressed by saying that the function $x_1x_2+x_3x_4$ is *transformed into itself* by the substitution (x_1x_2). It is clearly also transformed into itself by the substitution (x_3x_4). The fact that the two substitutions (x_1x_2), (x_3x_4) are to be performed successively is indicated by $(x_1x_2)(x_3x_4)$, and this substitution is called the **product** of the two substitutions (x_1x_2), (x_3x_4). It is clear that if each of two substitutions transforms a function into itself their product must also transform this function into itself. A set of distinct substitutions which has the property of including the square of each of the set as well as the product of any two of them is called a **substitution group.** As $(x_1x_2)^2=(x_3x_4)^2=[(x_1x_2)(x_3x_4)]^2=1$, or the identity, where 1 implies that all the elements of the function under consideration are left unchanged, it is clear that the four substitutions

$$1,\ (x_1x_2),\quad (x_3x_4),\quad (x_1x_2)(x_3x_4)$$

form a substitution group. This group is of order 4, the *order* being the number of substitutions in a group. It plays a fundamental rôle in many mathematical considerations and is known abstractly under various names as follows: the axial group, the anharmonic ratio group, the quadratic group, the four group, the group of the rectangle, etc.

The given function is evidently also transformed into itself by the additional substitutions $(x_1x_3)(x_2x_4)$, $(x_1x_4)(x_2x_3)$ $(x_1x_3x_2x_4)$, $(x_1x_4x_2x_3)$ where the last two substitutions indicate that the letters x_1, x_3, x_2, x_4; x_1, x_4, x_2, x_3, respectively, are permuted cyclically in the given order. It is easy to verify that the eight substitutions

$$\begin{gathered}1,\quad (x_1x_2),\quad (x_3x_4),\quad (x_1x_2)(x_3x_4),\quad (x_1x_3)(x_2x_4),\\ (x_1x_4)(x_2x_3),\quad (x_1x_3x_2x_4),\quad (x_1x_4x_2x_3)\end{gathered}$$

form a group and that these are the only substitutions on these letters which transform the given function into itself. A group that is contained in another group is called a **subgroup.** The first four substitutions of this group of order 8 therefore constitute a subgroup of order 4, while the first two substitutions constitute a subgroup of order 2. The reader can readily verify the fact that the given group of order 8 contains two and only two other subgroups of order 4, and four other subgroups of order 2. This group is known abstractly as the **octic group** or the **group of the square.**

While the theory of substitutions is essential to attain an insight into what is known as the *Galois theory* of the algebraic equations and is very important also in other domains of mathematics, we shall make no explicit use of it in what follows, in view of the facts that the elements of this subject are not as generally known as they should be, and a proper development of the subject *ab initio* would demand too much space for the present monograph. It seems, however, desirable to state a few general theorems depending on this theory, whose import can be at least partially appreciated by means of the development of the preceding paragraphs.

It was observed above that the function $x_1x_2+x_3x_4$ is transformed into itself by all the substitutions of a certain group of order 8, but by no other substitution on these letters. This fact is commonly expressed by saying the function $x_1x_2+x_3x_4$ *belongs* to this group. It is easy to find other functions in these letters, for instance $(x_1+x_2-x_3-x_4)^2$, which belong to the same group; and it has been proved that an infinite number of distinct rational functions belong to any given substitution group while such a function belongs to only one substitution group. That is, there is an $(\infty, 1)$ correspondence between rational functions involving certain letters, and the substitution groups on these letters, and it is an important fact that all these functions which belong to the same group are rational functions of each other. *Lagrange* observed that the number of values which such a function assumes when its n elements are permuted in every possible manner is a divisor of $n!$ For instance, $x_1x_2+x_3x_4$ assumes the following three values:

$$x_1x_2+x_3x_4,\ x_1x_3+x_2x_4,\ x_1x_4+x_2x_3.$$

This is in accord with the general theory, as 3 is a divisor of 24; but it is not possible to construct a rational function in four letters which assumes exactly five distinct values when its elements are permuted in every possible way, since 5 is not a divisor of 24.

Although the number of values which a rational function whose degree does not exceed n assumes when its letters are permuted in every possible manner is a divisor of $n!$ it does not follow that there is such a function for every divisor of $n!$ In fact, it has been proved that whenever $n>4$ it is not possible to construct a function for every divisor of $n!$ while it is possible to construct such a function whenever $n<5$. The fact that it is not possible to construct a rational function with five letters which assumes either 3, 4, or 8 values when these letters are permuted in every possible manner was proved by *Ruffini* in his Teoria generale delle equazioni, in cui si dimostra impossible la soluzione algebraica delle equazioni generali di grade superiore al quarto, published at Bologna in 1799. This fact is equivalent to the theorem that there is no substitution group on five or a smaller number of letters having for its order one of the numbers 40, 30, 15.

12. Linear equations. Every linear equation with one unknown can be reduced to the form

$$ax=b,$$

where a and b are known, and x is the unknown.

Necessary and sufficient conditions that this equation can be solved are that either a and b are both equal to zero, or that a is not zero. If the former condition is satisfied the equation has an infinite number of solutions, as x may have any value. On the contrary, the equation has only one solution when the latter condition is satisfied. In this case the value of x is obtained by dividing b by a. As this is a rational process the root of the equation must be in the domain of rationality (a, b) constituted by a and b. The root is, however, not necessarily in the integral domain $[a, b]$ constituted by a and b.

If a and b are restricted to be *natural* numbers it is not possible to reduce every linear equation to a single form, but all such equations can, in this case, be reduced to one of the two forms

$$ax=b, \quad ax+b=0.$$

This is also true in case a and b are only restricted to be *positive* rational numbers. The ancient and the mediæval mathematicians generally imposed the latter restriction on a and b as well as on the root.* Hence the second form was not solvable. The general solution of the linear equation as noted above therefore calls for the extension of the number concept so as to include both negative and fractional numbers in

* This was done by the great French algebraist *Vieta* (1540–1603) and even *Descartes* called negative roots *false roots* in his Géometrie.

addition to the natural numbers. With this extension of the number concept the linear equation is solvable except when $a=0$ and $b\neq 0$. The further extension of this concept so as to include the irrational and the ordinary complex numbers does not affect the given discussion of the linear equation.

13. Quadratic equations. Every quadratic equation with one unknown can be reduced to the form

$$a_0x^2+a_1x+a_2=0.$$

If we put $x=z+k$ this equation becomes

$$a_0z^2+(2a_0k+a_1)z+a_0k^2+a_1k+a_2=0.$$

Since $a_0\neq 0$, it results from the preceding paragraph that it is always possible to solve the following linear equation in k:

$$2a_0k+a=0,$$

and thus arrive at an equation of the form

$$z^2=A,$$

which involves only the extraction of the square root of a number. The most important thing about the solution of the quadratic equation is the extraction of the square root of a number. In fact, this is the only operation which enters into the solution of the quadratic equation but not into the solution of the linear equation, as can be deduced from the general solution sketched above. The extraction of the square root is, however, not a little thing in mathematics. It opens up the question of irrational numbers as well as that of ordinary complex numbers—two very profound and far-reaching questions.

As the number A is a rational function of the coefficients a_0, a_1, a_2, it must lie in the domain of rationality constituted by these coefficients. Hence *the quadratic equation in one unknown can always be solved provided we can extract the square root of all the numbers in the domain of rationality constituted by the coefficients of the equation.* As it is known that we can extract the square root of any real number as well as of any ordinary complex number, it results, in particular, that the quadratic equation with one unknown can always be solved provided its coefficients are ordinary real or complex numbers.

While the root of a linear equation in one unknown lies in the domain of rationality constituted by its coefficients this is not necessarily true of the roots of a quadratic equation, since the operation of extracting the square root is not a rational operation. If the coefficients of the quadratic are rational numbers the domain of rationality constituted by one root clearly includes the other root, but this is not necessarily true when the coefficients are either irrational or complex numbers. It is, however, always true that the two roots of a quadratic equation in one unknown must be in the domain of rationality constituted by the coefficients and one of the roots, since each root may be obtained by a rational process from the coefficients and the other root. In other words, the quadratic in one unknown is always *reducible* in the domain of rationality constituted by its coefficients and one of its roots, but in no smaller domain of rationality.

The reduction of the quadratic equation to the form

$$z^2 = A$$

is a special case of the removal of the second term in the equation

$$a_0x^n + a_1x^{n-1} + \ldots + a_n = 0.$$

If we substitute $z+k$ for x in this equation, there results

$$a_0(z+k)^n + a_1(z+k)^{n-1} + \ldots + a_n = 0.$$

The coefficient of z^{n-1} in this equation is

$$a_0nk + a_1.$$

As a_0 and n are both different from zero (otherwise the equation would not be of degree $n>0$) a number can always be found which when substituted for k will reduce a_0nk+a_1 to zero. This number is sometimes called the **zero of the function** a_0nk+a_1, but it is more commonly known as the root of the following linear equation in k:

$$a_0nk + a_1 = 0.$$

Hence the solution of a linear equation suffices to determine a number by means of which the coefficient of x^{n-1} can be reduced to zero. In general, the solution of an equation of degree α suffices to reduce the coefficient of $x^{n-\alpha}$ to zero. In particular, to reduce the absolute term a_n to zero it is necessary to solve an equation of degree n.

14. Extensions of the number concept due to the quadratic. The solution of the general quadratic calls for numbers of the form $a+b\sqrt{-1}$, where a and b are real, even when coefficients of the equations (a_0, a_1, a_2) are rational numbers. It has been proved that numbers of this form likewise suffice for the solution of the equation of the nth degree in one unknown even if the coefficients are also any numbers of this form. It should, however, not be inferred that the numbers of the form $a+b\sqrt{-1}$ which are required to solve the quadratic equation with rational coefficients are coextensive with those required to solve the equations of the nth degree. In 1770 *Lagrange* proved that the real irrational numbers which are roots of a quadratic equation with rational coefficients have the characteristic property that they may be represented by periodic continued fractions whose elements are integers.* The quadratic equation merely opened the great problem of distinguishing the different kinds of irrational numbers—a problem which is to-day the object of important investigations.

The quadratic equation opened also the question as to the number of possible roots of an equation. It should be emphasized that the answer given to this question depends upon the point of view. For *Diophantus* and the older mathematicians who did not admit negative, irrational, or complex numbers as roots of an equation, most of the quadratic equations did not have any root; others had one root, but no instance is known where the ancient Greeks, or the older mathematicians, observed that at least some quadratic equations may have two roots. On the contrary, *Bhaskara*, a

---

* Cf. *Cahen*, Elements de la Théorie des Nombres, 1900, p. 183. This theorem was extended by *Minkowski* in *Göttingen Nachrichten*, 1899, p. 64.

Hindu mathematician of the twelfth century of our era, observed that some quadratic equations have two roots, but even for him many quadratic equations had no root whatever, since he did not use complex numbers. He gave the following interesting rule: "The square of a positive as well as that of a negative number is positive, and the square root of a positive number is double, positive and negative. There is no square root of a negative number because a negative number is not a square."

Problems leading to quadratic equations are frequently viewed so narrowly that only one root, or even no root, seems to have meaning, and the existence of two roots has often led to a more comprehensive conception of the problem. This equation has thus contributed to more accurate and deeper thought as to the real nature of the problem. It is very important to observe that the study of the nature and the properties of the roots of an equation has not only led to a clearer comprehension of the essence of an equation, but also to a deeper insight into the nature of the subject giving rise to the equation. This point of view was taken by *Poinsot* in his important article entitled "Réflexions sur les principes fundementeux de la théorie des nombres," in contradicting a view expressed earlier by *d'Alembert* to the effect that the additional roots, beyond those to which the problem was supposed to give rise, were an inconvenience and were not to be attributed to the richness of algebra as some had supposed.*

The question as to the number of roots of an equation is not entirely confined to the number domain in which the values of the unknown are supposed to be. The additional difficulty is opened by the quadratic which is a perfect square. For instance, there seems to be good reason for saying the equation,

$$x^2 - 2x + 1 = 0,$$

has only one root, since 1 is the only solution of this equation. On the other hand, when the first member of this equation is

* *Poinsot, Journal de Mathématique,* Vol. X, 1845, p. 8.

written in the form $(x-1)(x-1)$, it is evident that $x=1$ will make each of its factors vanish, and hence we may say that 1 is a **repeated** root. This should, however, be regarded as merely a convention which tends toward simplicity and clearness—two of the most potent factors in shaping the development of mathematics. The statement that *a quadratic equation has always two and only two roots* is thus seen to be heavily laden with historical facts of great significance, and it opens up the way for harmony and brevity in the theory of the general equation.*

15. Cubic equations. The solution of the general cubic equation requires the operation of extracting the cube root in addition to the operations involved in the solution of the quadratic. The preparation for root extraction is, however, not so evident in the case of the cubic as it is in the case of the quadratic. In fact, many mathematicians attempted these preliminary transformations in vain before an Italian, *Scipione del Ferro*, professor in Bolgona from 1496 to 1526, finally succeeded. Since this time, a large number of different solutions have been given and a very extensive literature on the cubic has been developed, as may be seen by consulting the " Subject Index " of the Royal Society of London Catalogue of Scientific Papers, 1800—1900, pp. 170–71. Many of these methods of solution are based upon considerations which do not apply to the general equation of the nth degree but are very elegant as regards the cubic. On the contrary, we shall first give a method which involves many very interesting general theorems but requires lengthy computations, for far-reaching thoughts are a greater desideratum for the mathematician than brief special methods.

Remove the second term of the general cubic by the method indicated in sec. 13. The equation may thus be reduced to the form,

$$x^3+qx+r=0.$$

---

* Professor *E. R. Hedrick* has given several reasons why the beginner should not be taught that every quadratic equation has exactly two roots, *School Science and Mathematics*, Vol. IX, 1909, p. 563.

Let x_1, x_2, x_3 be the roots of this equation, and consider the functions:

$$(x_1-x_2)(x_1-x_3)(x_2-x_3),$$
$$(x_1+\omega x_2+\omega^2 x_3)^3,$$
$$(x_1+\omega^2 x_2+\omega x_3)^3,$$

where ω is an imaginary cube root of unity. Observe that whenever any one of these functions remains unchanged under any given substitution on the roots, the other two do so also. That is, each of these functions is transformed into itself by the same substitutions on the roots. From the fact that two rational functions which are transformed into themselves by the same substitutions can be expressed rationally in terms of each other (sec. 11), it results that each of these functions can be expressed rationally in terms of each of the others.* As the square of the first of these functions is symmetric, this square can be expressed rationally in terms of the elementary symmetric functions q and r, as was noted above in sec. 11.

These general theorems enable us to see how the cubic can be solved. We express $(x_1-x_2)(x_1-x_3)(x_2-x_3)$ as the square root of a rational function of q and r. Then we express each of the other functions as a rational function of this square root and extract the cube root of this rational function. In this way we find the values of

$$x_1+\omega x_2+\omega^2 x_3 \quad \text{and} \quad x_1+\omega^2 x_2+\omega x_3.$$

As we know that $x_1+x_2+x_3=0$ we have three linear equations in three unknowns from which the values of the unknowns can be readily found. It should be observed that this general method enables us to see, before we do any calculating, how we may proceed to find the roots, and it illustrates an important tendency in mathematics to see things without calculating. Normally, thought should precede rather than follow calcu-

---

* Cf. *Dickson,* Introduction to the theory of algebraic equations, 1903, p. 24.

lations in pure mathematics. The calculations will come out as follows:

$$(x_1-x_2)(x_1-x_3)(x_2-x_3)=\sqrt{-4q^3-27r^2};$$

$$x_1+\omega x_2+\omega^2 x_3=\sqrt[3]{-\frac{27}{2}r-\frac{3}{2}\sqrt{12q^3+81r^2}};$$

$$x_1+\omega^2 x_2+\omega x_3=\sqrt[3]{-\frac{27}{2}r+\frac{3}{2}\sqrt{12q^3+81r^2}};$$

$$x_1+x_2+x_3=0.$$

On adding the last three equations we obtain

$$x_1=\sqrt[3]{-\frac{r}{2}+\sqrt{\frac{r^2}{4}+\frac{q^3}{27}}}+\sqrt[3]{-\frac{r}{2}-\sqrt{\frac{r^2}{4}+\frac{q^3}{27}}}.$$

This is known as *Cardan's* formula, because he first published it. The substance of it had been obtained by *Cardan* from *Tartaglia* under the promise of secrecy, but *Cardan* broke his promise and published the formula in his "Ars Magna," in 1545.*

An elegant and brief solution of the cubic was given in 1591 by *Vieta*, a noted French mathematician. The general equation is first reduced to the form,

$$x^3+3ax=2b.$$

Letting $x=\frac{a-y^2}{y}$ this becomes

$$y^6+2by^3=a^3.$$

As this is in the form of a quadric it is very easy to find the possible values of y, and after these are known the values of x result from $x=\frac{a-y^2}{y}$. Numerous other brief methods are known and may be found in works on the Theory of Equations.

16. Biquadratic equations. We shall see that the solution of the general biquadratic equation requires no non-rational

---

* For a clear statement of the extenuating circumstances the reader may consult, *Tropfke's* Geschichte der Elementar-Mathematik, Vol. I, p. 275.

operation except the extraction of the square and the cube root. Hence the operations which enter into this solution are of the same type as those which enter into the solution of the cubic. As in the case of the cubic we shall begin with a method which is valuable on account of its perspicuity and the far-reaching thoughts which it involves, but is not the simplest from the standpoint of practical applications. For numerical equations the methods of the following section are generally to be preferred.

We shall suppose that the general biquadratic has been reduced to the form,

$$x^4+qx^2+rx+s=0,$$

and that its roots are x_1, x_2, x_3, x_4. The following three functions are clearly transformed either into themselves or into each other by every substitution on the roots

$$(x_1+x_2-x_3-x_4)^2, \quad (x_1-x_2+x_3-x_4)^2, \quad (x_1-x_2-x_3+x_4)^2.$$

Hence the cubic equation which has these functions as roots must have for its coefficients symmetric functions of x_1, x_2, x_3, x_4. As these symmetric functions can be expressed as integral functions of the elementary symmetric functions q, r, s, it results that this cubic lies in the domain of rationality constituted by these elementary symmetric functions. As a matter of fact, this cubic is

$$y^3+8qy^2+(16q^2-64s)y-64r^2=0.$$

Solving this cubic and denoting its root by θ_1, θ_2, θ_3, we have the following system of four linear equations in four unknowns:

$$x_1+x_2+x_3+x_4=0;$$
$$x_1+x_2-x_3-x_4=\sqrt{\theta_1};$$
$$x_1-x_2+x_3-x_4=\sqrt{\theta_2};$$
$$x_1-x_2-x_3+x_4=\sqrt{\theta_3}.$$

By adding these equations we observe that x_1 is one-fourth of the sum of the square roots of the roots of the given cubic.

After x_1 is known it is easy to find the values of the other three roots.

The discovery of a solution of the general biquadratic is due to *Ferrari*, who was a pupil of *Cardan*. It is especially interesting since *Ferrari* was not yet twenty-three years old when he discovered it. In this connection, it is interesting to note that both *Abel* and *Galois* did their fundamental work on the theory of equations before they were twenty-three years old. The substance of Ferrari's solution was as follows: Write the biquadratic in the form,

$$x^4+px^3+qx^2+rx+s=0.$$

Add $(ax+b)^2$ to both members and then assume that the first member is a perfect square. That is,

$$x^4+px^3+(q+a^2)x^2+(r+2ab)x+s+b^2=(x^2+\tfrac{1}{2}px+k)^2.$$

By equating coefficients of the like powers of x and eliminating a and b there results a cubic in k. After finding the value of k by means of this cubic it is only necessary to factor,

$$(x^2+\tfrac{1}{2}px+k)^2-(ax+b)^2=0,$$

in order to reduce the solution of the biquadratic to that of two quadratics. The solutions of these quadratics must include the roots of the original equation.

17. Equations whose degrees exceed 4. The brilliant discoveries of the Italian mathematicians regarding the solution of the cubic and biquadratic equation led to numerous attempts to solve general equations of higher degrees by rational operations and the extraction of roots, as these were the only known algebraic operations at that time. All such efforts were destined to failure, but it required nearly three hundred years from the time when *Ferrari* first solved the biquadratic until *Abel* discovered, at the age of twenty-two, the first rigorous proof of the fact that the general quintic equation cannot be solved by these elementary operations. It is interesting to note that *Abel* began his scientific career by attempts to solve the quintic by radicals and he believed for some time that he had actually found a solution, but he afterward discovered his own error. His apparent success won for him the life-long friendship and support of his countryman, *Hansteens.*

Abel was not the first who attempted to prove that the general quintic cannot be solved by the extraction of roots. About a quarter of a century earlier *Paolo Ruffini* did much to develop methods which were of sufficient power to prove this fundamental fact. In particular, he gave a number of theorems on *groups of substitutions*, as was noted above. The difficulties which the general solution of the quintic presented have thus become a source of great riches for the later development of mathematics. Besides *Ruffini*, some of the most eminent among those who started these developments are: *Tschirnhaus, Euler, Lagrange, Gauss, Galois*, and *Hermite.*

The work of *Galois* (1811–32) was especially fundamental as regards the establishment of more definite relations between the theory of equations and the theory of substitution groups, by proving that every equation belongs to a certain substitution group, and that the properties of this group give definite information as to the solvability by radicals of the equations belonging to the group. The important theorem that two rational functions of the roots of any equation may be expressed rationally in terms of each other, in the domain of rationality of the coefficients of the equations, had been proved earlier by *Lagrange.* For an introduction to the elegant theory of equations based upon these theorems we may refer the reader to the following works: *Dickson,* Introduction to the Theory of Algebraic Equations, 1903; *Cajori,* An Introduction to the Modern Theory of Equations, 1904; *Mathews,* Algebraic Equations, 1907.

IV. EQUATIONS WITH ONE UNKNOWN AND WITH NUMERICAL COEFFICIENTS

18. General statement. Although numerical algebraic equations have a prehistoric origin, the arithmetical epigrams of the Greek Anthology, among other things, support the assumption that they resulted from puzzles and word-equations. The fully developed equations represent highways of exact thought without by-ways, and the coefficients determine the possible destinations of these highways. The ancient problems of duplicating a cube and trisecting an angle, among many others, directed attention to the need of such highways, but their construction for coefficients, which may be regarded as arbitrary, presented great difficulties. Even in the case of the cubic with three real roots (*casus irreducibilis*) *Cardan's* formula represents the real root in the form of the sum of two imaginary expressions, and it has been proved that it is impossible in this case to represent the roots of the cubic in a real form by means of radicals.* On the other hand, the great French algebraist, *Vieta* (1540–1603), showed how the real values of the three roots may be obtained by means of trigonometry.

From the preceding paragraph it results that the solution of numerical equations of a given degree may present difficulties even after a formula for the roots of the general equation of this degree is known. These difficulties, combined with those of finding such general formulas, directed attention to special methods of solution in case the coefficients are numbers. It is of especial importance to observe that for many applications of algebra only approximate values of the real roots are needed. This need has led to a vast literature

* Cf. Encyklopädie der Mathematischen Wissenschaften, Vol. I, p. 518. The French edition of this work, to which we have already referred, treats many subjects more completely than the German. This is especially true as regards algebra and arithmetic. Neither of these editions is completely published, but the German is considerably further advanced than the French. They constitute at present the most important mathematical works of reference.

which embodies some of the most beautiful results relating to alegbraic equations. As the solutions of the general linear and quadratic equations are so easily available for numerical equations, we shall assume, in what follows, that the degrees of the equations under consideration exceed 2. The solutions of numerical equations may frequently be simplified by considering the special properties of the coefficients, and hence they demand great alertness as regards details.

A large part of the theory of numerical equations confines itself to real numbers, since these are frequently the only numbers applying directly to the conditions which give rise to an equation. This is especially true as regards the coefficients of an equation. When the coefficients of the rational integral function $f(x)$ involve complex numbers it is evidently possible to write this function in the form,

$$f(x)=\phi(x)+i\psi(x),$$

where the coefficients of the rational integral functions $\phi(x)$ and $\psi(x)$ are real numbers. After multiplying both members of this equation by the conjugate value, $\phi(x)-i\psi(x)$, we obtain a new rational integral function of x, which involves all the roots of $f(x)=0$, but has only real coefficients. Hence it results that if we can find all the roots of every rational integral function of x with real coefficients we can also find those of such a function with complex coefficients. It is also important to observe from the given form of $f(x)$ that any real root of $f(x)=0$ is a common root of $\phi(x)=0$, $\psi(x)=0$, and hence it is a root of the highest common factor of $\phi(x)$ and $\psi(x)$. In view of these facts and for the sake of brevity and perspicuity we shall assume throughout the rest of the present section that all the coefficients of $f(x)$ are real numbers.

19. Multiple roots. If $f(x)$ is divisible by $(x-r)^\alpha$ but not by $(x-r)^{\alpha+1}$, r is said to occur exactly α times as a root of the equation $f(x)=0$; sometimes it is also called such a root or a zero of $f(x)$. When $\alpha>1$, r is called a multiple root of $f(x)=0$, or multiple zero of $f(x)$. To determine the multiple roots of $f(x)=0$ it is convenient to use the well-known property that any root which occurs exactly α times in $f(x)=0$ must occur exactly $\alpha-1$ times as a root of $f'(x)=0$, where $f'(x)$ is the first derivative of $f(x)$. Hence a multiple root of $f(x)$ is also a root of the highest common factor of the two functions, $f(x), f'(x)$. Since the first derivative of $f(x)$ may be found by a rational process it results that $f(x)$ is reducible in the domain of rationality of its coefficients whenever it has multiple roots, but the converse of this theorem is evidently not necessarily true.

From the preceding paragraph it results that the multiple roots of $f(x)=0$ may be found by means of the highest common factor of $f(x)$ and $f'(x)$. As the multiple roots of this highest common factor may be found in a similar manner it results that whenever $f(x)=0$ has no more than β distinct multiple roots, all these roots may be found by rational operations and by solving equations whose degrees do exceed β. In particular, if $f(x)=0$ has only one multiple root it may be found by rational operations. It is frequently possible to find the rational multiple roots by inspection

Since the quotient obtained by dividing $f(x)$ by the highest common factor of $f(x)$ and $f'(x)$ involves each root of $f(x)$ once and only once, we may suppose in what follows that $f(x)=0$ involves no multiple root. This hypothesis will conduce to brevity of statements.

20. Sturm's theorem. This theorem (proved in 1829) furnishes the scientific foundation for every method of finding the approximate values of the unknown in an algebraic equation with real coefficients, as it gives definite information in regard to the number of real roots between two arbitrarily assigned numbers.* Moreover, the proof of this theorem is not difficult, being based upon the following two elementary facts: (1) The continuity of $f(x)$, and (2) the fact that if α is a real root of $f(x)=0$ and h is a sufficiently small positive number, then $f(\alpha-h)$ and $f'(\alpha-h)$ have different signs, while

* Encyklopädie der Elementar-Mathematik von Weber und Wellstein. 1906, Vol. I, p. 337.

$f(\alpha+h)$ and $f'(\alpha+h)$ must have the same sign, where $f'(x)$ is the first derivative of $f(x)$. A proof of these two facts is found in many elementary text-books; e.g., *Burnside* and *Panton's* Theory of Equations, Vol. I, 1899, pp. 9 and 161.

To obtain Sturm's Series we proceed exactly as in the process of finding the highest common factor of $f(x)$ and $f'(x)$ with the single exception that the sign of each remainder is changed. In this way we obtain the following relations:

$$\begin{aligned} f(x) &= q_1(x)f'(x) - r_1(x), \\ f'(x) &= q_2(x)r_1(x) - r_2(x), \\ r_1(x) &= q_3(x)r_2(x) - r_3(x), \\ &\cdots\cdots\cdots \\ r_{n-2}(x) &= q_n(x)r_{n-1}(x) - r_n(x), \end{aligned}$$

where $r_n(x)$ is a constant, different from zero, since $f(x)=0$ has no multiple root. The series,

$$f(x),\ f'(x),\ r_1(x),\ r_2(x),\ \ldots,\ r_n(x),$$

has the following properties: No two adjacent functions can vanish for the same value of x; otherwise all the succeeding functions would have to vanish for this value of x, but this is impossible since $r_n(x)$ cannot be 0. When any function vanishes the two adjacent functions must have opposite signs in order to satisfy the given equations. In finding the number of changes of sign in this series as x increases continuously from the real number a to a larger real number b we need therefore not consider the vanishing of any function except the first one. In case this vanishes a change of sign is lost, as was observed in the preceding paragraph. This proves Sturm's Theorem, which may be stated as follows:

If any two real numbers a and b be substituted for x in Sturm's Series,

$$f(x),\ f'(x),\ r_1(x),\ r_2(x),\ \ldots,\ r_n(x),$$

the difference between the number of changes of sign in the series when a is substituted for x and the number when b is substituted for x is exactly the number of real roots of the equation $f(x)=0$ between a and b.

The total number of real roots of $f(x)=0$ is equal to the difference between the changes of sign in these functions when $-\infty$ is first substituted for x and then $+\infty$. The total number of positive roots may be found by first substituting 0 and then $+\infty$, and of the negative roots by first substituting $-\infty$ and then 0. This theorem is more general than Descartes' Rule of Sign, as the latter gives merely an upper limit for the number of real roots. The disadvantage of Sturm's Theorem is that it requires considerable labor to find Sturm's Series, especially when the degree of $f(x)$ is large, since the coefficients in the successive function of the series may become large. It is evident that the successive remainders may be multiplied or divided by any positive number and that it is not necessary to find the exact value of $r_n(x)$, since only its sign is considered in the application of the theorem.

Sturm's Series suffices to find the rational roots of an equation and to approximate the irrational roots to any desired degree of accuracy, but other methods generally require much less computation. One of the most useful auxiliary theorems in locating the roots of an equation may be stated as follows: *There must be an odd number of roots between a and b whenever* $f(a)$ and $f(b)$ *have opposite signs.* This theorem results directly from the fact that $f(x)$ is continuous and hence can change its sign between a and b only by passing through zero. It is evident that the number of roots between a and b must be zero or even whenever $f(a)$ and $f(b)$ have the same sign.

21. Rational roots. *Descartes* observed that every root of

$$f(x)=a_0x^n+a_1x^{n-1}+\ldots+a_n=0$$

is a divisor of $\frac{a_n}{a_0}$. Moreover, if a root is rational and reduced to its lowest terms, its numerator is a divisor of a_n and its denominator is a divisor of a_0, as results directly from substituting such a root $\left(\frac{m}{l}\right)$ in $f(x)=0$. In fact, all the terms of

$$a_0l^{n-1}\left[\left(\frac{m}{l}\right)^n+\frac{a_1}{a_0}\left(\frac{m}{l}\right)^{n-1}+\ldots+\frac{a_n}{a_0}\right],$$

except possibly the first are evidently integers. As the sum of all these terms is zero the first must also be an integer. On the other hand, since m divides all these terms except possibly the last it must also divide the last. If $f(x)=0$ has a second rational root and this root is also reduced to its lowest terms, its numerator evidently divides $a_n \div m$ and its denominator divides $a_0 \div l$, etc. As the numerator of every rational root in its lowest terms divides a_n and the denominator divides a_0, it results that we can find all the rational roots of $f(x)=0$ by a finite number of trials and that the number of these trials is small when a_n and a_0 have only a small number of factors.

22. Irrational roots. It is always possible, in accord with the preceding theory, to find two rational numbers, whose difference is less than any assigned finite number, such that one of these numbers is greater than the required irrational root while the other is less than this root. We may choose these rational numbers successively so as to differ from each other by powers of $\frac{1}{10}$. That is, we may first find two integers which differ by $10^{\circ}=1$ such that the root lies between them, then we may find two rational numbers differing by 10^{-1}, such that the root lies between them, then we may find two rational numbers differing by 10^{-2} and inclosing the root, etc. The smaller of these two rational numbers is called the approximate value of the root, and the process of finding it is known as **approximating the root.** In practice this process is greatly modified in details so as to require much less labor.

In 1767 *Lagrange* published a theoretically simple method for finding the approximate value of an irrational root by means of continued fractions. The main features of this method are as follows: After finding that a root of $f(x)=0$ lies between the integers r and $r+1$ we substitute for x in $f(x)=0$,

$$x=r+\frac{1}{y_1}=\frac{ry_1+1}{y_1},$$

and thus obtain another equation of degree n, $f_1(y_1)=0$, which has the same number of real roots greater than 1, as $f(x)=0$

has real roots between r and $r+1$. We then find an integer $r_1>0$, such that there is a root between r_1 and r_1+1 and substitute in $f_1(y_1)=0$,

$$y_1=r_1+\frac{1}{y_2}=\frac{r_1y_2+1}{y_2}.$$

In this way there results an equation of the nth degree in y_2 which has as many real roots greater than 1 as $f(y_1)=0$ has real roots between r_1 and r_1+1.

By continuing this process we must arrive at an equation which has only one root greater than 1, and this root may be traced as far as may be desired. The value of a root of the original equation is then given by the continued fraction,

$$x=r+\cfrac{1}{r_1+\cfrac{1}{r_2+}}.$$

Although this method is perspicuous and exhibits clearly the reason for each step, it has not been used as widely as the well-known Horner's Method.

23. Solutions by means of graphs and machines. If an exact graph of $y=f(x)$ could be constructed and if it were possible to measure exactly the abscissas of the points where this graph crosses the x-axis, the numerical measures of these abscissas would furnish all the real roots of $f(x)=0$. This method has the advantage that it exhibits the values of $f(x)$ for all the values of x within certain limits. Its disadvantage is that a graph cannot be said to represent a function accurately on account of the imperfections in measurement and drawing. It serves the purpose of a hypothesis by bringing unity into what might otherwise appear as disconnected, and hence it serves a very useful purpose, especially for the beginner. It is a convenient receptacle for a large number of facts whose significance might otherwise not be so clear.

The ancient Greeks used geometric constructions to solve certain problems of geometry which are equivalent to the solutions of equations of the second degree, but the present graphic methods for solving equations were developed mostly since the beginning of the nineteenth century. In many cases these methods serve only to show that certain solutions are possible and in some cases they serve as a rough check on the accuracy of the calculations, but there are a large number of cases where such solutions are sufficiently accurate for the problems on hand. As they are especially well adapted to the saving of thought as regards details they are doubtless destined to play a more and more prominent rôle as mathematical methods find wider and wider use in the development of science and industry.

Instead of drawing the graph of $y=f(x)$ as noted above, it is often more convenient to construct two curves such that the abscissas of the points of intersection are the roots of $f(x)=0$. Sometimes one curve is fixed for all the equations of the same degree, while the other curve is made to vary so as to correspond to the different values of the coefficients. As early as 1637 *Descartes* employed a fixed parabola and a variable circle to solve equations of the third and fourth degrees, and he also solved equations of the fifth and sixth degrees by means of a certain fixed curve of the third order and a circle. The literature on graphic algebra is very extensive and is growing rapidly. Among the introductory treatises we may mention the Graphic Algebra by *Phillips* and *Beebe*.

Closely related to the graphic methods are the various machines for finding the approximate values of the roots of a numerical equation. Some of these are very ingenious, employing principles of equilibrium of forces and of hydrostatics as well as of electricity. Although the ancient Greeks solved the Delian problem, involving the solution of a cubic equation, by means of mechanical devices, the machines suitable for finding the roots of a great variety of equations are comparatively recent inventions. One of the most noted was invented in 1893 by a Spanish engineer named *M. L. Torrès*. For a detailed description of this and other machines to solve equations and to simplify other calculations we may refer to Le Calcul Simplifié par *Maurice d'Ocagne*, 1905. The large mathematical encyclopedias, especially the Encyclopédie des Sciences Mathématiques, tome 1, Vol. IV, contain a large amount of information on this subject.

24. A few fallacies and notes of caution. While the chief aim of mathematics is the construction of permanent and attractive highways of thought leading as directly as possible to important treasures of the intellect, it is of some interest to observe where one is led by following by-ways regardless of the danger signals. One of the most prominent of these signals is: *Never divide both members of an equation by an expression whose value is zero.* If it were allowable to divide by such an expression it would be easy to prove that every number is equal to zero. One such proof would be as follows: From $x=1$ there would result successively,

$$x^2=1,\quad x^2-1=0,\quad x+1=0,\quad x=-1,\quad 1=-1,\quad a=-a,\quad 2a=0.$$

As a may be so selected that $2a$ is an arbitrary number, it would result from this that any arbitrary number is zero.

A fallacy of a somewhat different nature results from the fact that we are so apt to forget that a number has n nth roots. This is illustrated in the following two examples:

$$\frac{1}{-1}=\frac{-1}{1}.$$

Extracting the square root of both members gives

$$\frac{\sqrt{1}}{\sqrt{-1}}=\frac{\sqrt{-1}}{\sqrt{1}}.$$

Clearing of fractions and observing that $(\sqrt{1})^2=1$ and $(\sqrt{-1})^2=-1$, if $\sqrt{\ }$ stands for a single root, there results,

$$1=-1.$$

The danger signal here is *remember that a number has n nth roots.*

The use of radicals in elementary mathematics is not as uniform as it should be. For instance, the symbol $\sqrt{\ }$ should either imply two values and hence should never be preceded by $\pm$, or we should have a slightly modified symbol to denote the arithmetic square root. If we assume that the symbol $\sqrt{}$ indicates merely a positive square root, such equations as

$$\sqrt{x+a}+\sqrt{x}=1, \quad a>1,$$

are clearly impossible. On the other hand, they are possible when this symbol indicates either of the two possible square roots, and the possible value of x may be found by clearing of radicals in the ordinary way. Such equations should therefore not be called impossible without stating that symbol $\sqrt{}$ is to be given an arithmetic meaning.

The equation,

$$\left(x^{\frac{1}{q}}\right)^p = \left(x^p\right)^{\frac{1}{q}},$$

where p and q are integers, should not be regarded as an identity, as is evident from the fact that $(x^{\frac{1}{4}})^4$ has only one value while $(x^4)^{\frac{1}{4}}$ has, in general, four distinct values. All the values of the first member of the given equation are evidently values of the second, but the converse is not true.* Such equations must therefore be used with great care. For more detailed information along this line the reader may consult *Catalan*, Sur un paradoxe algébrique, Nouv. Annales de Math., Vol. VIII, 1869, p. 456.

V. SIMULTANEOUS EQUATIONS

25. Introduction. In sec. 5 it was observed that simultaneous equations appear on some of the oldest mathematical papyri and that the solution of a special case of a system of n simultaneous equations was known to the ancient Greeks. A satisfactory treatment of such equations was, however, not possible until *determinants* had been developed. This subject is comparatively modern, having its origin in the writings of *Leibnitz* (1693), and assuming a significant position in mathematical literature during the latter part of the eighteenth and the first part of the nineteenth century. In what follows we shall

* Cf. *Vallès*, Nouvelles Annales de Mathématiques, Vol. IX, 1870, p. 20.

assume a knowledge of the elementary properties of determinants.

In the case of a single equation in one or more unknowns, it is known that it can always be solved in the sense that at least one value of each of the unknowns exists which will satisfy the equation. The only exception to this rule is when all the coefficients of the unknown, or the unknowns, are equal to zero,* while the known term is not equal to zero. In the case of a system of equations, a number of other possibilities arise and one of the first questions in regard to such a system is whether it can be solved. If this can be done the system is said to be **consistent.**

A set of mn quantities arranged in rectangular array of m rows and n columns is called a **matrix.** When $m=n$ it is called a **square matrix,** so that the matrix of a determinant is always a square matrix. The rank of a matrix is the order of the largest non-vanishing determinant contained in the matrix.

26. Consistency of a system of linear equations.† Consider the following system of m equations in n unknowns:

$$a_{11}x_1+a_{12}x_2+\ldots+a_{1n}x_n+b_1=0,$$

$$a_{21}x_1+a_{22}x_2+\ldots+a_{2n}x_n+b_2=0,$$

$$\cdots\cdots\cdots\cdots\cdots$$

$$a_{m1}x_1+a_{m2}x_2+\ldots+a_{mn}x_n+b_m=0,$$

where m and n are any two positive integers. The three cases that can arise are:

(1) The equations may have no solution and hence be *inconsistent*.

(2) They may have only one solution.

(3) They may have more than one solution.

---

* We consider only finite values of the unknowns in the solutions of equations.

† In this article we have, in the main, adopted the mode of presentation given in the Introduction to Higher Algebra, by *Maxime Bôcher*, 1907.

It will soon appear that they must have an infinite number of solutions whenever they have more than one (in fact, each unknown has none, one, or an infinite number of values), so that the possible cases are: No solution, one solution, or an infinite number of solutions. To prove this it will be convenient to consider the two matrices:

$$A=\begin{vmatrix} a_{11}a_{12} & \dots & a_{1n} \\ a_{21}a_{22} & \dots & a_{2n} \\ \cdot\ \cdot & \cdot\ \cdot & \cdot \\ a_{m1}a_{m2} & \dots & a_{mn} \end{vmatrix}, \qquad B=\begin{vmatrix} a_{11}a_{12} & \dots & a_{1n}b_1 \\ a_{21}a_{22} & \dots & a_{2n}b_2 \\ \cdot\ \cdot & \cdot\ \cdot & \cdot\ \cdot \\ a_{m1}a_{m2} & \dots & a_{mn}b_m \end{vmatrix}.$$

The latter is obtained by adding the column of b's to the former, and hence it is called the **augmented** matrix of the system, while A is the **matrix of the system.** It is evident that the rank of B cannot be less than the rank of A and that the former cannot exceed the latter by more than unity. Hence we have the two possible cases: (1) The rank of A is equal to that of B, (2) the rank of A is one less than that of B.

Suppose that the given system of equations comes under the latter of these two possible cases. We may therefore suppose that the rank of B is r while the rank of A is $r-1$. The given system of equations may be supposed to have been arranged in such a manner that the non-vanishing determinant of order r in B is in the upper right-hand corner of this matrix. Since the rank of A is $r-1$ it results that the homogeneous parts $(f_1, f_2, \dots, f_r)$ of the first r equations of the given system may be multiplied by constants $(c_1, c_2, \dots, c_r)$, so that

$$c_1f_1+c_2f_2+\dots+c_rf_r=0,$$

independently of the values of the unknowns, where at least one of the c's is not 0. If we represent the first members of the given system by $F_1, F_2, \dots, F_m$, so that

$$F_i=f_i+b_i, \qquad (i=1,\ 2,\ \dots,\ m),$$

it follows from the above that

$$c_1F_1+c_2F_2+\dots+c_rF_r=c_1b_1+c_2b_2+\dots+c_rb_r=c.$$

Since the rank of B is r it is necessary that $c \neq 0$, otherwise each of the elements in one row of the matrix of a non-vanishing determinant would be the same linear function of the corresponding elements in the other rows.

The fact that $c \neq 0$ for any possible values of the unknowns proves the inconsistency of the system, for if they were consistent there would be values of the unknowns which would cause each of the functions $F_1, F_2, \ldots, F_r$ to vanish and hence c would be 0. Having proved that the given system of equations is inconsistent when the rank of B is larger than the rank of A we proceed to prove that the system must be consistent when the rank of A is equal to that of B. Suppose that each of these two matrices is of rank r and that the equations are so arranged that a non-vanishing determinant of order r appears in the upper left-hand corner of each of these matrices. Since each of the determinants of order $r+1$ must vanish we have the relation,

$$c_1F_1 + c_2F_2 + \ldots + c_rF_r + c_{r+1}F_{r+1} = 0,$$

independently of the values of the unknowns. As $c_1F_1 + c_2F_2 + \ldots + c_rF_r \neq 0$ independently of the values of the unknowns, it results that $c_{r+1} \neq 0$. Hence we may divide the given equation by c_{r+1} and thus express F_{r+1} in terms of $F_1, F_2, \ldots, F_r$. As the same argument holds for $F_{r+2}, F_{r+3}, \ldots, F_m$ it results that any solutions of the first r equations must also be solutions of all the rest.

If in the first r of the given system of equations we assign arbitrary values to $x_{r+1} \ldots x_n$ we obtain a system which can be solved in the ordinary way by means of determinants, since the determinant of the system does not vanish. In this way we obtain one and only one value for each of the unknowns $x_1, \ldots, x_r$. The preceding considerations prove the following theorem: *A necessary and sufficient condition for a system of linear equations to be consistent is that the matrix of the system has the same rank as the augmented matrix.* Since the values assigned to $x_{r+1} \ldots x_n$ are arbitrary, it also follows that a system of linear equations has an infinite number of solutions whenever it has more than one solution.

To provide very elementary illustrations of the preceding theorem we consider the following systems:

$$\text{I.}\begin{cases}3x-2y+z=8,\\ x-4y+2z=6.\end{cases}\qquad \text{II.}\begin{cases}3x+4y=7,\\ 6x+8y=10.\end{cases}$$

$$\text{III.}\begin{cases}x+2y=5,\\ 2x-y=0,\\ 4x+3y=10.\end{cases}\qquad \text{IV.}\begin{cases}x-y+3z=4,\\ 2x+3y-z=5,\\ 3x+2y+2z=10.\end{cases}$$

In system I the rank of the matrix of the system is 2, since

$$\begin{vmatrix}3 & -2\\ 1 & -4\end{vmatrix}\neq 0.$$

As the rank of the augmented matrix is also 2 this system is consistent and arbitrary values may be assigned to either y or z. On the other hand, the only value that x can have is 2.* The rank of system II is 1, while the rank of the augmented matrix is 2; hence this system has *no* solution. In system III the rank of the matrix as well as that of the augmented matrix is 2. Hence this system has a solution and it is evident that it has only one solution, viz., $x=1$, $y=2$. As the matrix system of IV is of rank 2, while the augmented matrix is of rank 3, this system has no solution.

27. Geometrical interpretation. As a linear equation involving no more than three unknowns may be conveniently represented as a plane in ordinary space, clearness is often attained by thinking of the planes which represent given systems of equations. For instance, system I of the preceding paragraph represents two planes intersecting on the plane $x=2$, and hence these planes are cut in parallel lines by every plane parallel to the plane $x=2$, while they are cut in two

* A necessary and sufficient condition that a given unknown in a consistent system of linear equation has the same value in every possible solution of the system is that the rank of the matrix of the system is decreased when the coefficients of this unknown are omitted from the matrix of the system. Cf. *American Mathematical Monthly*, Vol. XVII, 1910, p. 137.

intersecting lines by the planes parallel to $y=0$ or $z=0$. System II represents two parallel planes, while system III represents three planes through a line parallel to the z-axis. Finally, system IV represents three planes intersecting in three parallel lines. These interpretations follow directly from solid analytic geometry, and they tend to elucidate the theory of systems of linear equations, but they do not form an essential element of this theory.

28. Consistency of two equations in one unknown. Suppose that two rational integral equations in x,

$$f_1(x)=0, \qquad f_2(x)=0,$$

have a common root. If $f_1(x)$ is of degree m and $f_2(x)$ is of degree n, we obtain $m+n$ equations in the $m+n-1$ unknowns, $x, x^2, \ldots, x^{m+n-1}$ by multiplying $f_1(x)$ successively by $x, x^2, \ldots, x^{n-1}$, and $f_2(x)$ by $x, x^2, \ldots, x^{m-1}$. The consistency of this system of $m+n$ equations requires that the determinant of the augmented matrix of the system be equal to zero.* This determinant is known as the **resultant** of the equations and the method by which we obtained it is known as **Sylvester's dialytic method of elimination.** The resultant of the two linear equations,

$$ax+b=0, \qquad a_1x+b_1=0$$

is

$$\begin{vmatrix} a & b \\ a_1 & b_1 \end{vmatrix} = ab_1 - a_1b = 0;$$

and the resultant of the two quadratic equations,

$$ax^2+bx+c=0, \quad a_1x^2+b_1x+c_1=0,$$

is the determinant of the fourth order.

$$\begin{vmatrix} a & b & c & o \\ o & a & b & c \\ a_1 & b_1 & c_1 & o \\ o & a_1 & b_1 & c_1 \end{vmatrix} = 0.$$

* It has been proved that this condition is sufficient as well as necessary. The arguments here employed prove only the latter.

For instance, the two equations,

$$x^2+4x-21=0, \quad x^2+2x-15=0,$$

are consistent, since their resultant is 0. It is evident that this method may also be employed to eliminate one of the unknowns from two simultaneous equations in two unknowns.

29. Equivalent equations. In elementary algebra two equations are generally regarded as **equivalent** by definition if they have all their roots in common.* Similarly, two systems of simultaneous equations are regarded as equivalent by definition if all the solutions of one system are solutions of the other, and vice versa. On the other hand, it is frequently desirable to define the term equivalent with regard to a certain set of transformations, and to say that two expressions, or sets of expressions, are equivalent as regards a certain set of transformations if this set includes at least one transformation which carries the first of these expressions over into the second, and also at least one which carries the second over into the first. Two expressions which are equivalent as regards one set of transformations need not be equivalent as regards another set.

In the present article we shall adopt the former of these definitions of equivalence, and we shall first inquire what effect clearing of fractions may have upon certain rational equations in one unknown. It is convenient to premise the evident theorem: A necessary and sufficient condition that the sum of the n rational numerical fractions,

$$\frac{a_1}{b_1}, \frac{a_2}{b_2}, \ldots, \frac{a_n}{b_n},$$

in the form

$$\frac{a_1b_2b_3 \ldots b_n + a_2b_1b_3 \ldots b_n + \ldots + a_nb_1b_2 \ldots b_{n-1}}{b_1b_2 \ldots b_n},$$

* In *Jordan's* Traité des substitutions, p. 271, two equations of the same degree are called equivalent if the roots of the one may be represented as rational functions of the roots of the other.

shall be in its lowest terms is that each of the n given fractions shall be in its lowest terms and that the denominators, $b_1, b_2, \ldots, b_n$, are relatively prime. Let

$$\frac{f_1(x)}{\phi_1(x)}+\frac{f_2(x)}{\phi_2(x)}+\ldots+\frac{f_n(x)}{\phi_n(x)}=0, \quad . \quad . \quad . \quad . \quad (1)$$

be an equation in which each fraction is reduced to its lowest terms and the denominators are relatively prime, $f_1, \ldots, f_n$, $\phi_1, \ldots, \phi_n$ representing rational integral functions of x, not excluding the case when some of these are constants. When cleared of fractions this equation becomes

$$f_1(x)\,\phi_2(x)\ldots\phi_n(x)+\ldots+f_n(x)\,\phi_1(x)\ldots\phi_{n-1}(x)=0. \quad (2)$$

Suppose that α is a root of (2), and hence

$$f_1(\alpha)\,\phi_2(\alpha)\ldots\phi_n(\alpha)+\ldots+f_n(\alpha)\,\phi_1(\alpha)\ldots\phi_{n-1}(\alpha)=0. \quad (3)$$

It is easy to see that none of the ϕ's is equal to 0. For instance, $\phi_1(\alpha)=0$ would imply that

$$f_1(\alpha)\,\phi_2(\alpha)\ldots\phi_n(\alpha)=0.$$

As α is not a root of any of the functions $f_1(x)$, $\phi_2(x), \ldots,$ $\phi_n(x)$ it cannot be a root of their product. That is, $\phi_1(\alpha)\neq 0$. Since none of the ϕ's is 0 we may divide Eq. (3) by

$$\phi_1(\alpha)\,\phi_2(\alpha)\ldots\phi_n(\alpha),$$

and thus obtain

$$\frac{f_1(\alpha)}{\phi_1(\alpha)}+\frac{f_2(\alpha)}{\phi_2(\alpha)}+\ldots+\frac{f_n(\alpha)}{\phi_n(\alpha)}=0.$$

This proves that every root of Eq. (2) is also a root of Eq. (1) and it is evident that every root of Eq. (1) is also a root of Eq. (2), since no root can be lost by multiplying both members of an equation by a rational integral function. Hence it results that Eqs. (1) and (2) are equivalent equations. That Eqs. (1) and (2) are not necessarily equivalent if we omit either of the conditions that the ϕ's are relatively prime or that the fractions are in their lowest terms results directly from the following examples:

The equation

$$\frac{x}{x-1}-\frac{1}{x-1}=0$$

has no root, since dividing by 0 is excluded, and 1 is the only number that requires consideration, but

$$x(x-1)-x+1=0$$

has 1 as a repeated root. It should be observed that the equation obtained by multiplying the former of these equations by the least common multiple of the denominators is

$$x-1=0,$$

and hence this has a root which is not a root of the equation in the fractional form. On the other hand, of the two equations,

$$\frac{x-1}{x^2-1}+\frac{1}{x}=0, \quad 2x^2-x-1=0,$$

the latter has the root $x=1$, while the former does not have this root. It is of especial interest to observe that all the roots of the former must be roots of the latter, since the latter was obtained by multiplying both members of the former by a rational integral function of x.

Geometrical considerations frequently throw additional light on the subject of equivalence of equations. For instance, the two equations,

$$\frac{1}{x}+\frac{1}{y}=2 \quad \text{and} \quad x+y=2xy,$$

represent two loci which have every point except the origin in common. The latter of these is a hyperbola, and if the former could be plotted accurately its graph would be so nearly like that of the latter that no microscope would reveal the difference, since such an instrument could not reveal the missing point. It may be added that the rigid exclusion of division by 0 is not followed by all mathematicians and that many of the leading mathematicians of earlier times did not completely exclude the possibility of such division.

29. A few tests for equivalence of equations. If the two members of an equation are either multiplied or divided by a rational expression of the unknowns, which cannot be zero or infinity in the domain of rationality to which the unknowns are restricted, the resulting equation is equivalent to the original. Let $A=B$ be any equation, and let K be any expression which cannot be zero or infinity for any of the values of the unknowns under consideration. The equations,

$$KA=KB, \qquad \frac{A}{K}=\frac{B}{K},$$

may be written as follows:

$$K(A-B)=0, \qquad \frac{1}{K}(A-B)=0.$$

Since $K\neq 0$, or ∞, these equations can be satisfied only by those values of the unknowns which make $A=B$. It results directly that two equations which are equivalent in one domain of rationality are not necessarily equivalent in another. For instance, if the values of the unknowns are confined to real numbers, K could be x^2+1, but K cannot have this value if x may be any complex integer.

If the two members of an equation are increased or diminished by the same expression, the resulting equation is evidently equivalent to the original. This clearly includes the transposing of any term from one member of an equation to the other as well as the changing of the sign of each term of an equation. In transforming equations it is very important to observe whether the derived equations are actually equivalent to the original. If a derived equation contains all the roots of the original and some others it is said to be **redundant**, if it lacks some of the roots of the original it is **defective**. From what precedes it is clear that the ordinary process of clearing of fractions leads either to an equivalent or to a redundant equation.

VI. A FEW REFERENCES

30. Text-books. The algebraic equation occupies a prominent place in algebra and some of its elementary properties are developed in the text-books on algebra for the secondary schools. More extensive developments of these properties may be found in the advanced text-books on this subject, such as

(1) *Chrystal,* Algebra, an elementary text-book, 2 vols., 2d edition, 1900.

(2) *Capelli,* Istituzioni di analisi algebrica, 4th edition, 1909.

(3) *Weber,* Lehrbuch der Algebra, 2 vols., 2d edition, 1898–99.

(4) *Serret,* Cours d'algèbre supérieure, 2 vols., 6th edition, 1910.

The last two of these works include a treatment of the *Galois* theory of equations while the first two omit this theory, but they give an elementary introduction to the theory of substitutions. In the first this introduction is very brief and incomplete.

A large number of special treatises on the general theory of the algebraic equation have appeared, beginning with the works of *Vieta* in the early part of the seventeenth century. Among the modern works in the English language *Burnside* and *Panton's* Theory of Equations is probably the most generally known. The first three editions of this work appeared in one volume and excluded the *Galois* theory, while the fourth and fifth appeared in two volumes and include an introduction to substitution groups and the *Galois* theory of equations. Among the other treatises on this subject we may mention

(1) *Dickson,* Introduction to the Theory of Algebraic Equations, 1903.

(2) *Cajori,* An Introduction to the Modern Theory of Equations, 1904.

(3) *Mathews,* Algebraic Equations, 1907.

(4) *Netto-Cole,* Theory of Substitutions and its Applications to Algebra, 1892.

(5) *Barton,* An Elementary Treatise on the Theory of Equations, 2d edition, 1903.

(6) *Bianchi,* Lezioni sulla teoria dei gruppi di sostituzioni e delle equazioni algebriche secondo Galois, 1900.

(7) *Vogt,* Leçons sur la résolution algébrique des equations, 1895.

(8) *Matthiessen,* Grundzüge der antiken und modernen Algebra der litteralen Gleichungen, 1878.

The last of these works contains an account of many of the ancient methods which were used to solve equations and is rich in historical material. As a result of the rapid growth of historical knowledge during recent years some of this material has been found not entirely reliable. Certain phases of the theory of equations are presented in a very instructive manner in *Klein's* .Elementarmathematik vom höheren Standpunkte aus, Autogr., 1908–09; and also in *Bôcher's* Introduction to Higher Algebra, 1907. An extensive list of treatises on this and other mathematical subjects may be found in the Mathematischer Bücherschatz by *Ernst Wölffing.* This extensive work is supposed to give a systematic list of the principal books and monographs appearing during the nineteenth century. It appeared in the Abhandlungen zur Geschichte der Mathematischen Wissenschaften, 1903.

31. Articles. (1) *Pierpont,* Galois "Theory of algebraic equations," *Annals of Mathematics,* Vols. I and II, 1900, pp. 113 and 22.

(2) *Bôcher,* Gauss's "Third proof of the fundamental theorem of algebra," *Bulletin of the American Mathematical Society,* Vol. I, 1895, p. 205.

(3) *Sylvester,* "On an elementary proof and generalization of *Sir Isaac Newton's* hitherto undemonstrated rule for the discovery of imaginary roots," *Proceedings of the London Mathematical Society,* Vol. I, 1865, p. 1.

(4) *Van Vleck,* "A sufficient condition for the maximum number of imaginary roots of an equation of the *n*th degree," *Annals of Mathematics,* Vol. IV, 1903, p. 191.

(5) *Baker,* "A balance for the solution of algebraic equations," *American Mathematical Monthly,* Vol. II, 1904, p. 224.

(6) *Emch,* "Hydraulic solution of an algebraic equation of the *n*th degree," *ibid.,* Vol. VIII, 1901, p. 58.

(7) *Moritz,* "On certain proofs of the fundamental theorem of algebra," *ibid.,* Vol. X, 1903, p. 159.

(8) *McClintock,* "A method for calculating simultaneously all the roots of an equation," *American Journal of Mathematics,* Vol. XVII, 1895, p. 89.

(9) *Tanner,* "A graphical representation of the theorems of *Sturm* and *Fourier,*" *Messenger of Mathematics,* Vol. XVIII, 1889, p. 95.

(10) *Kellogg,* "A necessary condition that all the roots of an algebraic equation are real," *Annals of Mathematics,* Vol. XI, 1908, p. 97.

(11) *Lambert,* "On the solution of algebraic equations in infinite series," *Bulletin of the American Mathematical Society,* Vol. XIV, 1908, p. 467.

(12) *Allardice,* "On a limit of the roots of an equation that is independent of all but two of the coefficients," *ibid.,* Vol., XIII, 1907, p. 443.

(13) *Dickson*, "On the theory of equations in a modular field," *ibid.*, Vol. XIII, 1906, p. 8.

(14) *Bauer*, "Ueber die verschiedenen Wurzeln einer algebraischen Gleichung," *Mathematische Annalen*, Vol. LII, 1899, p. 113.

(15) *Dedekind*, "Ueber Gleichungen mit rationalen Coefficienten," *Jahresbericht der deutschen Mathematiker-Vereinigung*, Vol. I, 1892, p. 33.

(16) *Lucas*, "Résolution electromagnétique des equations," *Comptes rendus de l'Académie des Sciences*, Paris, Vol. CXI, 1890, p. 965.

A very extensive list of additional references to articles may be found in the Royal Society of London Subject Index Catalogue of Scientific Papers, Vol. I, 1908, pp. 156–87. A selected list of treatises and articles is contained in *Felix Müller's* Führer durch die mathematische Literatur, 1909, pp. 55–62.

VI

THE FUNCTION CONCEPT AND THE FUNDAMENTAL NOTIONS OF THE CALCULUS

By Gilbert Ames Bliss

CONTENTS

VI

THE FUNCTION CONCEPT AND THE FUNDAMENTAL NOTIONS OF THE CALCULUS

By Gilbert Ames Bliss

I. INTRODUCTION

1. Euclidean geometry a logical model. The mathematical historian tells us that the most important contribution by *Euclid* to mathematical science was his systematization of geometrical principles already known to the mathematicians of his day, rather than the additions which he made to the science in the form of new theorems. His development of the structure of Euclidean geometry has itself not been kept inviolate from criticism in recent years. But whatever may be the faults of his presentation from the standpoint of present-day methods, it must nevertheless be recognized that he was among the earliest exponents of a now well-established logical form for the application of mathematics to the phenomena of nature. The structure of such an application consists of two essential parts: first, a set of postulates suggested by our intuitive interpretation of natural phenomena; and second, a collection of definitions and of theorems stated in terms of the definitions and deduced by logical processes from the initial assumptions. The postulates are the foundation, and the definitions and theorems the superstructure of the science.

2. Imperfections in the presentation of other subjects. The Euclidean theory of geometry, which was presented thus early to mankind in a form attractive alike to the intuitive or to the logical type of mind, has for centuries occupied a prominent place in educational curricula, and it is no wonder that the theory remains to the present day the gem of our elementary mathematical courses. The marvel is, on the other hand, that the characteristics of the Euclidean theory which make it seem logically so complete, and so interesting to the mind sympathetically inclined to mathematical thinking, have apparently been overlooked to a very large extent in the presentation of other elementary subjects. Especially is this true in the case of algebra. To be convinced one needs only to take a cursory glance through the table of contents of almost any college or elementary text-book on the subject, and to note the heterogeneity of the subjects presented. Topics, related perhaps inherently but with no indicated relationships, follow each other in a confusion of radicals, exponents, progressions, imaginaries, probabilities, and other algebraic conceptions, in a way which must tend to develop a very disjointed understanding on the part of the beginner. It is true that efforts have been made with considerable success, in some of the more recent text-books, to effect unity of presentation by grouping the usual elementary algebraic conceptions about the equation as a central notion. It is true also that heterogeneity of presentation is much less marked in the cases of trigonometry and analytics, largely because the mathematical material designated by those titles is in itself more homogeneous. But very little conscious effort seems to have been made to make these subjects appear in their proper light as interrelated parts of a larger mathematical theory.

3. A remedy in the function concept. It is one of the purposes of the present paper to show how this lack of unity may be remedied with the help of a very important mathematical conception which is called a function. The notion of a function has been inserting itself into the consciousness of mathematicians in its most general guise since the time of *Dirichlet*, though long before present and recognized in more special forms. It is interesting to note that the definition of *Dirichlet*, which seems very abstract in comparison with those of the earlier mathematicians, was really devised as a result of his consideration of a practical problem involving the representation of functions by means of series, that of the flow of heat. His definition is a simple one, though at first sight it seems to be too general to serve as a basis for any extensive theory of functions or to have important applications in other branches of science. In order to explain it one must first consider what is meant by a variable in terms of which the notion of a function is defined.

II. VARIABLES AND FUNCTIONS

4. Definition of a variable. A **variable** is simply a symbol, say x, which in a given discussion may be used to denote any one of a given set of objects. By means of a variable we are enabled to express in terms of a single statement involving x, a property which is common to all objects of the set. Thus we may say that for any positive integer x the number $3x+2$ will have a remainder 2 when divided by 3, and we express thereby a property of each of the positive integers. Or if we wish to say that any curve joining two given points p and q is longer than the straight line pq, we may designate by C any one of the curves and state that C is longer than the line pq. The set of objects, any one of which is represented by x, is called the **range of the variable,** and in elementary mathematics it usually consists of numbers, though the example just given shows that it may contain elements of a quite different character.

5. Example of a function. The word function was used by Leibnitz to designate geometrical magnitudes of various kinds associated with a variable point on a curve, but with the development of the calculus it came to mean any mathematical expression involving a variable x, the value of which could be calculated when that of x was assigned. The definition of *Dirichlet* is more general still, and we may understand it better perhaps by examining first some simple examples. Consider the accompanying table, in which the numbers in the first column are hours of the day, and the numbers in the second the corresponding temperatures. If x is a variable which may stand for any one of the hours of the day, and y a variable representing the temperatures, then the table sets up a correspondence between the values of x and y in such a way that whenever a value is assigned to x a corresponding value of y is uniquely determined, and y is said to be a **function of x.** Similarly the mathematical formula $y=x/(x^2-1)$ makes a unique value of y correspond to any given value of x with the exception of $x=\pm1$, and y is again said to be a function of x. The range of the variable x is in this case the totality of real numbers excluding the values ±1, and it may be seen without much difficulty that y takes all values between $-\infty$ and $+\infty$.

Hour.	Temperature.
8	52.2
9	53.4
10	61.0
11	69.8
12	75.7
1	77.8
2	78.1
3	76.9
4	72.5
5	67.8
6	66.8
7	60.0
8	51.1

6. Definition of a function. With these examples in mind we may now define with *Dirichlet* **a single-valued function of a variable x to be a second variable y so related to x that whenever a value is assigned to x from the x-range, a corresponding value of y is uniquely determined in the y-range.** The correspondence between the objects in the x- and y-ranges need not be made, however, by means of what is usually called a mathematical expression, but may be determined in any way whatsoever, provided only that it is unique for each object which can be represented by x. The essentials in the definition are evidently the independent variable x with its range, and the correspondence between x and y. The range of the dependent variable y is of course not necessarily exhausted by the correspondence; it may contain elements which do not correspond to any object in the x-range.

7. Examples of functions. To a person encountering this definition for the first time, it would no doubt seem very artificial and too general to be of any great service. It is possible, however, to develop an elaborate and important theory of functions for the very general case when the range of x is left entirely arbi trary while that of y consists of real numbers, as has recently been shown by Professor *Moore** in his study of a field of mathematics which he has called General Analysis. The generality of the definition depends not only upon the absence of any specification as to the character of the ranges of x and y, however, but also upon the freedom which it leaves in the choice of the functional correspondence, even when the ranges consist of real numbers.

The example of the hours and temperatures above illustrates the existence of functions which do not involve a mathematical expression of any kind, and many similar examples could be found in the tabulated results of statistical observations or of physical experiments. But the correspondence may also be entirely artificial. For let x range over all the real numbers from zero to one. Corresponding to any rational values of x suppose that y is to have the value $+1$, and for irrational values of x the value -1. Then y is a function of x over the interval from zero to one, and the range of y consists only of two elements. This example suggests the definition of a constant function, that is, one for which the dependent variable y takes but a single value over the whole x-range. A constant, in general, may be regarded as a variable for which the range consists of a single number.

For the function last given the x-range has an infinity of values while the y-range consists of only two values, and a table could be arranged which would indicate this functional correspondence. But if the y-range contained also an infinity of different y-values, it might be impossible to express the correspondence by listing the values of x opposite the corresponding values of y in a table. For by far the majority of functions met with in mathematical theories the correspondence is specified not by means of a table, but by means of a mathematical formula which takes the place of the table, and which often implicitly defines the range of the independent variable x,

* *E. H. Moore*, the New Haven Mathematical Colloquium. The lectures in this volume were delivered by Professor Moore and others in September 1906.

as well as the correspondence. Thus the formula $y=x/(x^2-1)$ given above defines a function of x which is well defined for all real values of x except the values $x=\pm 1$, and as has been noted the y-range consists of all values between $-\infty$ and $+\infty$.

8. Functions with other than numerical ranges. The preceding examples illustrate the definition of a function when the range of the independent variable consists of numbers. It is easy to find functions for which this range has elements of a different kind. If two points p and q are joined by a curve C, the area $pqrs$ shown in the figure is uniquely determined and depends upon the form of the curve. A functional correspondence is thus set up between the variable C whose range is the totality of curves joining the points p and q, and the variable A which represents the area. The statement that a dependent variable y is a function of an independent variable x, is usually expressed in the form of an equation $y=f(x)$, where the symbol $f(x)$ is an abbreviation for the phrase "function of the independent variable x." If we wish, therefore, to express the fact that the area A described is a function of C, we may represent it by the symbol $A(C)$. Similarly the length of the curve C is another function of C which may be denoted by $L(C)$, as is also the surface area $S(C)$ generated by the arc C when the whole figure is revolved about the horizontal line rs as an axis.

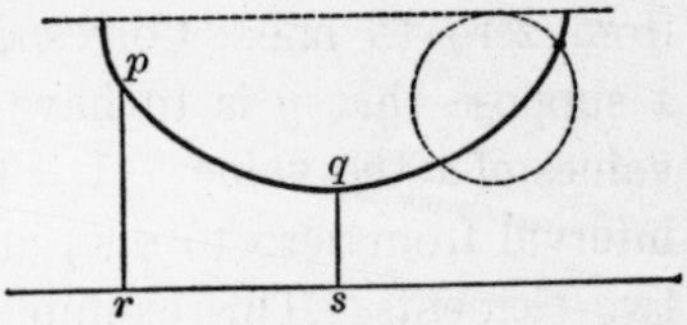

FIG. 1.

There is a famous problem from a domain of mathematics called the calculus of variations, which gives rise to a function of precisely the type which has just been considered. Suppose that it is desired to find the curve C along which a marble will roll in the shortest time from p to q. The time T in this case depends upon the form of the curve C and is a function $T(C)$. It is impossible to describe here the interesting controversy which arose between *John Bernoulli*, the proposer of the problem, and his brother *James* as a result of their rival solutions, or to undertake a detailed study of the methods by means of which they found the minimizing curve. Suffice it to say that in their work is found the origin of the whole subject of the calculus of variations. But it may not be uninteresting to see the result which they obtained. The minimizing curve is a **cycloid,** that is, the locus of a point on the circumference of a circle which rolls along a straight line. In the figure the cycloid is shown inverted with its steeper part, as it should be, near the point p, so that the marble accumulates a high velocity at the beginning of its fall.

Similar minimum problems can be stated with respect to two others of the functions described above. For the length function $L(C)$ the curve which provides the minimum value is evidently the straight line joining p and q; and the curve which describes the surface of minimum area when it is revolved about the horizontal line rs is a **catenary,** whose form is that of a heavy chain allowed to hang freely from two points of suspension.

An example of a function whose independent variable has a range of still a different kind would be the shortest or straight-line distance $D(q)$ between a fixed point p and a variable point q. The independent variable is now the point q, which may range over the whole plane, while the range of the dependent variable D is the totality of numbers between 0 and ∞. This and the preceding examples show that there are important examples in which the elements of the range of the independent variable are real numbers, arcs of curves, or points of a plane, and many other examples could be devised to exhibit a variety of ranges which it would not be possible to enumerate here, even if the patience of the reader permitted. In all of the examples which have been given the range of the dependent variable has consisted of real numbers, but this is also not necessarily the case, as appears in the theory of the so-called integral equations and in parts of the General Analysis of Professor *Moore*, referred to above.

9. Graphs of functions. For functions both of whose ranges are real numbers a graphical representation was devised by *Descartes,* which is too familiar to need a detailed description here. But a few remarks concerning it may not be amiss. A horizontal line is taken with a zero point O and a unit of measure (see Fig. 2), so that to each value of x there corresponds a point of the line to the right of O if x is positive, and to the left if negative. In order to represent the value of a function at a point x, a perpendicular is erected equal in length to the number $f(x)$. When $f(x)$ is positive, the distance is measured upward; when negative, downward. The horizontal axis is called the axis of abscissas, and the vertical lines are called ordinates. It is customary to erect a perpendicular called the y-axis at the point O, but such a line is not at all essential to the representation of the function, and it is interesting to note that in some of the early editions of *Descartes'* Analytical Geometry the line does not appear.

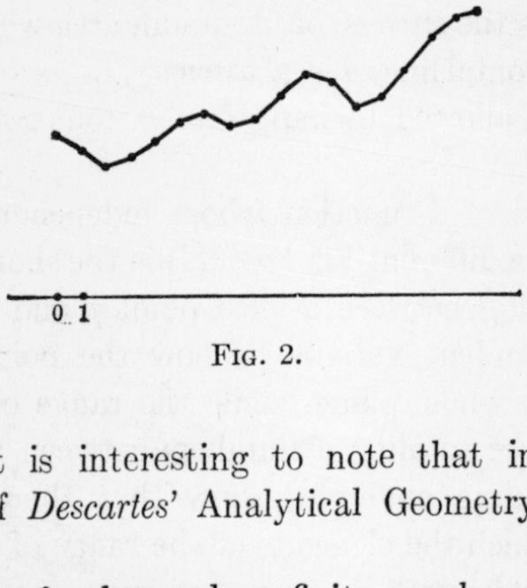

FIG. 2.

If the range of x has only a finite number of elements, as in a statistical table, then all the values of the function may be plotted in this way, the result being a picture which is much more suggestive and easy of interpretation than the table of values itself. For example, the accompanying graph shows a baby's ages measured in weeks as abscissas, and weights measured in pounds as ordinates. Even a bachelor's eye suffices to discover at a glance the unhappier periods, which are suggested only after some study by the table from which the graph was made. The ordinates under the dots represent the values of the weight function in this case, the straight sides of the broken line being drawn only to assist the eye in passing from one significant point to the next.

On the other hand if the x-range contains an infinity of elements it is usually impossible to make a complete picture of the function. One must be satisfied with plotting as many points as is convenient or desirable from the nature of the problem, and these may then be joined by a continuous curve which will give an idea of the functional values and their variation as x is changed. For example consider the function $y=x/(x^2-1)$. If only the points indicated by the dots are

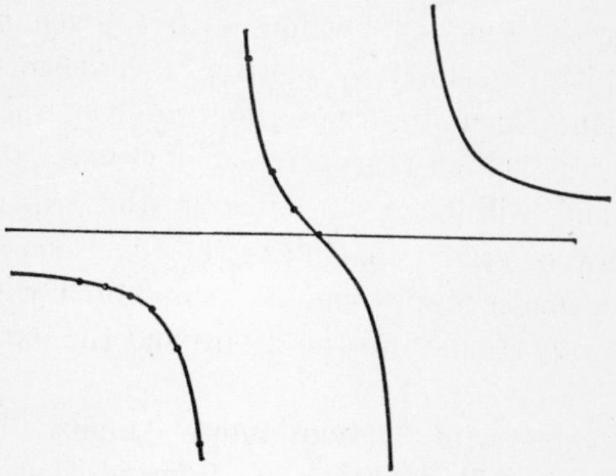

FIG. 3.

actually calculated, the rest of the figure must be drawn free hand. (See Fig. 3.)

At the best the graph can only be regarded as an approximate representation of a function, the errors which occur being essentially of the following two different kinds. Since it is impossible to represent distances exactly by means of marks which have finite dimensions, a first source of error would be in the use of the drawing instruments and would depend not only upon the inadequacy of the instruments themselves, but also upon the skill of the draughtsman. A second source of error lies in our inability to plot more than a finite number of points and the consequent necessity of filling in arbitrarily by far the major portions of the graph. The magnitude of the errors due to the first cause can be estimated only by an experimental examination of the accuracy of the instruments and the personal equation of the operator. Similarly it is quite impossible without experimental evidence to say what the error will be which is due to the process of "filling in" the curve, provided that the curve joining the plotted points is drawn arbitrarily. But if the inaccuracies of the instruments are neglected, and if it is agreed to join the finite number of points which are actually plotted by straight lines, then it is possible to show that certain types of functions are fairly represented by such broken lines, and to show also that the error of representation for the functional values over a given interval can be made arbitrarily small by plotting a sufficient number of points sufficiently near together. The proof of this statement is made with the help of a property of functions called uniform continuity, and will be given later in the paper. For the present it may be stated that all of the functions which occur in elementary mathematics can be represented with a degree of accuracy proportionate to the desire and the patience of the investigator.

10. Functions with discontinuous graphs. From what has been said it will doubtless be inferred that there exist functions which cannot properly be represented by a graph, and in fact the function referred to above which is equal to $+1$ for rational values of x between 0 and $+1$, and equal to -1 for irrational values, is of this character. For, a line parallel to the x-axis representing the values of the function for rational points would, according to the usual interpretation of the graph, imply $+1$ as the values of the function for irrational values of x also. Nor is it true, as might be supposed, that any function for which the functional correspondence is defined by means of a mathematical formula, can be represented by a curve. Professor *Pierpont* * has set up a number of interesting formulas which have curious geometrical interpretations, one of which represents the function having no proper

* The Theory of Functions of Real Variables, p. 202.

graph, which has just been mentioned. He begins by considering a function which he calls **signum x**, or sgn x, and which is defined by the following conditions:

$$\text{sgn } x = +1 \quad \text{for} \quad 0 < x \leqq 1,$$

$$\text{sgn } x = 0 \quad \text{for} \quad x = 0,$$

$$\text{sgn } x = -1 \quad \text{for} \quad -1 \leqq x < 0.$$

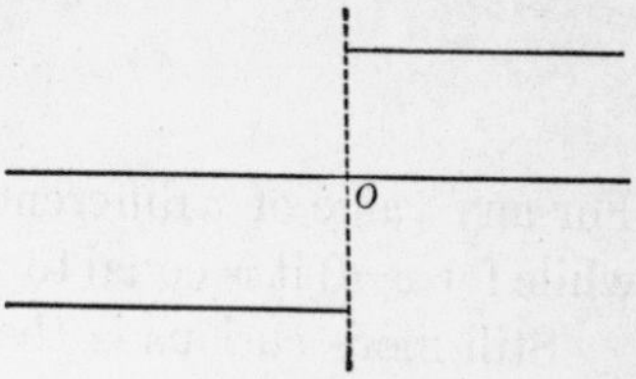

FIG. 4.

This function has the relatively simple formula:

$$\text{sgn } x = \frac{2}{\pi} \lim_{n=\infty} \text{arc tan } nx. \quad . \quad . \quad . \quad . \quad (1)$$

For if x is positive the limit has the value $\pi/2$, if x is zero the value 0, and if x is negative the value $-\frac{\pi}{2}$.

By means of the function sgn x a formula can be found for the function which takes any given value a for rational values of x, and any other number b for irrational values. For consider the function

$$g(x) = a + (b - a) \lim_{n=\infty} \text{sgn } (\sin^2 n!\,\pi x). \quad . \quad . \quad (2)$$

If x is a rational number the expression in the parenthesis becomes and remains equal to zero for a sufficiently large n, since $n!\,\pi x$ becomes an integral multiple of π. Hence

$$\text{sgn } (\sin^2 n!\,\pi x) = 0,$$

and $g(x)$ has the value a, as a result of the properties of sgn x. For an irrational x the product $n!\,\pi x$ is never a multiple of π, and hence $\sin^2 n!\,\pi x$ is some number between 0 and 1. For such values of x

$$\text{sgn } (\sin^2 n!\,\pi x) = 1,$$

and $g(x)$ has the value b.

Another example which Professor *Pierpont* gives is the function

$$y = \lim_{n=\infty} \frac{x}{\frac{1}{n}+x}.$$

For any value of x different from zero this has the value unity, while for $x=0$ it is equal to zero.

Still more curious is the function

$$y = \lim_{n=\infty} \frac{(1+\sin \pi x)^n - 1}{(1+\sin \pi x)^n + 1},$$

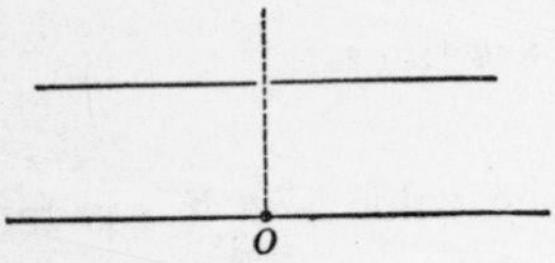

FIG. 5.

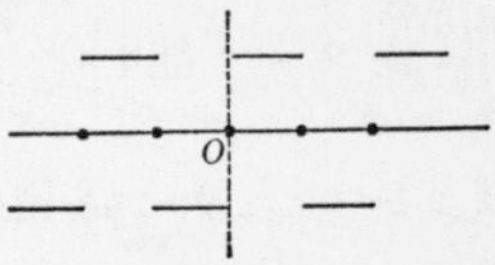

FIG. 6.

which has the discontinuous graph shown in the accompanying figure. If x is any integer this expression is evidently equal to zero. For any value of x between 0 and 1 the parenthesis $(1+\sin \pi x)$ is greater than unity and its nth power approaches infinity as n increases indefinitely. Hence the limit of the fraction is $+1$. On the other hand, if x is between 1 and 2, then $(1+\sin \pi x)$ is less than one and approaches zero as n increases, so that the limit of the fraction is in this case -1.

11. Classification of functions. The examples which have just been given and those which precede show clearly the necessity of some methods of classifying functions, if an intelligent study of them is to be made. There are several methods in use, each of which is important in some branch of the function theory, but one of them, which will presently be explained, is especially interesting from the standpoint of the elementary functions. On the basis of this classification some suggestions will also be made with regard to the presentation of the elementary subjects, suggestions which it is hoped will not seem too radical to be useful. In endeavoring to introduce any pedagogical improvement the teacher is always hampered by the conservatism of the printed page. An alteration in method, in order to be successful with elementary students, must be mild enough to be adapted to the printed machinery already at hand; or if it is a radical reform, it must be accompanied by a well-written and practical text, in order to be at all effective or far reaching. The suggestions which are to be made here are of the milder sort, with the possible exception of those referring to algebra, where it seems to the writer that a thorough reorganization of subject-matter might lead to a very great improvement.

12. Algebraic functions. The simplest type of a function is the polynomial

$$y=a_0x^m+a_1x^{m-1}+\ .\ .\ .\ +a_m,$$

sometimes called a rational integral function, after which come the rational functions or quotients of two polynomials,

$$y=\frac{a_0x^m+a_1x^{m-1}+\ .\ .\ .\ a_m}{b_0x^n+b_1x^{n-1}+\ .\ .\ .\ b_n}. \quad . \quad . \quad . \quad . \qquad (3)$$

Both these types of functions are formed with the help only of the four processes of addition, subtraction, multiplication, and division, and the next class of functions which would naturally suggest themselves would be those expressible by means of the four processes just mentioned with the addition of extraction of roots. But it is better to regard functions so constructed, as well as the polynomials and rational functions, as belonging to a larger category called algebraic functions which are defined as follows. Suppose an equation

$$a_0(x)y^n+a_1(x)y^{n-1}+\ .\ .\ .\ +a_{n-1}(x)y+a_n(x)=0 \quad . \qquad (4)$$

is given, in which the coefficients of the powers of y are themselves polynomials in x. If any value is assigned to x, the resulting equation in y will have a certain number of roots, in general n. To any x, therefore, the equation assigns a number of values of y, and y is said to be a multiple-valued function of x. Evidently a polynomial or a rational function is an algebraic function, the equation which y satisfies in the latter case being easily found from equation (3) by making a common denominator. It is not so easy to show that any function which is expressible by means of radicals is algebraic, but a few examples will indicate very well how this may be the case. Take the functions

$$y=\sqrt[3]{x+\sqrt{x}}, \quad y=\sqrt{1+x}+\sqrt{1-x}.$$

By the usual algebraic methods of rationalization the variables x and y are found to satisfy, respectively, the equations

$$y^6-2xy^3+x^2-x=0, \quad y^4-4y^2+4x^2=0,$$

and in general it can be proved that any function found by addition, subtraction, multiplication, division, and extraction of roots, satisfies an equation of the type (4).* The various values which can be assigned to the radicals account for the multiple values of the function. If it is remembered that equations of the fifth degree and higher can be solved by radicals only in special cases, it appears at once that the class of algebraic functions includes many which cannot be calculated by means of these elementary processes alone. The generalization of the properties of functions determinable in terms of radicals to the corresponding properties for algebraic functions of the most general type, has furnished one of the most fruitful and interesting fields of mathematical research.

13. Transcendental functions. The trigonometric functions and the inverse trigonometric functions, the logarithm and the exponential, as well as an infinity of other functions which appear only in the higher analysis, do not satisfy any equation of the type (4) and have been given the name **transcendental functions.**† The values of these functions cannot be calculated analytically by a finite number of additions, subtractions, multiplications, and divisions, but depend upon an infinity of

---

* See Monograph V. sec. 7; Monograph IV, Appendix II.

† For proof of the transcendence of the numbers e and π see Monograph IX.

such operations indicated by means of a power series. As examples of such series may be cited the well-known ones for the sine, logarithm, and exponential:

$$\sin x = x - \frac{x^3}{3!} + \frac{x^5}{5!} - \frac{x^7}{7!} + \dots,$$

$$\log(1+x) - x + \frac{x^2}{2} + \frac{x^3}{3} + \dots,$$

$$e^x = 1 + x + \frac{x^2}{2!} + \frac{x^3}{3!} + \dots.$$

A function whose values are expressible by means of a power series is called an **analytic function,** and it can be shown that not only transcendental functions, but also all of the algebraic functions are expressible in this way. Even this very general category of analytic functions does not exhaust all of the possibilities for functions of a real variable, but for the purposes of the present paper it will be unnecessary to pursue the classification further. The function (2) which has so often been used as an illustration before, is an example of a function which for real values of x is not expressible by means of a power series, and there are many others. The results of the classification, as far as it has been made, can be summarized most concisely in the form of the following table:

- Analytic functions.
  - Algebraic functions.
    - Rational function.
      - Polynomials.
      - Rational fractions.
    - Irrational functions.
      - Those expressible by means of radicals.
      - Those not so expressible.
  - Transcendental functions.
    - The trigonometric functions and their inverses.
    - The logarithm and the exponential.
    - Other functions of less elementary character.
- Non-analytic functions.

14. The trigonometric and exponential functions are transcendental. There is an objection to this classification from the elementary standpoint, which ought to be mentioned. It is the difficulty in proving that all functions expressible in terms of radicals are algebraic, and the necessity of proving that the transcendental functions do not have this property. In one of the accompanying monographs * it has been shown that all the numbers expressible in terms of quadratic radicals only are the roots of an algebraic equation, and a similar proof could be made for functions of x which are so expressible. But for the radicals of higher orders the problem is a much less elementary one and cannot be undertaken here. Professor *Pierpont* has given a simple proof that the function $y=\sin x$ cannot satisfy an equation of the form (4). For if there were such an equation satisfied by $y=\sin x$, then there would be one of the lowest degree with the same property and of the form

$$y^n+a_1(x)y^{n-1}+\ldots a_n(x)=0, \quad . \quad . \quad . \quad . \quad (5)$$

where the coefficients are now rational fractions in x. On account of the periodicity of the sine function, the two equations

$$y^n+a_1(x+2m\pi)y^{n-1}+\ldots+a_n(x+2m\pi)=0,$$

$$[a_1(x+2m\pi)-a_1(x)]y^{n-1}+\ldots+[a_n(x+2m\pi)-a_n(x)]=0,$$

would also have to be satisfied by $y=\sin x$ for any integral value of m. Since a rational fraction in m can vanish for only a finite number of values, it follows that if m is properly chosen the coefficients of the last equation do not vanish, and hence the hypothesis that Eq. (5) is an equation of lowest degree satisfied by y is contradicted. If the function $y=\sin x$ is not algebraic, then the inverse function $x=\text{arc} \sin y$ cannot be; for an equation of the type (4) for one of these functions would determine the algebraic character of the other also. Similar proofs can be made for all of the trigonometric functions, and also for the exponential $y=e^x$ and its inverse $x=\log y$, provided that

* Monograph VIII, secs. 5, 6.

imaginary values of the variable x are admitted. The proof given above depends upon the periodicity of the sine function, and it is known that the exponential has similarly the imaginary period $2m\pi\sqrt{-1}$.

15. Applications of the function concept in collegiate teaching. In a preceding paragraph it was suggested that the classification of functions which has been made might be helpful in relating to each other the different parts of the undergraduate curriculum. In order to see how this may be done let us first of all consider the topics which are treated in the elementary courses in their relation to the table. The subject of study in trigonometry is the group of functions which have been classified as transcendental, emphasis being laid on the trigonometric functions and their inverses. The exponential is usually considered only as an introduction to logarithms, and the logarithmic function itself only so far as is necessary to enable the student to make a successful mechanical use of logarithmic tables. It is hard to say with precision where the topics treated of in algebra belong in the table, but most of them are related to the polynomials or rational fractions, and it is proposed to show in a following paragraph precisely how this relationship may profitably be employed. Analytic geometry, on the other hand, is concerned with the graphical representation of functions and with the properties of the elementary algebraic functions which are defined by equations

$$ay+bx+c=0,$$

$$ay^2+(bx+c)y+(dx^2+ex+f)=0,$$

of the first and second degrees in x and y.

16. Objections to present methods. There are numerous objections which might be made to the way in which these subjects are usually presented, a few of which will suffice to show at least the possibility of improvement. In the first place there is one toward the removal of which much has recently been done. That is the now somewhat obsolete tendency to confine the graphical study of functions entirely to the courses in analytics. The graphical representation of a function is a device of the utmost importance not only in the study of the conic sections and the straight line, but also in the study of all the other elementary functions, and the student cannot be made familiar with it too early in his mathematical course. A second and more justifiable objection is the lack of attention given to the exponential and logarithm. It is safe to say that none of the functions listed in our table have wider or more frequent applications, and yet there is none which the student understands with so little thoroughness at the end of his freshman year, his only study of them having been for the purpose of enabling him to attain a certain mechanical skill in the use of logarithmic tables. The lack of unity in algebra courses and the desirability of graphical methods have already been pointed out. It may also be added that the elementary notions of the calculus can be introduced with much profit at suitable points in both algebra and analytics. In the analytics, especially the process of finding the tangent line to a conic involves the calculus notion of the slope of the tangent, and yet it is a common custom of writers on the subject to avoid carefully the notions and notations of the more advanced subject. It is difficult to account for this tendency on the part of our text-book writers, except on the theory that one should never encroach on a neighbor's property, a principle which is good when applied to real estate, but hardly commendable in a scientific treatise.

17. Suggestions for improvement. What are then the conclusions and the suggestions for improvement which can be drawn from these objections? In the first place does it not seem proper that each elementary course, since mathematics under our present collegiate mechanism must be divided into courses, should have to do with a particular class of functions, and should not the purpose of the course as a study of those functions be set clearly before the student at the beginning and re-emphasized at proper intervals until it is clearly understood? If the answer is affirmative, not only should trigonometry be concerned with the elementary transcendental functions and analytics a study of the simple irrational algebraic functions, but the subject-matter of algebra should be related to the study of the rational algebraic functions, the polynomials and the rational fractions. What is unrelated should be relegated to its proper place in some other part of the mathematical curriculum. Furthermore, the treatment of these functions should be complete as far as possible at the stage in which the student finds himself, and illumined by a foresight on the part of the instructor of the conceptions of the calculus. There are good reasons why the differentiation of the transcendental functions should not be considered in trigonometry, for the limiting processes involved are too complicated for the elementary student, but much can be said in favor of the early consideration of derivatives and anti-derivatives of polynominals—notions which will be explained later in this paper—in a course in algebra, and in favor of the study of the derivatives of the elementary algebraic functions which occur in analytical geometry.

Let us outline then a course of study for the freshman year in college, which is not to depart too radically from the present plan as usually followed, and yet which may afford a systematic treatment of the elementary functions. The course should begin with a consideration of the function concept, by means of special examples perhaps, and with frequent applications of the graphical representation of a function which should be continued throughout the entire course. The exponential and the logarithm might well be studied next on account of their importance in numerical computation, in particular in the plotting of other functions. Their graphs can be readily drawn without the use of a table, if it is noticed that $y=a^x$ can be plotted very easily, and that the graph of the logarithm can then be found by simply rotating the plane about a line through the origin making an angle of 45° with the x-axis. After these preliminaries the usual course in trigonometry can be given with considerable economy in time on account of the familiarity which the student has already gained with graphical methods and the use of the logarithmic tables.

The course in algebra is the one in which it seems that the notion of a function can be used to effect the greatest improvement. It is perhaps not easy to see how all of the topics usually studied in algebra can be related to the study of the rational functions, and on this account a brief outline of a course which might be given is to be inserted here.

Let the course begin with an explanation of the kinds of functions which are to be studied, and show by means of examples, or more generally, that any function formed with the four elementary operations only is a rational fraction. This will give plenty of opportunity to exercise the student in the reduction of complex fractions. Following this a chapter on operations with polynomials should be given, including the division equation

$$f(x)=g(x)\cdot q(x)+r(x),$$

synthetic division, and the computation of the coefficients of a polynomial

$$a_0(x+a)^m+a_1(x+a)^{m-1}+\ .\ .\ .\ +a_{m-1}(x+a)+a_m$$

by means of synthetic division.* Then take up linear functions and study their graphs and intersections, with the aid of determinants of the second order. The theory of quadratic functions affords occasion to emphasize the notion of a root of a polynomial, and may be used to introduce two new conceptions, the slope of a curved line by means of which maxima and minima may be determined, and imaginary numbers. A short treatment of imaginary numbers and DeMoivre's theorem will not be amiss at this stage, to be followed by a graphical study of polynomials of higher degrees, including the theory of maxima and minima with the help of the derivative. The roots of polynomials should then be studied systematically with the remainder theorem as basis, the theorems upon which Horner's method is based receiving due attention. After a chapter on the numerical determination of roots, including Horner's method, take up the study of polynomials of special types. For example the polynomials x^n-a lead to the theory of rad-

* See for example *Fine's* College Algebra, sec. 422.

icals and fractional exponents, whose properties can all and perhaps best be derived from that equation $x^n = a$; the polynomial $(a+x)^m$ suggests the binomial theorem, and the polynomials

$$a+(a+x)+(a+2x)+\ \ldots\ (a+nx),$$

$$a+ax+ax^2+\ \ldots\ +ax^n$$

are progressions. When the elementary properties of polynomials have been exhausted, the graphical theory of rational fractions may be developed, followed by a study of indeterminate forms and undetermined coefficients as applied to partial fractions. Chapters on series, permutations and combinations, and probabilities fit less easily into the elementary function theory, although series may be regarded as a natural generalization from polynomials with a finite number of terms to those with an infinite number, and a new proof of the binomial theorem might be made the excuse for the introduction of the formulas for combinations. The number of combinations of n things k at a time is $\frac{n!}{(n-k)!n!}$, and it can be argued that the number of terms of the form $a^{n-k}x^k$ which occur in the product $(a+x)^n$ is also equal to this number. No mention has been made of a place for probabilities or the theory of determinants. The former might well give place to topics which are more important at this stage of the student's course, and the latter really belongs in a course in the theory of equations, or else in solid analytical geometry.

The course in plane analytic geometry needs but few remarks aside from those which have been made above. It should be devoted to the theory of the simple irrational functions, including the solution of simultaneous quadratic equations, with applications to intersections of conics, and an introduction to the process of finding the derivative of an algebraic function with its interpretation in the problem of determinating the slopes of tangents.

The detailed study of the differentiation of transcendental functions and of algebraic functions in general must of course be left for the course in calculus, where functions are studied from a somewhat different standpoint. In the calculus the continuity, differentiation, and integration of functions hold the most prominent place in our attention, and as the basis of the behavior of functions under these operations, other classifications besides the one given in the table above can also be made, which are more important for purposes of the higher analysis.

18. Continuity of a function. A discussion of functions would not be complete without a description of what is meant by the property of continuity mentioned in the preceding paragraph. Speaking very roughly, a function is continuous when it has an unbroken graph. Thus the function $y=\frac{x}{(x^2-1)}$ is continuous for every value of x except the values $x=\pm 1$. The function (1), Sec. 10, is not continuous at $x=0$, for its functional values jump from -1 to 0 and to $+1$, as x increases through this value. Analytically a function $f(x)$ is said to be continuous at a value $x=a$ if a belongs to the range of x-values for which $f(x)$ is defined, and if the difference $f(x)-f(a)$ can be made arbitrarily small by taking x sufficiently near to a. If a function has this property it is evident that $f(x)$ must approach $f(a)$ as x approaches a. The definition is made still more precise by saying that $f(x)$ is continuous provided that for any positive number ε, however small, a second positive number δ can be found, such that $f(x)-f(a)$ is numerically less than ε whenever x differs from a by less than δ. Graphically interpreted, this means again that on the interval from $a-\delta$ to $a+\delta$ the difference of any pair of ordinates, $f(x)$ and $f(a)$, of the curve $y=f(x)$ is less than ε.

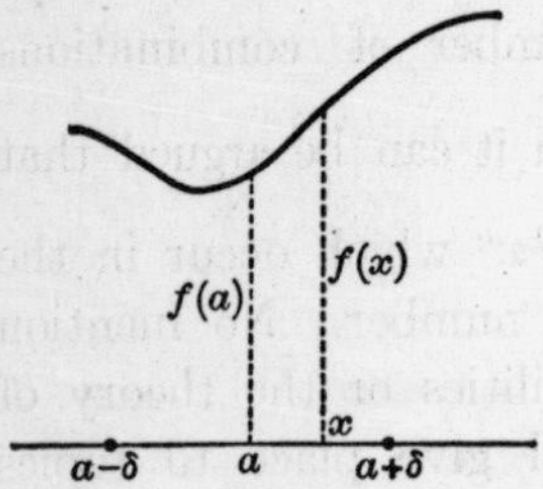

FIG. 7.

It will be understood readily, from their graphs, and it may be proved analytically, that polynomials are continuous functions for every value of x, and that a rational fraction is continuous at every value except those which make its denominator vanish. It is true of any other elementary functions also that they are continuous for every value of x, with the possible exception of certain isolated ones. Thus the trigonometric sine and cosine are everywhere continuous, while the tangent becomes infinite and therefore has a discontinuity for values of x which are odd multiples of $\frac{\pi}{2}$. But other functions may be discontinuous in a much more complicated way, as in the case of the function (2) which is discontinuous at every point. The continuity properties of the elementary functions are evidently relatively simple, and we may therefore leave them at this point in order to consider other important properties of functions which occur in the calculus.

III. THE FUNDAMENTAL NOTIONS OF THE CALCULUS

19. The three fundamental notions of the calculus. The differential and integral calculus has to do with three fundamental notions associated with functions, to which are due most of the applications of the function theory in geometry, mechanics, and physics, as well as other branches of science. These three conceptions are called the **derivative,** the **anti-derivative** or **indefinite integral,** and the **definite integral.** All three may be interpreted geometrically and illustrated simply by means of polynomials, and it is proposed to explain them briefly here. The real difficulties of the calculus arise in applying the fundamental notions mentioned to the irrational algebraic and transcendental functions.

20. The derivative function and its interpretations. Let us agree to consider from this point on in our discussion only functions $f(x)$ which are defined for x on the whole range of real numbers, or on a certain interval $a \leqq x \leqq b$ of that range. If x is thought of as indicating the time at any moment and increasing uniformly from the value at one end of its range to that at the other, the variable $y=f(x)$ will simultaneously change in value. At each value of x the function will have a certain rate of change relatively to x, which may be defined in the following way. Consider an interval of x-values between x and $x+\Delta x$, where Δx is simply a symbol used to denote a quantity which is to be added to x. At the value $x+\Delta x$ the function y will have a value which may be represented by $y+\Delta y=f(x+\Delta x)$, and the difference between the values of y at the beginning and end of the interval, is therefore

$$\Delta y=f(x+\Delta x)-f(x).$$

The quotient

$$\frac{\Delta y}{\Delta x}=\frac{f(x+\Delta x)-f(x)}{\Delta x} \quad . \quad . \quad . \quad . \quad . \quad (6)$$

represents then the average rate of change of the function as x varies from x to $x+\Delta x$. The limit of this quotient, as Δx decreases in size and approaches zero, is what is meant by the *rate of change*, of the function at the value x. Evidently if this limit exists it will be a variable which is uniquely determined at each value of x, and is therefore itself a new function usually denoted by the symbol $f'(x)$.

The function $f'(x)$, which is called the derivative or rate of change of $f(x)$, does not exist for every function, as might easily be shown for some of those which have already been defined. But for the elementary functions the rate of change can always be found. The manner in which it is calculated can be well illustrated by the familiar problem of the falling body. When a heavy particle falls from rest, the distance through which it has fallen in the time t is a function of t defined by the well-known formula

$$s=\tfrac{1}{2}gt^2.$$

If the distance fallen through in the time $t+\Delta t$ is denoted by $s+\Delta s$, then the equation

$$s+\Delta s=\tfrac{1}{2}g(t+\Delta t)^2$$

holds, and the average velocity during the time Δt is

$$\frac{\Delta s}{\Delta t}=\tfrac{1}{2}g\frac{(t+\Delta t)^2-t^2}{\Delta t}=gt+\tfrac{1}{2}g\Delta t.$$

As Δt approaches zero this average velocity approaches the limit gt, which is the actual velocity of the falling body at any given moment t.

The rate of change which has just been calculated was that of a very simple polynomial in t. The rate of change of any polynomial can readily be found by a similar method with the help of the binomial theorem. For consider first the function $y=ax^n$. By the process described above the value of the average rate of change in the interval from x to $x+\Delta x$ is the quotient

$$\begin{aligned}\frac{\Delta y}{\Delta x} &= a\frac{(x+\Delta x)^n - x^n}{\Delta x}\\ &= anx^{n-1} + \text{terms containing powers of } \Delta x.\end{aligned}$$

Hence the rate of change of ax^n is the function anx^{n-1}, a formula which holds for any positive integral value of n. Similarly if y is the polynomial

$$y=2x^3-x+5,$$

the average rate of change in the interval between x and $x+\Delta x$, will be

$$\frac{\Delta y}{\Delta x}=2\,\frac{(x+\Delta x)^3-x^3}{\Delta x}-\frac{(x+\Delta x)-x}{\Delta x},$$

and the limit of this expression is the derivative function $6x^2-1$. From this last example it may be inferred that *the derivative of any polynomial can be found by applying the formula for the rate of change of* ax^n *to each term separately and adding the results.*

The above definition of the derivative function as a rate of change is the one which gives this function importance in mechanical problems, but the derivative has also an interesting geometrical interpretation. Suppose that the function $y=f(x)$ has the graph shown in the accompanying figure. At any value of x the vertical line xp has a length equal to the value of the function $f(x)$, and at $x+\Delta x$ the corresponding ordinate from $x+\Delta x$ to q has the value $f(x+\Delta x)$. Hence, in Fig. 8

$$pr=\Delta x,\ rq=f(x+\Delta x)-f(x),$$

and the value of the quotient of Eq. (6) is evidently the same as that of the quotient rq/pr, the slope of the secant pq. As Δx

approaches zero the point q approaches p and the secant pq approaches the tangent at p as a limiting position. The slope of pq must therefore simultaneously approach the slope of the tangent, so that *the value of the derivative function* $f'(x)$ *is numerically equal to the slope of the tangent line pt.*

21. Maxima and minima of functions. Perhaps the most important application of the geometrical notion of a derivative is in the determination of the maximum and minimum values of functions. Evidently the slope of the tangent at the maximum and minimum points, a, b, c, Fig. 8, must have the value zero. If, therefore, the derivative function $f'(x)$ can be found for a given function $f(x)$, then the maximum or minimum

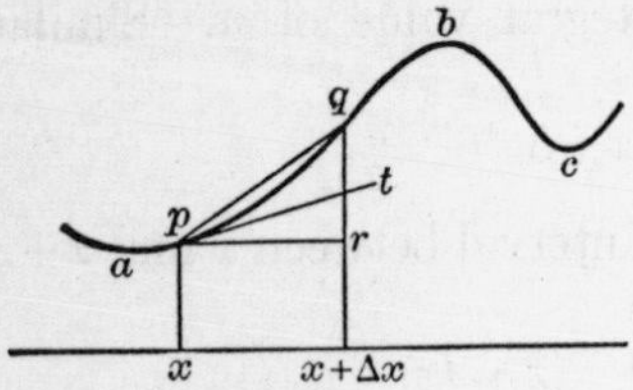

FIG. 8.

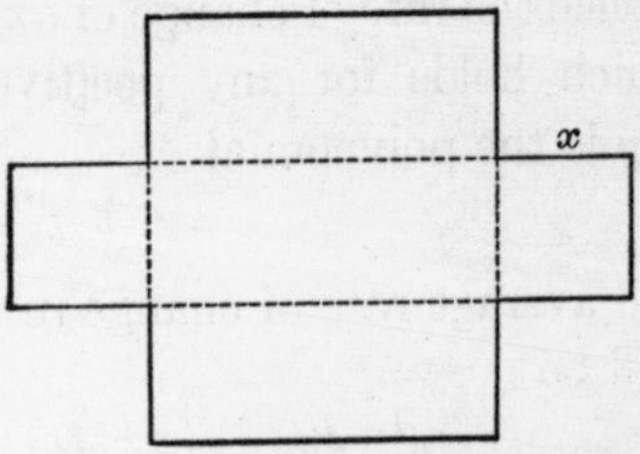

FIG. 9.

values $f(x)$ will be determined by values of x for which $f'(x)$ vanishes.

As an example, suppose that it is required to find the dimensions of the largest box which can be made by cutting squares of side x out of a piece of tin as in Fig. 9, and then folding along the dotted lines. If the dimensions of the tin are 4×6 inches the volume of the box will be a function of x defined by the equation

$$v = (6-2x)(4-2x)x = 24x - 20x^2 + 4x^3,$$

This function has the graph shown in Fig. 10. The slope of the tangent to the curve at any point is given by the derivative function

$$v' = 24 - 40x + 12x^2$$

which must vanish at the point a where v is a maximum. The roots of the last function are

$$x=\frac{5+\sqrt{7}}{3},\ \frac{5-\sqrt{7}}{3},$$

the latter being the value of x for the point a. In order, therefore, to get a box of the greatest capacity, the corners must be cut in a distance equal to $\frac{5-\sqrt{7}}{3}$ inches.

If a function $f(x)$ has everywhere the same value c, its rate of change is evidently zero, and its graph is a straight line

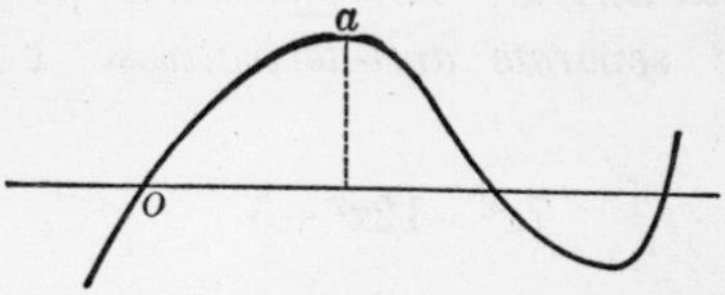

FIG. 10.

parallel to the x-axis. Conversely it is reasonable to infer that any function $f(x)$ whose rate of change is zero must have a graph which is a straight line parallel to the x-axis, and must therefore have the same value for every value of x. Consider now two functions $f(x)$ and $g(x)$ which have the same rate of change. Their difference $f(x)-g(x)$ will be a new function of x whose rate of change is everywhere zero, since it is the difference of the rates of $f(x)$ and $g(x)$. But it has just been seen that such a function is always equal to a constant c, and it follows at once that if two functions have the same derivative they are always related to each other by an equation of the form

$$f(x)=g(x)+c.$$

22. The Anti-derivative functions. With this remark in mind we may undertake a study of the second fundamental notion of the calculus, that of the anti-derivative. It has already been seen that in general any function $f(x)$ has associated with it a derivative function $f'(x)$ which expresses its rate of change. But it may also be asked whether or not there exists a function of which $f(x)$ is itself the derivative. The answer is that in general such a function exists, and it is called the anti-derivative of $f(x)$. It is easy to find an anti-derivative for any polynomial by inspection, if the formula for the derivative of x^n is borne in mind. By an application of this formula it is seen at once that the function $ax^{n+1}/(n+1)$ has for its derivative ax^n, and hence is an anti-derivative of ax^n. *The anti-derivatives of each term of a polynomial can therefore be found by adding one to the exponent of each term, and dividing the term by the exponent so increased. The anti-derivative of the whole polynomial is then the sum of these separate anti-derivatives.* For example the polynomial

$$7x^6 - 12x^2 + 5$$

is the rate of change of the polynomial

$$x^7 - 4x^3 + 5x,$$

as may be verified easily by applying to the last polynomial the formula previously given for differentiation.

The anti-derivative of a function $f(x)$ is unlike the derivative in that it is not *uniquely* determinable when $f(x)$ is given. For convenience let us denote the anti-derivative by $a(x)$, the letter a serving to indicate the relation between the two functions. If $A(x)$ is any other anti-derivative of $f(x)$, then $A(x)$ and $a(x)$ by definition have the same derivative and they must be related by an equation of the form

$$A(x) = a(x) + c.$$

It follows that although the anti-derivative is not unique, yet *if one anti-derivative $a(x)$ is known, then all the others are found by adding constants to $a(x)$.*

23. A typical mechanical application. One of the uses of the anti-derivative is well illustrated by the problem of determining at any moment the height of a ball thrown vertically upward with a given initial velocity. Physical experiments tell us that the velocity of the ball will decrease uniformly by an amount equal to $-g$ in each second, where g is approximately 32.2 feet. In other words the rate of change of the velocity is a constant $-g$. If any anti-derivative of $-g$ were known, the velocity v would necessarily differ from it by a constant only. Such an anti-derivative can readily be found by means of the formula given above, the result being $-gt$, and the corresponding expression for v is

$$v = -gt + c.$$

The constant c may be determined in terms of the initial velocity v_0 at the time $t = 0$ when the ball was thrown. For since the equation just written is true for all values of t, it will be true also when $t = 0$, and it follows readily that $c = v_0$. In a similar way a formula for the height s in terms of the time can be derived by seeking an anti-derivative of its rate of change v. The value of the anti-derivative is $-\frac{1}{2}gt^2 + v_0 t$, and hence this function and s must satisfy an equation of the form

$$s = -\tfrac{1}{2}gt^2 + v_0 t + d.$$

Here the constant d turns out to be zero on account of the fact that $s = 0$ when $t = 0$, and the final formula for s is therefore

$$s = v_0 t - \tfrac{1}{2}gt^2.$$

The problem of the thrown ball, and many others involving similar principles, show clearly the importance of having a method for finding an anti-derivative, as well as the derivative, of any given function. The **integration** of a function is the term applied to the process of finding an anti-derivative, and **differentiation** is the process of finding the derivative. One of the chief problems of the calculus is the determination derivatives and anti-derivatives for as many different types of functions as possible.

24. Relations between a function and its anti-derivatives. The graphs of the functions $a(x)$ and $f(x)$ are related to each other by two very interesting properties, one of which follows immediately from the definition of an anti-derivative. For any value of x the slope of the tangent to the anti-derivative curve, at the point n in Fig. 11, is equal numerically to the number of linear units in the corresponding ordinate xq of the original curve $y=f(x)$. Evidently when $y=a(x)$ has a maximum or minimum the curve $y=f(x)$ must intersect the x-axis, since the slope of the former, and therefore the ordinate to the latter, is zero at such a point.

The second relation between the curve is more interesting and more important, but in order to exhibit it we must first

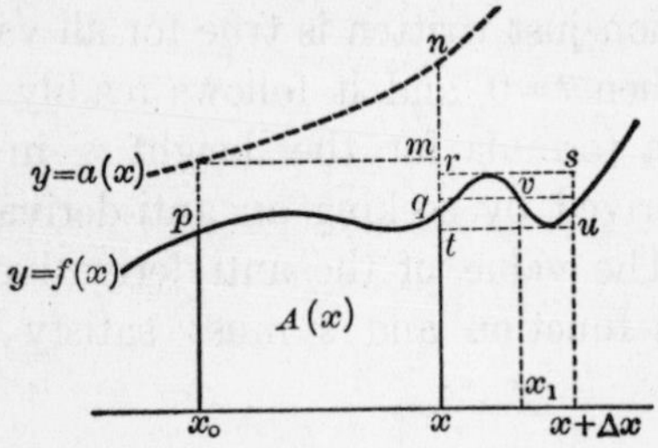

FIG. 11.

prove a property of the curve $y=f(x)$ itself. Consider the area A bounded by the two ordinates at x_0 and x, the curve itself, and the x-axis. For every value of x the value of A is uniquely determined, and, according to the definition of a function, it is therefore a function $A(x)$. The derivative of this function can readily be calculated. For the difference $A(x+\Delta x)-A(x)$ is the area under the curve bounded by the ordinates at x and $x+\Delta x$ in Fig. 11. This latter area is less than the rectangle whose corners are x, r, s, $(x+\Delta x)$ in the figure, greater than the rectangle x, t, u, $(x+\Delta x)$, and therefore equal to some rectangle intermediate between the two whose upper side cuts the curve in a point v with an abscissa which may be denoted by x_1.

Since the altitude of this rectangle is $f(x_1)$, its area has the value $f(x_1)\Delta x$, and

$$A(x+\Delta x)-A(x)=f(x_1)\cdot\Delta x.$$

The quotient

$$\frac{A(x+\Delta x)-A(x)}{\Delta x}=f(x_1)$$

will therefore have the limit $f(x)$, since the value of x_1 is always between x and $x+\Delta x$, and must approach x as Δx approaches zero. We have then this striking result that *the rate of change of the area $A(x)$ is numerically equal to the length of the ordinate $f(x)$ at the boundary of the area.*

25. Representation of an area by a line. Consider now the two functions $A(x)$ and $a(x)$. They are both anti-derivatives of the function $f(x)$ and hence must satisfy an equation of the form

$$A(x)=a(x)+c, \quad \ldots \ldots \quad (7)$$

where c is a constant whose value may be determined by putting $x=x_0$. The value of $A(a)$ is seen to be zero, so that for $x=x_0$ the last equation becomes

$$0=a(x_0)+c,$$

and the relation (7) takes the form

$$A(x)=a(x)-a(x_0). \quad \ldots \ldots \quad (8)$$

Interpreted geometrically this important equation means that *the number of square units in the area $A(x)$ is equal to the number of linear units in the line mn, which is the difference of the ordinates $a(x)$ and $a(x_0)$ of the anti-derivative curve.* (See Fig. 11.)

Consider for example the curves

$$y=3x^2=f(x), \quad y=x^3+1=a(x).$$

In Fig. 12 the area under $y=3x^2$ between the origin and the ordinate at $x=2$ is equal numerically to the length of the line *mn*, which in this case is

$$a(2)-a(0)=(2^3+1)-1=8$$

The curve $y=e^x$, shown in Fig. 13, where $e=2.718+$, has the interesting property that it is its own derivative curve. Hence the area enclosed between the curve, the x-axis, and any two ordinates is equal numerically to the difference between the two ordinates.

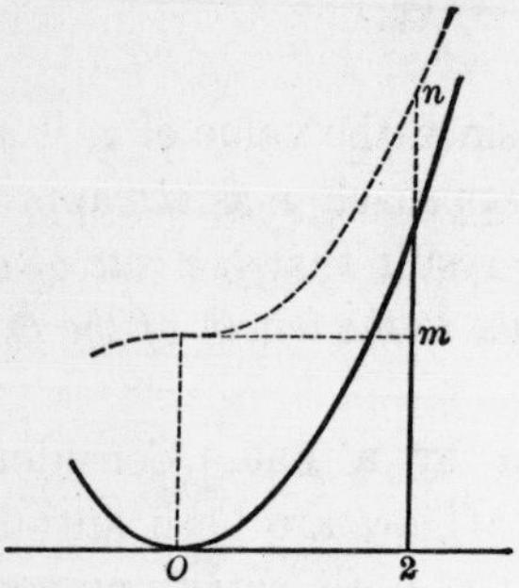

FIG. 12.

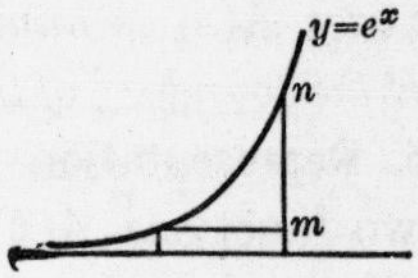

FIG. 13.

Similarly the area under any arch of the cosine curve can be calculated as soon as it is known that the sine is its antiderivative. For by the theorem just proved this area is equal to the difference

$$\sin\frac{\pi}{2}-\sin\left(-\frac{\pi}{2}\right)=2.$$

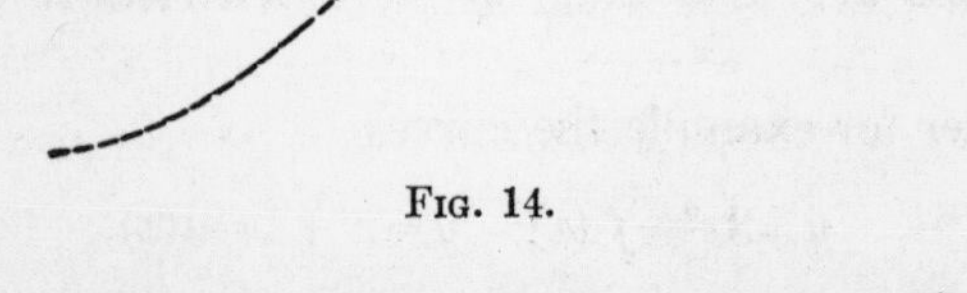

FIG. 14.

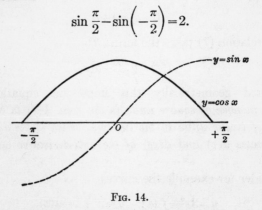

26. The definite integral. Fluid pressure. The relation which has just been exhibited between the derivative and antiderivative curves is interesting geometrically, but its importance really lies in its application to the evaluation of the third fundamental notion of the calculus, the definite integral. Let us consider first some examples which lead to definite integrals. Suppose that a cylindrical vessel full of water is at hand and that it is required to find the pressure of the water on the sides of the vessel. It is a well-known principle of physics that the horizontal pressure at any point in the liquid is the same as the pressure vertically downward. If w is the weight of a cubic unit of water, and x the depth of the point in question, then the pressure per unit of area at that depth is equal to the weight $w \cdot x$ of a column of water one square unit in cross section and x units high. Let the cylindrical surface between the top and the bottom of the liquid be divided by planes parallel to the bottom of the vessel into n horizontal rings of width $\Delta x_1, \Delta x_2 \ldots \Delta x_n$. If r is the radius of the cylinder, then the area of any one of these rings will have the value $2\pi r \Delta x_k$. The pressure on this area is less than the product of $2\pi r \Delta x_k$ by the pressure at the lower edge of the ring, greater than the product of $2\pi r \Delta x_k$ by the pressure at the upper edge, and therefore equal to $2\pi r w x_k \Delta x_k$, where x_k is some properly chosen depth in the interval Δx_k between the two extremes. The sum

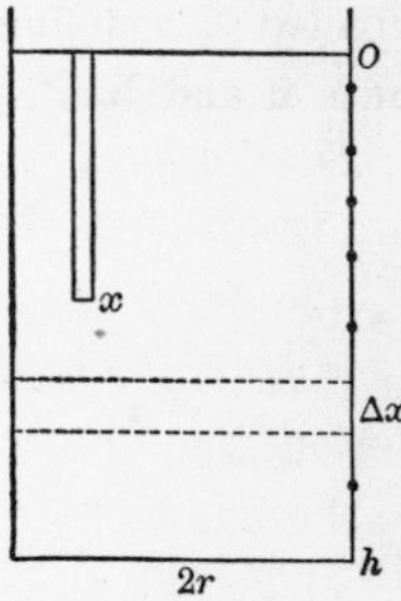

FIG. 15.

$$2\pi r w\{x_1 \Delta x_1 + x_2 \Delta x_2 + \ldots + x_n \Delta x_n\} \quad . \quad . \quad . \quad (9)$$

is the total pressure. In its present form this sum would be difficult to calculate on account of the indeterminateness of the values x_k, but it turns out that the limit of the sum as the intervals Δx_k are decreased in size, can be very easily found by a rule which will be explained a little later. Since the sum is always equal to the desired pressure its limit will have the same value.

It would be laborious to write down for many examples a detailed description of a sum such as (9) and its limit, and consequently a notation has been devised which suggests at a glance the essential steps in the process. For the examples just given the limit is denoted by the symbol

$$\int_0^h 2\pi rwxdx, \quad . \quad . \quad . \quad . \quad . \quad . \quad . \qquad (10)$$

where h denotes the total depth of the water. In this notation the integral sign $\int$ is a metamorphosed old English letter s, and suggests that the limit of a sum has been taken; the limits o and h indicate the interval for which the sum has been constructed; and the "integrand" $2\pi rwxdx$ shows the nature of the terms which have been summed. The whole expression is called the **definite integral of the function $2\pi rwx$ between the limits o and h.**

27. Volumes of solids of revolution. Another simple problem which may be solved with the help of a definite integral

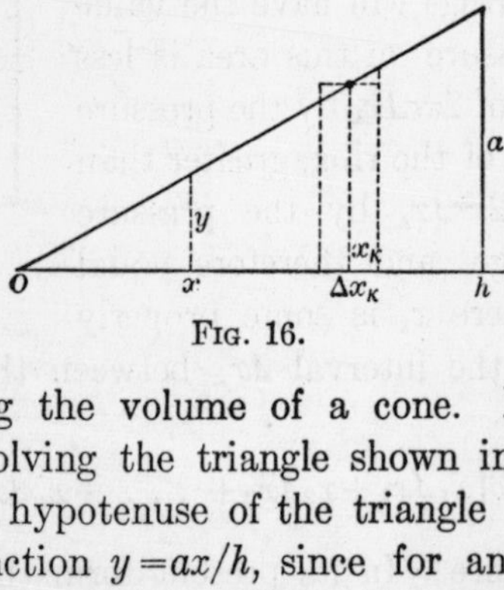

FIG. 16.

is that of finding the volume of a cone. Let the cone be generated by revolving the triangle shown in Fig. 16, about the x-axis. The hypotenuse of the triangle is a part of the graph of the function $y=ax/h$, since for any point of it y and x have the ratio $a:h$. Divide the interval from o to h into n parts Δx_k as before. The volume generated by the trapezoid over Δx_k will be equal to that generated by a properly chosen rectangle with base Δx_k and altitude $y_k=ax_k/h$. The volume generated by the rectangle is cylindrical and equal to the product of its base $\pi a^2x_k^2/h^2$ by its altitude Δx_k. The whole volume of the cone will then be a sum of terms of the type $\pi a^2x_k^2\Delta x_k/h^2$, and according to the description of the definite integral symbol given above, the limit of this sum can be denoted by

$$\int_0^h \pi \frac{a^2}{h^2} x^2 dx. \quad . \quad . \quad . \quad . \quad . \quad . \quad . \quad (11)$$

The volume of a cone of course can be calculated by the methods of elementary geometry. But the process just described enables us to find with equal ease an expression for the volume generated by revolving about the x-axis the area x_0pqx (Fig. 11) under any arbitrary curve $y=f(x)$, a problem quite beyond the scope of the usual elementary methods. The only differences in this case are that the type of the terms to be summed is $\pi f^2(x_k) \Delta x_k$ instead of $\pi a^2 x_k{}^2 \Delta x_k / h^2$, and the interval over which the sum is to be taken extends from x_0 to x instead of from o to h. The definite integral expressing the value of the volume has therefore the form

$$\int_{x_0}^x \pi f^2(x) dx. \quad . \quad . \quad . \quad . \quad . \quad . \quad (12)$$

28. Areas. The area x_0pqx in Fig. 11 can also be expressed as a definite integral. For, the part of the area underneath the curve and over the interval Δx_k is greater than the product of Δx_k by the highest ordinate over the interval, less than the product of Δx_k by the shortest ordinate, and therefore equal to Δx_k multiplied by some intermediate ordinate $f(x_k)$. The total area is consequently a series of terms of the type $f(x_k)$ Δx_k and is equal to the definite integral

$$\int_{x_0}^x f(x) dx,$$

which is the limit of this sum as the Δx_k approaches zero.

29. Computation of definite integrals. The fundamental theorem. The fact that the area x_0pqx can be expressed as a definite integral suggests at once a formula by means of which the values of many definite integrals can be calculated with considerable ease. In discussing the relation between the curves belonging to a function and its anti-derivative, it was found that the area x_0pqx for the curve $y=f(x)$ is equal to the difference of the ordinates of the anti-derivative curve at the values x_0 and x. By comparing these two results we have at once a remarkable theorem which is called the **fundamental theorem of the integral calculus.** According to it, *the value of the definite integral*

$$\int_{x_0}^{x} f(x)dx = \lim_{\Delta x = 0} \{f(x_1)\Delta x_1 + f(x_2)\Delta x_2 + \ . \ . \ . \ + f(x_n)\Delta x_n\}$$

is given by the formula

$$\int_{x_0}^{x} f(x)dx = a(x) - a(x_0),$$

where the function $a(x)$ is any anti-derivative of the function $f(x)$.

30. Applications. The values which the formula would give for the definite integral if two different anti-derivatives were used are evidently the same, since the difference of the anti-derivatives is always a constant. The theorem has been derived with the help of geometrical conceptions, but the definite integral is really an analytic notion with a geometrical interpretation, and the theorem itself is essentially analytic in character. It enables us to calculate the values of any definite integral for which an anti-derivative function can be found, irrespective of its geometrical or mechanical interpretation. Thus in the first example discussed above the function under the integral sign in (10) is $2\pi rwx$, and an anti-derivative, formed by the usual rule for functions of the type ax^n, is πrwx^2. The total pressure on the walls of the cylindrical vessel is therefore

$$\int_0^h 2\pi rwxdx = \tfrac{1}{3}\pi rwh^2 - \pi rw0^2 = \pi rwh^2.$$

Similarly the anti-derivative for the integral (11) which expresses the volume of a cone is $\pi a^2x^3/3h^2$, and the volume itself turns out to have the well-known value

$$\int_0^h \pi \frac{a^2}{h^2} x^2 dx = \tfrac{1}{3}\pi a^2 h,$$

one-third of the product of the base by the altitude.

In a similar way the volume of a sphere can be calculated by means of the formula (12). At any point of semicircle of radius r about the origin the abscissa x and ordinate y satisfy the relation $x^2+y^2=r^2$, so that the function which is represented by the circle has the equation

$$y=\sqrt{r^2-x^2}.$$

The volume generated by rotating the semicircle about the horizontal axis is that of a sphere of radius r. The definite integral which represents the volume, formed from the formula (12) by substituting the radical $\sqrt{r^2-x^2}$ in place of $f(x)$, has the form

$$\int_{-r}^{+r} \pi(r^2-x^2)dx,$$

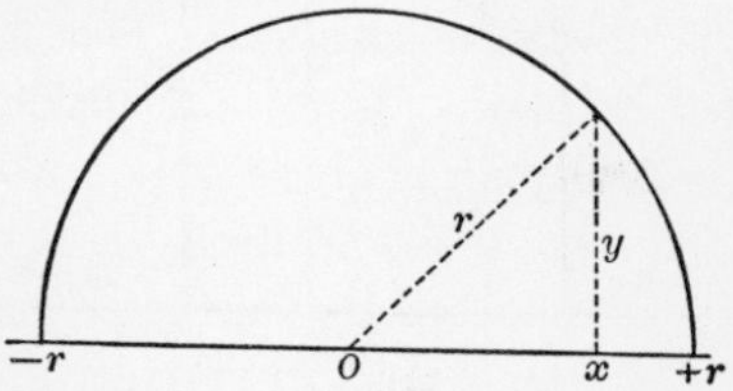

FIG. 17.

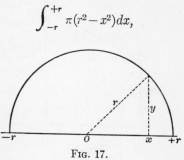

and an anti-derivative of the integrand function is $\pi(r^2x-\frac{1}{3}x^3)$. The volume has therefore the value

$$\int_{-r}^{+r} \pi(r^2-x^2)dx=\pi(2r^3-\tfrac{2}{3}r^3)=\tfrac{4}{3}\pi r^3.$$

If the area under the curve $y=3x^2$ in Fig. 12 is rotated about the x-axis, the volume generated is easily found from the same formula. In this case the integral is

$$\int_0^2 \pi 9x^4dx=\tfrac{9}{5}\pi(2^5-0^5)=\frac{288\pi}{5}.$$

31. Relations between functions and graphs. Let us conclude our brief study of the more important notions of the calculus with a consideration of a question which was proposed earlier in the paper with regard to the representation of a function by means of a graph. If a function is continuous at every point of an interval $\alpha \leq x \leq \beta$, then the difference $f(x') - f(x'')$ for any two values x' and x'' in the interval can be made arbitrarily small by choosing x' and x'' sufficiently near together. The proof that this property of a continuous function is a consequence of its continuity at the individual points between α and β is somewhat complicated, and cannot well be given here. The property itself is called the "uniform continuity of $f(x)$ in the interval $\alpha \leq x \leq \beta$." Assuming that it is true, we can without difficulty see that any continuous function can be approximately represented by a polygon. For

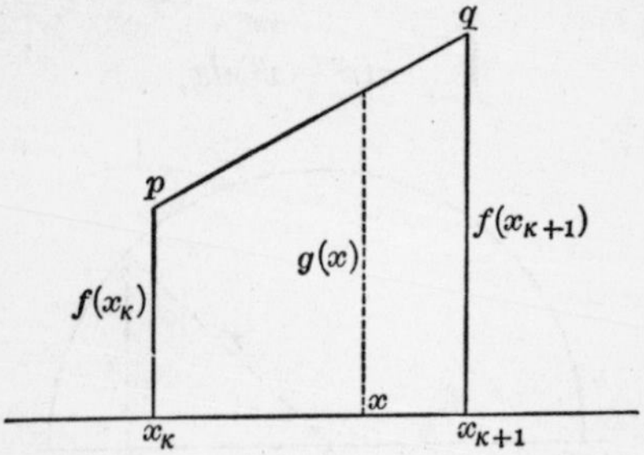

FIG. 18.

suppose that the interval from α to β has been divided into segments by a set of values x_k so near together that the difference $f(x) - f(x_k)$ for any value x between x_k and x_{k+1} is less than an arbitrarily chosen number ε. If the points p and q corresponding to any two successive values x_k and x_{k+1} are plotted, and the ordinate to the straight line joining p and q is represented by $g(x)$, it follows that the difference $g(x) - f(x_k)$ will also be less than ε, since $f(x_k) - f(x_{k+1})$ is less than ε and $g(x)$ lies between $f(x_k)$ and $f(x_{k+1})$. Since $f(x)$ and $g(x)$ both differ from $f(x_k)$ by less than ε it follows that their difference can itself not exceed 2ε. This result will hold for each segment Δx_k, however small the constant ε is taken, provided only that the points of division in the interval between α and β are taken sufficiently near together. It is evident then that a continuous function can be represented with any desired degree of numerical accuracy by plotting a finite number of points sufficiently near together, and joining them by straight lines.

The numerical accuracy of the representation is not the only characteristic of the graph, however, which should be taken into consideration. The broken line represents the values of the function with some degree of fairness, but it does not in general indicate other properties satisfactorily, and a smooth curve drawn through the corners of the polygon might be equally misleading. A smooth curve, for example, suggests to the eye that at each point of the curve there is a tangent line whose direction changes continuously as the point of tangency moves along the curve, and whose slope also changes continuously. Hence the function $f(x)$ which such a curve represents should have a continuous derivative, which is

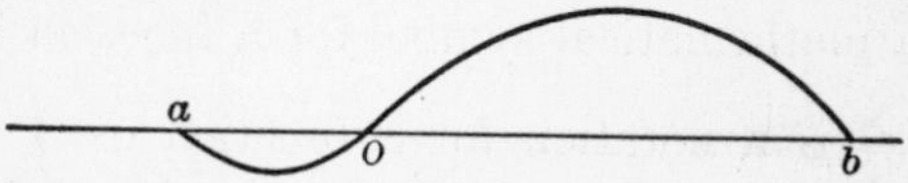

FIG. 19.

not always the case. A function may in fact be continuous in an interval and yet not have a derivative at any point of it, as is shown by a classical example of such a function due to *Weierstrass*.* The graph does not indicate as much, however, with regard to the rate of change of the slope of the tangent, which is denoted by $f''(x)$ and called the second derivative, and very little indeed concerning the rate of change of $f''(x)$ and the successive rates of change of higher orders. The second derivative is positive along an arc *ao* convex downward where the slope of the tangent is increasing, and negative on an arc *ob* which is concave downward. It vanishes presumably and changes sign at *o*, though at such a point it may change abruptly, as it would if for example *ao* and *ob* were arcs of the two curves

$$y=x+x^2, \quad y=x-\tfrac{1}{2}x^2.$$

* Mathematische Annalen, Vol. XIX, p. 591.

Both of these curves pass through the origin o, and their derivatives, $1+2x$ and $1-x$, have the same value for $x=0$, so that the two curves are tangent to each other at that point. On the other hand the second derivatives are respectively 2 and -1. From this and other examples which might be constructed it follows that a curve which appears perfectly smooth to the eye may represent a function which has a discontinuous second derivative, or possibly no second derivative at all.

32. The graph as a mathematical symbol. From the remarks which have been made it may be inferred that graphs have two distinct and important uses, the first of which is the numerical representation of the values of a function. It has been seen that such a representation may have significance, even if the function is only continuous without having any of the derivatives. But a graph is most useful, in theoretical work at least, as a mathematical symbol for a function in the same way that $f(x)$ is a notation for a function or $\int_\alpha^\beta f(x)dx$ for a definite integral. The variety of characteristics which may be suggested by a glance at a graph is, however, much greater than is suggested by the symbol $f(x)$ which indicates only functional dependence upon x, and its value as a symbol is proportionately enhanced. From the graph of the function $y=x/(x^2-1)$ in Fig. 3, for example, we read that this function is continuous and has a continuous derivative except at $x=\pm 1$; that it always decreases, varying from 0 to $-\infty$ as x increases from $-\infty$ to -1, from $+\infty$ to $-\infty$ as x increases from -1 to $+1$, and from $+\infty$ to 0 as x increases from $+1$ to ∞; that it vanishes only once, when $x=0$; that its derivative is negative with variations clearly indicated; that its second derivative vanishes at $x=0$; and so on; all of these properties being much more significantly suggested by the graph than by the corresponding and somewhat clumsy description in words.

As the usefulness of any mathematical notation depends upon the sharpness with which the conception for which it is to stand is defined, so the graph attains its greatest efficiency as a symbol only when the nature of the functions which are to be represented is clearly specified in advance, as well as the properties of functions which are to be represented by special features of the curve. As has been seen above, the characteristics of first and second derivatives seem to be particularly adapted to graphical representation, and it has been suggested that curves possess their fullest significance as symbols of functions when the functions are continuous, have only a finite number of maxima and minima in any given interval, and have continuous derivatives of the first and second orders. The elementary functions have these properties, in common with all of the other functions which have been designated as analytic. But it is not necessary that the functions represented be thus restricted in character, provided only that the correspondence between the analytical characteristics of the function on the one hand and the graphical characteristics of the curve on the other, is expressly understood. In the elementary courses it is evidently impossible to discuss the niceties of the relation of graphical to analytical conceptions, and it is highly desirable that graphical methods should be used. But they should always be formulated with special reference in the mind of the instructor to the correspondence between the graphical and the analytical processes, with which the student will later be familiar.

We have now come to the end of our brief survey of the elements of the calculus, the threshold of the higher mathematics. The technical difficulties which would arise have prevented the application of the processes of differentation and integration to any but the simplest functions, the polynomials. By means of these alone, however, it has been possible to explain the meaning of the derivative, the anti-derivative, and the definite integral, and some of their interrelations among themselves. The rest of the theory is for the most part an application in many different ways and to many different functions of these three fundamental conceptions. It is hoped that by his perusal of these pages the reader unfamiliar with

with the calculus will have lost whatever awe he may have had of one at least of the more advanced mathematical subjects, and at the same time have gained an insight into the variety and importance of its relations with problems of a practical nature and with other branches of science.

VII

THE THEORY OF NUMBERS

BY J. W. A. YOUNG.

CONTENTS

VII

THE THEORY OF NUMBERS

By J. W. A. Young

I. INTRODUCTION

1. The "Theory of Numbers" might, in a certain sense, include nearly all of the subject-matter usually treated in mathematics, since, with the exception of the non-metrical portions of Geometry, there are few domains of mathematics that are not fundamentally concerned with numbers. But the term is commonly used in a restricted, technical sense as meaning the theory of *integral* numbers (positive, negative, zero). Even this must be further restricted, for all numbers other than integers can be defined in terms of integers,* so that to study the whole body of theory that has been built up on integral numbers would still be tantamount to studying nearly the whole body of mathematical science. The restriction customarily made is to regard the "theory of numbers" as concerned with integers *as such;* their properties and their combinations by operations that lead to integral results. The operations of addition, subtraction, and multiplication are accordingly admitted when applied to any integers, and division is admitted when applied to integers such that the quotient is integral. The process of division may also be used to obtain equations between integers. For example, $9385 = 62 \cdot 151 + 23$.†

In all that follows the term *number* shall accordingly be understood to mean *integral number;* and other terms, for

---

* See Monograph IV, Appendix I.

† The dot indicates multiplication.

example, *factor*, shall be understood to be similarly restricted in meaning.

2. The treatment of our subject, as now delimited, might properly begin with a chapter studying the nature and genesis of the concept of integer, the fundamental definitions and postulates relating to integers and to the admitted operations thereupon, the "laws" of operation, and the like. This would be, in a measure, the treatment of the theoretic basis of elementary arithmetic.*

3. We, however, here assume a working knowledge of elementary arithmetic, and begin with a consideration of various properties, connected with the *factors* of numbers, that are not ordinarily treated in that subject.

II. FACTORS

4. Definition. A **prime number** (or briefly, a **prime**) is a number having no other factors than itself and unity.

5. Theorem. *The series of primes is endless.*

Proof. It is sufficient to show that there exists a prime larger than any given prime. Let the given prime be p.

Consider $$N=2\cdot 3\cdot 5\ \dots\ p+1,$$

---

* For a treatment of the corresponding questions relative to the numbers of algebra, which include those of arithmetic, see Monograph IV.

For the more strictly arithmetical theory see:

Dedekind, Was sind und was sollen die Zahlen? Braunschweig, 2d ed., 1893. English translation by *Beman* as the second essay of "Essays on Number," Chicago, 1901. *Stolz-Gmeiner*, Theoretische Arithmetik, Part I, 2d ed., Leipzig, 1900. (This work presents the theory of the natural numbers, published by Peano, under the title, "Arithmetices principia nova methodo exposita," Turin, 1889, in a symbolic notation. A brief account of this theory is given by *Huntington* in the Bulletin of the American Mathematical Society, 2d Series, Vol. IX, 1902, pp. 40–46.) *Padoa*, "Théorie algébrique des nombres entiers," Internat. Cong. de Philos., Paris, 1900, pp. 309–65. *Huntington*, "Complete sets of postulates for the theories of positive integral and positive rational numbers," Transactions American Mathematical Society, Vol. III, 1902, pp. 280–84. *Huntington*, pp. 27–29 of "The fundamental laws of addition and multiplication in elementary algebra," Annals of Math., Vol. VIII, 1906, pp. 1–44.

where the first term of N is the product of all the primes not greater than p.

Then it appears from the form of N, that if N be divided by any one of the primes just mentioned, the remainder will be 1. Consequently, every prime factor of N must be greater than p. Since N must have one or more prime factors, the *existence* of a prime greater than p is thus proved. But this is by no means tantamount to the *actual finding* of a prime greater than a given prime p. No general method for doing this has as yet been discovered.

This theorem may also be stated thus: *There is no largest prime number;* or thus: *The primes being arranged in order of increasing magnitude, after each prime there follows another;* or also thus: *The number of primes is infinite.* The last form of statement means neither more nor less than the others.

It has been conjectured that every even number is the sum of two primes, but this has not yet been proved.

6. The theorem above was known to *Euclid* two thousand years ago. In the nineteenth century *Dirichlet* proved an elegant generalization of it, viz., *There is an endless set of primes in every arithmetical progression whose first term and common difference have no common factor.*

Dirichlet's proof of this theorem makes use of numbers and operations not admitted in our subject* (which is often called **higher arithmetic**) thus furnishing an instance of a "non-arithmetical" proof of an arithmetical proposition.†

It is, however, easy to prove the theorem arithmetically for certain progressions.

For example, the progression

$$3, 7, 11, 15, 19, 23, \ldots 4n-1, \ldots$$

contains an endless sequence of primes.

---

* See sec. 1.

† Such proofs abound in the development of the theory of numbers. For an introduction to this division of the subject see: *Bachman*, Analytische Zahlentheorie, Leipzig, 1892 (proof of the above theorem, pp. 74–88); *Kronecker-Hensel*, Zahlentheorie, Leipzig, 1901 (above theorem, pp. 438 et seq.).

To prove this it is sufficient to show that for every prime p there exists a larger prime of the form $4n-1$.

Consider $$N=2(2\cdot3\cdot5\cdot7\ldots p)+1,$$

where the number in the parenthesis is the product of all primes not greater than p.

Then it is clear from the form of N, that none of the primes $2, 3\ldots p$ is a factor of N. All the prime factors of N are therefore greater than p.

All odd primes are of the form $4n+1$ or $4n-1$. The product of two numbers of the form $4n+1$ is also of the form $4n+1$. But N is of the form $4n-1$. Hence at least one of its prime factors must be of the form $4n-1$. The existence of a prime of this form larger than the given prime, p, is thus proved.

It can be proved quite analogously that the progression,

$$5, 11, 17, 23, 29, 35, \ldots, 6n-1, \ldots$$

contains an unending set of primes.

7. Various important general problems have been studied relating to primes. For example:

(1) To determine the number of primes in a given interval.

(2) To determine a prime larger than a given prime.

(3) To determine the prime next larger than a given prime.

(4) To determine whether or not a given number is prime; or, more generally, to determine the factors of a given number.

No general solution of these problems has as yet been found.

8. The simplest method of finding factors is by actual trial. It is sufficient to try only primes, and of these, only those whose squares are smaller than the given number. But this method is impracticable for large numbers. For these, use is made of various results and methods that are developed in our subject.

9. Tables of the factors of all members up to ten millions have been published.* A manuscript in the Archives of the

* *Lehmer*, Factor Table for the First Ten Millions, Washington 1909. *Carr's* Synopsis of Pure Mathematics, London, 1886, contains a table extending to 99,000. Still smaller tables are found in *Jones'* Logarithmic Tables, Ithaca, N. Y., 1889, and elsewhere.

Academy of Vienna gives the factors of numbers from 3,000,000 to 100,000,000. (This MS. is known to contain many errors.)

10. Factors of particular numbers much larger than those in the tables have also been found. For example, in the theory of the construction of regular polygons* it is important to know whether or not $2^{2^n}+1$ is a prime number. It has been shown that

$$2^{2^5}+1=4,294,967,297$$
$$=641 \cdot 6,700,417$$

Also that $2^{2^{36}}+1$, a number of more than twenty billion places, has the prime factor:

$$2,748,779,069,441.†$$

11. Definition. Two numbers having no common factor but unity, are called **relatively prime.** Each is said to be **prime to** the other.

12. Definition. The number of (positive) integers not greater than m and prime to m is called the **totient** of m, and denoted by $\phi\ (m)$.

Thus $\phi(1)=1;\ \ \phi(2)=1;\ \ \phi(3)=2;\ \ \phi(4)=2;$

$\phi(5)=4;\ \ \phi(6)=2;\ \ \phi(7)=6;\ \ \phi(8)=4.$

If p is prime, $\phi(p)=p-1.$

13. Problem. *To determine* $\phi(m)$.

Solution. Let $m=p^a q^b r^c \ldots v^h$, where $p,\ q,\ r \ldots v$ are different primes, $a,\ b,\ c, \ldots h$ positive integers.

If from the series of numbers

$$1, 2, 3, 4, 5, \ldots m-1, m,$$

we strike out all those that have as factor p or q, or r, etc., the numbers that remain will be prime to m, and the number of such numbers is the desired totient.

---

* Monograph No. VIII, sec. 26.

† Encyc. des Sciences Math., Tome I, Vol. III, p. 51.

First consider those having p as a factor.

They are: $p, 2p, 3p, \ldots \frac{m}{p} \cdot p.$

Their number is $\frac{m}{p}$.* There are therefore $m-\frac{m}{p}$ or $m\left(1-\frac{1}{p}\right)$ numbers of the series $1, 2 \ldots m$ that do not have the factor p. This may be stated generally thus:

Lemma. If M has the prime factor P, then $M\left(1-\frac{1}{P}\right)$ of the numbers $1, 2, 3 \ldots M$ do not have the factor P.

We next strike out the numbers having the factor q.

These numbers are

$$q, 2q, 3q, \ldots \frac{m}{q}, q.$$

Some of them may already be struck off as having the factor p. The number not having the factor p, is the number of the coefficients

$$1, 2, 3 \ldots \frac{m}{q},$$

not having the factor p. By the lemma this number is $\frac{m}{q}\left(1-\frac{1}{p}\right)$.

The number of numbers $1, 2, 3 \ldots m$, having neither p nor q as factor is therefore

$$m(1-p)-\frac{m}{q}\left(1-\frac{1}{p}\right)$$

or

$$m\left(1-\frac{1}{p}\right)\left(1-\frac{1}{q}\right).$$

Similarly, the numbers

$$r, 2r, 3r \ldots \frac{m}{r}, r$$

* This number is an integer, since p is a factor of m. For similar reasons, the other numbers indicated by fractions in what follows, are also integers.

have r as a factor. Some of them may have p or q as factor. The number of those that do not is the number of coefficients

$$1, 2, 3 \ldots \frac{m}{r},$$

that have neither p nor q as factor.

By the preceding result this number is

$$\frac{m}{r}\left(1-\frac{1}{p}\right)\left(1-\frac{1}{q}\right).$$

Consequently these are in the series $1, 2, \ldots m$,

$$m\left(1-\frac{1}{p}\right)\left(1-\frac{1}{q}\right)-\frac{m}{r}\left(1-\frac{1}{p}\right)\left(1-\frac{1}{q}\right),$$

or

$$m\left(1-\frac{1}{p}\right)\left(1-\frac{1}{q}\right)\left(1-\frac{1}{r}\right),$$

numbers not divisible by either p, q, r. The same reasoning may be repeated until all of the prime factors of m have been used. The numbers remaining will be prime to m, and we have thus:

$$\phi(m)=m\left(1-\frac{1}{p}\right)\left(1-\frac{1}{q}\right)\left(1-\frac{1}{r}\right)\ldots\left(1-\frac{1}{v}\right).$$

REMARKS. (1) The repetition of the reasoning for all of the prime factors of m is formally accomplished by the process of *mathematical induction*, that is, we show that if a result of the above type holds for any k different prime factors of m, such a result also holds for $k+1$ of the prime factors of m, consisting of the k already considered and any other one. Since such results have been proved above for one, two, and three factors, it would follow that a similar result holds for four factors, therefore for five factors, etc., therefore for all the factors.

(2) If the reader has any difficulty in following the reasoning above for a general m, he should first carry it through for one or more particular values (say, $60=2^2\cdot 3\cdot 5$, $48=2^4\cdot 3$, $55=5\cdot 11$), and then generalize. This remark applies to our whole subject—the theory of *numbers*. It cannot be mastered without much work with specific numbers, and recourse should always be had to particular instances, whenever the general theory becomes in any way hazy.

14. Problem. *To find the sum of all the factors of any number, m.*

Solution. Let $m=p^aq^br^c \dots v^l$, where $p, q, r, \dots v$ are different primes, and $a, b, c \dots l$ are positive integers. Let all the factors of m, including unity and m itself, be $d_1, d_2, d_3 \dots d_k$, and let $d_1+d_2+d_3+\dots+d_k=S(m)$.

Every factor of m is of the form:

$$d=p^{a'}q^{b'}r^{c'} \dots v^{l'},$$

where $a'\ b'\ c' \dots l'$ have any combination of the values:

$$a'=0, 1, 2 \dots a$$
$$b'=0, 1, 2 \dots b$$
$$\cdot \quad \cdot \quad \cdot \quad \cdot \quad \cdot$$
$$l'=0, 1, 2 \dots l$$

and, conversely, all expressions of this form are factors.

Further, every expression of this form occurs once, and only once, as a term of the following product, and the product contains no other terms:

$$P=(1+p+p^2+\dots+p^a)(1+q+q^2+\dots+q^b)\dots$$
$$(1+v+v^2+\dots+v^l).$$

Consequently P is the sum of the d's, and since each factor of P is a geometric series, we obtain:

$$S(m)=\frac{p^{a+1}-1}{p-1}\cdot\frac{q^{b+1}-1}{q-1}\dots\frac{v^{l+1}-1}{v-1}.$$

EXAMPLES. 1. Since $25=5^2$,

$$S(25)=\frac{5^3-1}{5-1}=31.$$

2. Since $72=2^3\cdot3^2$,

$$S(72)=\frac{2^4-1}{2-1}\cdot\frac{3^3-1}{3-1}=15\cdot13=195.$$

3. Since $100{,}800=2^6\cdot3^2\cdot5^2\cdot7$,

$$S(100{,}800)=\frac{2^7-1}{2-1}\cdot\frac{3^3-1}{3-1}\cdot\frac{5^3-1}{5-1}\cdot\frac{7^2-1}{7-1}$$
$$=127\cdot13\cdot31\cdot8=409{,}448.$$

15. Definition. A number that is equal to the sum of all its factors, except itself, is called **a perfect number.**

For example, 6 and 28 are perfect numbers, since

$$6 = 3+2+1,$$

$$28 = 14+7+4+2+1.$$

16. Theorem. *If* 2^k-1 *is a prime, then* $2^{k-1}(2^k-1)$ *is a perfect number.* (This theorem is given by *Euclid.*)

Proof. Let

$$n = 2^{k-1}(2^k-1)$$

and let

$$p = 2^k-1.$$

Then

$$n = 2^{k-1}p.$$

And by sec. 14,

$$S(n) = \frac{2^{(k-1)+1}-1}{2-1} \cdot \frac{p^2-1}{p-1}$$

$$= (2^k-1)(p+1)$$

$$= (2^k-1)2^k.$$

Subtracting n from both members we have:

$$S(n)-n = (2^k-1)2^k - 2^{k-1}(2^k-1)$$

$$= (2^k-1)(2^k-2^{k-1})$$

$$= (2^k-1)(2\cdot 2^{k-1}-2^{k-1})$$

$$= (2^k-1)2^{k-1}$$

$$= n.$$

That is, n is a perfect number.

17. It is not difficult to prove * that every even perfect number is of the form given above. No odd perfect number has been found, and it is not known whether or not any exists.

18. The question naturally arises as to what values of k will make 2^k-1 a prime. It is easy to see that a first condition is that k itself must be prime. For if $k=ab$, $2^{ab}-1$ has (according to elementary algebra) the factor 2^a-1.

---

* See, for example, *Lucas*, Théorie des Nombres, Paris, 1891, p. 375.

In 1644 *Mersenne* asserted that when p is a prime not greater than 257, 2^p-1 is a prime if and only if

$$p=2, 3, 5, 7, 13, 17, 19, 31, 61, 127, 257.$$

Numbers of the form 2^p-1, $p \leqq 257$, are called **Mersenne's numbers.**

The statement that 2^p-1 is prime has been verified for the first 9 values of p, which, consequently, when substituted in Euclid's formula gives the nine known perfect numbers. The first eight of them were known as early as the sixteenth century, the ninth (whose value is

$$2,658,455,991,569,831,744,654,692,615,953,842,176)$$

was verified late in the nineteenth century. The values $p=127$ and $p=257$ are still in doubt. The statement that 2^p-1 is composite for values of $p<257$ other than those of the list above has been verified in a large number of instances,* but not yet in all. It is believed that *Mersenne* knew some more powerful and general method of dealing with these questions, which his successors have not yet succeeded in rediscovering.

III. DIOPHANTINE EQUATIONS

19. Definition. An equation in two or more unknowns whose values are to be integral is called a **Diophantine** equation; also an **indeterminate equation.**

Linear Diophantine equations are best studied in connection with another division of our subject (Congruences, secs. 31–33).

20. An interesting instance of a quadratic Diophantine equation is the equation

$$x^2+y^2=z^2. \qquad . \quad . \quad . \quad . \quad . \quad . \quad . \quad (1)$$

The numbers of any set x, y, z satisfying these equations are the lengths of the sides of a right triangle. So that the two problems of finding all integral solutions of the above equations and of finding all right triangles with sides of integral length are equivalent. Such triangles are called **Pythagorean triangles.**

---

* For list, see *Lucas,* Théorie des Nombres, p. 375.

A solution in which x, y, z have no common factor is called **a primitive** solution. It will be sufficient to find all the primitive solutions, for every non-primitive solution can be deduced from some primitive solution by multiplying all its numbers by the proper factor.

We begin the search for the primitive solutions by showing that in any primitive solution of one of the numbers, x and y, say x, is even and the other, y, is odd. For (*a*) if x and y were both even, z would also be even; the common factor, 2, would be present and the solution would not be primitive. (*b*) If x and y were both odd (that is, of the form $2n+1$), x^2 and y^2 would both be of the form $4n+1$; and hence z^2 would be of the form $4n+2$. But this is impossible, since the square of every even number is of the form $4n$, and that of every odd number is of the form $4n+1$. Since suppositions (*a*) and (*b*) are both incorrect one of the numbers x and y must be even, the other, odd. Let x denote the even one. Then y and z are odd.

From (1):

$$\begin{aligned} x^2 &= z^2 - y^2 \\ &= (z+y)(z-y). \end{aligned}$$

Since z and y are both odd we may put,

$$\left.\begin{aligned} z+y &= 2k \\ z-y &= 2l \end{aligned}\right\} \quad . \quad . \quad . \quad . \quad . \quad . \quad . \quad . \qquad (2)$$

Hence,

$$x^2 = 4kl.$$

Since x, y, z are relatively prime, k and l must also be relatively prime; for, from equations (2),

$$z = k+l \quad \text{and} \quad y = k-l;$$

hence if k and l had a common factor y and z would have that factor in common also.

Since $4kl$ is a square, it follows that k and l must be square. We therefore put:

$$\begin{aligned} k &= m^2 \\ l &= q^2 \qquad (m,\ q,\ \text{relatively prime}). \end{aligned}$$

Consequently, in any primitive solution of equation (1), x, y, z must be of the forms:

$$\left.\begin{aligned} x &= 2mq \\ y &= m^2 - q^2 \\ z &= m^2 + q^2 \end{aligned}\right\} \quad . \quad . \quad . \quad . \quad . \quad . \quad (3)$$

It is readily seen by substitution that every set of values of this form, whether primitive or not, satisfies the equation. To pick out these solutions of form (3) that are primitive, we proceed as follows:

If m and q have a common factor, then x, y, z evidently have that factor in common also. The primitive solutions will therefore all be among those obtained under the restriction that m and q shall be relatively prime.

Further, since $z+y=2m^2$, and $z-y=2q^2$, any common factor of z and y would be a common factor of $2m^2$ and of $2q^2$, or, if m and q are relatively prime, of 2. That is, if m and q are relatively prime, y and z can have, at most, the factor 2 in common. They do, indeed, have this common factor when m and q are both odd, and not otherwise (m and q being relatively prime). We have thus proved the following

Theorem. *All the primitive solutions and no others of the equation* $x^2+y^2=z^2$ *are given by the formulas* (3) *if* m *and* q *run through all possible sets of relatively prime values such that* $m>q$, *and that one of the two is even, the other odd.*

It is now simply a matter of substitution to prepare a table of the smaller primitive solutions.*

* A table of all primitive solutions in which $z \overline{\overline{<}} 2500$ is given by *Whitworth*, Proc. Lit. and Phil. Soc. of Liverpool, Vol. XXIX, 1874, p. 237.

m	q	x	y	z	m	q	x	y	z
2	1	4	3	5	7	6	84	13	85
3	2	12	5	13		4	56	33	65
4	3	24	7	25		2	28	45	53
	1	8	15	17	8	7	112	15	113
5	4	40	9	41		5	80	39	89
	2	20	21	29		3	48	55	73
6	5	60	11	61		1	16	63	65
	1	12	35	37					

Theorem. Of the three numbers, x, y, z, one is divisible by 3, one (perhaps the same one) by 4 and one by 5.

Proof. Since either m or q is even, x is divisible by 4. If either m or q is divisible by 3 or by 5, x is divisible by 3 or by 5.

If neither m nor q is divisible by 3, they are both of the form $3n \pm 1$, and their squares are of the form $3n+1$. Therefore m^2-q^2 is of the form $3n$. That is y is a multiple of 3.

If neither m nor q is divisible by 5 they are of one of the forms $5n \pm 1$, $5n \pm 2$, and their squares are of the form $5n \pm 1$. If both m^2 and q^2 are of the same form (either $5n+1$ or $5n-1$) m^2-q^2 is of the form $5n$; while if one is of the form $5n+1$ and the other of the form $5n-1$, m^2+q^2 is of the form $5n$. That is, in the former case y is a multiple of 5, in the latter case, z is a multiple of 5.

All of these statements may be verified for the particular instances occurring in the table above, and they should be so verified if the reader has the slightest difficulty in understanding the general reasoning. (See note, sec. 13.)

21. As it has been easy to solve completely the equation $x^2+y^2=z^2$, it would be natural to expect corresponding success in the solution of $x^3+y^3=z^3$, but this expectation is doomed to disappointment. It has been proved* that the equation has *no solution.* In other words: no cube of an integer can be the sum of two cubes of integers. This is a special case of the following more general theorem announced by *Fermat:*

The equation $x^n+y^n=z^n$ admits no solution in integers, if n is a positive integer greater than two.

This famous theorem is commonly known as **Fermat's last theorem**, and was stated without proof by *Fermat* in the seventeenth century. Since then the theorem has stood as a standing challenge to arithmeticians. For various specific instances the proof has been found, including every $n \leqq 100$ and some others, but the general proof has not yet been made.

---

* *Euler*, Algebra, St. Petersburg, 1770.

22. Mere mention must suffice for the interesting and famous indeterminate equation:

$$x^2-Dy^2=\pm 1,$$

generally known as the **Pellian equation,** though it has recently been pointed out that *Pell* never published anything on this equation.* A method for the solution of this equation was known to the Hindus about 600 A. D., but it was solved independently by *La Grange* in the eighteenth century. The equation is treated in the works on the Theory of Numbers cited in the bibliography; these works also discuss many other indeterminate equations that cannot even be mentioned here.

IV. CONGRUENCES

23. It frequently happens that in a particular problem numbers whose difference is a multiple of a given number, are equivalent.

For example:

(1) With respect to the day of the week on which the last day of a certain period falls, numbers of days counted from a fixed day are equivalent if their difference is a multiple of 7.

(2) With respect to their trigonometric functions, angles are equivalent if they differ only by multiples of 360°.

(3) With respect to their numerical value, powers of -1 are equivalent if their exponents differ only by multiples of 2.

24. Definitions. If $a=b+cm$, that is, if $a-b$ is a multiple of m, we say that a is **congruent** to b with respect to the **modulus** m, and write:

$$a\equiv b(\text{mod. } m). \quad . \quad . \quad . \quad . \quad . \quad . \quad . \quad (1)$$

The modulus is supposed to be positive.

A relation of the form (1) is called a **congruence.** a and b are called **residues** of each other, **modulo** m.

The numbers on the two sides of the sign $\equiv$ are called the **members** of the congruence.

* Encyc. des Sc. Math., Tome I, Vol. III, p. 27.

The following are examples of congruences: The reader will readily convince himself of their correctness.

$$15 \equiv 8 \pmod{7} \qquad 60 \equiv 0 \pmod{12}$$

$$37 \equiv 19 \pmod{6} \qquad -18 \equiv 32 \pmod{10}$$

$$1 \equiv 41 \pmod{5} \qquad 3 \equiv -59 \pmod{31}$$

25. Every number is congruent (mod. m) to one and only one of the series:

$$0, 1, 2 \ldots m-1;$$

also to one and only one of the series:

$$0, -1, -2, \ldots -(m-1);$$

also, if m is odd, to one and only one of the series:

$$0, \pm 1, \pm 2 \ldots \pm \frac{m-1}{2};$$

and, if m is even, to one and only one of the series:

$$0, \pm 1, \pm 2 \ldots \pm \frac{m}{2}-1, +\frac{m}{2}.$$

These are called respectively the series of **least positive residues, least negative residues,** and **absolutely least residues** (mod. m).

26. In any congruence, multiples of the modulus may be added or subtracted at will, without disturbing the congruence. For $a \equiv b$ (mod. m) means that a differs from b by a multiple of m. This property is not affected if a or b, or both, are altered by a multiple of m.

Similarly, any factor may be increased or diminished by a multiple of the modulus without destroying the congruence. That is, if

$$ab \equiv c \pmod{m}$$

then also $\qquad (a+dm)b \equiv c \pmod{m}.$

The reader may supply the details of this reasoning.

27. We may, therefore, in any congruence reduce all numerical terms and coefficients to values less than the modulus without destroying the congruence.

Thus, the congruence $86c \equiv 7$ (mod. 11) may be replaced by $9c \equiv 7$ (mod. 11), and $437a + 289b \equiv 469c$ (mod. 27) may be replaced by $5a + 19b \equiv 8c$ (mod. 27).

The reader should practice with similar relations until he is quite familiar with the idea. These relations may be taken quite at random. Thus, $873 \equiv ?$ (mod. 36); $4729 \equiv ?$ (mod. 123). What congruences with coefficients smaller than the modulus are equivalent to the following?

$$83x \equiv 7 \text{ (mod. 13)}; \quad 439x \equiv 283 \text{ (mod. 20)};$$

$$11a - 23b \equiv 36 \text{ (mod. 5)}; \quad 4632y \equiv 367{,}832 - 439 \text{ (mod. 16)},$$

etc.

(But exponents may not be treated similarly. From $2^7 \equiv 3$ (mod. 5), it does not follow that $2^2 \equiv 3$ (mod. 5). A theorem which enables us to replace exponents larger than the modulus by smaller ones, will be proved later—secs. 34, 35.)

28. Fundamental properties of congruences.

I. If $b \equiv a$ (mod. m) and $c \equiv a$ (mod. m) then $b \equiv c$ (mod. m).

Proof. The given congruences mean:

$$b = a + dm$$

$$c = a + em.$$

Subtracting, $$b - c = (d - e)m$$

$\therefore$ by definition $$b \equiv c \text{ (mod. } m).$$

II. If
$$a_1 \equiv b_1 \text{ (mod. } m)$$
$$a_2 \equiv b_2 \text{ (mod. } m)$$
$$\cdot \quad \cdot \quad \cdot \quad \cdot \quad \cdot$$
$$a_l \equiv b_l \text{ (mod. } m).$$

then: $$a_1 + a_2 + \ldots + a_l \equiv b_1 + b_2 + \ldots + b_l \text{ (mod. } m).$$

The reader can readily supply the proof here, and in the case of the other properties of this list where the proof is omitted.

Corollary. Terms may be *transposed* from one member of a congruence to another; that is, they may be omitted where they stand, and inserted in the other member with their signs changed.

For if t represents the term to be transposed, this is equivalent to adding the members of the congruence $-t \equiv -t$ (mod. m) respectively to the members of the given congruence.

III. If $a \equiv b \pmod{m}$,

then $ka \equiv kb \pmod{m}$,

and also $ka \equiv kb \pmod{km}$.

IV. If $a \equiv b \pmod{m}$

and $c \equiv d \pmod{m}$

then $ac \equiv bd \pmod{m}$.

For by III, $ac \equiv bc \pmod{m}$

and $bc \equiv bd \pmod{m}$

$\therefore$ by I $ac \equiv bd \pmod{m}$.

Corollary 1. If

$$a_1 \equiv b_1 \pmod{m}$$
$$a_2 \equiv b_2 \pmod{m}$$
$$\cdot\ \cdot\ \cdot\ \cdot\ \cdot$$
$$a_l \equiv b_l \pmod{m}$$

then $a_1a_2 \ldots a_l \equiv b_1b_2 \ldots b_l \pmod{m}$.

Corollary 2. If $a \equiv b \pmod{m}$

then $a^r \equiv b^r \pmod{m}$.

V. If

$$a \equiv b \pmod{m_1}$$
$$a \equiv b \pmod{m_2}$$
$$\cdot\ \cdot\ \cdot\ \cdot\ \cdot$$
$$a \equiv b \pmod{m_l}$$

and if $M \equiv$ L. C. M. of $m_1m_2 \ldots m_l$,

then $a \equiv b \pmod{M}$.

Proof. By hypothesis $a-b=r_1m_1$

$$a-b=r_2m_2$$
$$\cdot\ \cdot\ \cdot\ \cdot$$
$$a-b=r_lm_l$$

and since $a-b$ is a multiple of $m_1, m_2 \ldots m_l$, it is a multiple of their least common multiple.

29. Those of the preceding properties that relate to a single modulus m, are analogous to the corresponding properties of algebraic equations; instead of "equal" we here say "congruent." These properties concern addition, subtraction and multiplication. We consider next the inverse operation of multiplication, namely, factoring, and shall see that in this case the analogy between the properties of equations and congruences is not so close.

In equations we know that if $ab=0$, then either $a=0$ or $b=0$. But we know that $4\cdot 6\equiv 0$ (mod. 12) while neither $4\equiv 0$ (mod. 12) nor $6\equiv 0$ (mod. 12). That is, from $ab\equiv 0$ (mod. m), we may not infer that necessarily either $a\equiv 0$ (mod. m) or $b\equiv 0$ (mod. m).

More generally, if we know that $ab=ac$, and that $a\neq 0$, we know that $b=c$.

But it is easy to show by an example that if $ab\equiv ac$(mod. m) and $a\not\equiv 0$ (mod. m) it does not necessarily follow that $b\equiv c$ (mod. m).

Thus: $2\cdot 21\equiv 2\cdot 17$ (mod. 8) and $2\not\equiv 0$ (mod. 8). But it is not true that $21\equiv 17$ (mod. 8).

The following property states what follows from $ab\equiv ac$ (mod. m).

VI. From $ab\equiv ac$ (mod. m), where a and m have the highest common factor d, it follows that

$$b\equiv c\left(\text{mod. }\frac{m}{d}\right).$$

Proof. The hypothesis means

$$ab=ac+km.$$

or

$$a(b-c)=km.$$

Since m is a factor of the left member and d is the largest factor of m that is a factor of a, it follows that $\frac{m}{d}$ is a factor of $b-c$. That is

$$b-c=k'\frac{m}{d},$$

or

$$b\equiv c\left(\text{mod. }\frac{m}{d}\right).$$

Corollary. Both members of any congruence may be divided by any factor that is prime to the modulus, but if the divisor have a factor common with the modulus, that factor must be taken out of the modulus also.

Thus:

(1) From $30 \equiv 78 \pmod{12}$,
it follows that $5 \equiv 13 \pmod{2}$.

(2) From $108 \equiv 192 \pmod{14}$,
it follows that $9 \equiv 16 \pmod{7}$.

(3) From $224 \equiv 44 \pmod{15}$,
it follows that $56 \equiv 11 \pmod{15}$.

30. Applications of the idea of congruence. The idea of congruence, together with the elementary properties that we have named, is sufficient for the solution of various interesting problems, of which we give a few examples.

I. *To find the remainder when large numbers are divided by a given number.*

(1) To find the remainder when 2^{40} is divided by 23:

We know that

$$2^5 = 32.$$

Hence $2^5 \equiv 9 \pmod{23}$.

Squaring $2^{10} \equiv 81 \pmod{23}$
$\equiv 12 \pmod{23}$.

Squaring $2^{20} \equiv 144 \pmod{23}$
$\equiv 6 \pmod{23}$.

Squaring $2^{40} \equiv 36 \pmod{23}$
$\equiv 13 \pmod{23}$.

That is, if 2^{40} is divided by 23 the remainder is 13.

(2) To show that $2^{2^5}+1$ has the factor 641 (sec. 10):

To show this it is sufficient to show that 2^{2^5} or 2^{32} has the remainder 640, or -1, when divided by 641.

We have

$$\begin{aligned} 2^2 &= 4, \\ 2^4 &= 16, \\ 2^8 &= (16)^2, \\ &= 256, \\ 2^{16} &= (256)^2 \\ &= 65{,}536 \\ &\equiv 154 \pmod{641}. \\ 2^{32} &\equiv (154)^2 \pmod{641} \\ &\equiv 23{,}716 \pmod{641} \\ &\equiv -1 \pmod{641}. \end{aligned}$$

In all such problems the work of multiplication is reduced by taking the absolutely least residue whether positive or negative.

(3) It is easily verified similarly that the following Mersenne's numbers (sec. 18), have the factor indicated:

Number	Factor
$2^{11}-1$	23
$2^{23}-1$	47
$2^{29}-1$	233
$2^{37}-1$	223
$2^{239}-1$	479
$2^{251}-1$	503

(4) At the expense of a somewhat longer computation it can be verified in precisely the same way that $2^{97}-1$ has the factor 11,447, that $2^{223}-1$ has the factor 18,287, that $2^{2^{12}}+1$ has the factor 114,689, and even the statement of sec. 10 with respect to $2^{2^{36}}+1$ could be verified by a calculation that would indeed be tedious in itself, but that nevertheless, in view of the enormous number whose factor is verified, would be a striking example of the power of the method.

It is easy to verify factors, such as the above, when once they are known, but it may be exceedingly difficult to find them.

II. *Criteria for divisibility.*

If the digits of a number N read from right to left are $a, b, c, d, e, f, g, \ldots$, we have

$$N = a + 10b + 10^2c + 10^3d + 10^4e + 10^5f + 10^6g + \ldots$$

(1) Since $10 \equiv 1 \pmod{9}$, and hence by sec. 28, IV. Cor. 2, $10^2 \equiv 1 \pmod{9}$, $10^3 \equiv 1 \pmod{9} \ldots$, we may write

$$N \equiv a + b + c + d + \ldots \pmod{9}.$$

If $a+b+c+d+\ldots$ is a multiple of 9, then N is a multiple of 9. This is the well-known criterion: *a number is a multiple of* 9 *if and only if the sum of its digits is a multiple of* 9.

(2) Since $10 \equiv -1 \pmod{11}$ and hence, $10^2 \equiv 1 \pmod{11}$, $10^3 \equiv -1 \pmod{11}$, $10^4 \equiv 1 \pmod{11}$, etc., we may write:

$$N \equiv a - b + c - d + e - f + \ldots \pmod{11}.$$

That is, *a number is a multiple of* 11 *if and only if the sum of the digits in the odd-numbered places diminished by the sum of the digits in the even numbered places is a multiple of* 11.

(3) Since $10^3+1=7\cdot 11\cdot 13$ we seek to obtain criteria for divisibility by 7, 11, or 13, by taking residues of the terms of N according to the modulus 10^3+1.

Since $10^3\equiv -1$ (mod. 10^3+1), we obtain according to sec. 28, III, the following congruences:

$$\left.\begin{aligned} 10^4 &\equiv -10 \\ 10^5 &\equiv -10^2 \\ 10^6 &\equiv -10^3 \equiv -(-1) \equiv 1 \\ 10^7 &\equiv 10 \\ 10^8 &\equiv 10^2 \\ &\text{etc.} \end{aligned}\right\} \pmod{10^3+1}.$$

Hence:

$$N\equiv (a+10b+10^2c)-(d+10e+10^2f) \\ +(g+10h+10^2j)-\ldots \pmod{10^3+1}.$$

Consequently we may state the following **criterion for divisibility by 7, 11, or 13.**

Beginning at the right, separate the given number into periods of three places each (the last period on the left may of course have fewer than three digits). Regard these periods as three place numbers and add them with alternating signs. If the algebraic sum thus obtained is divisible by 7, 11, *or* 13, *the original number is so divisible, and otherwise not.*

Thus: To examine 847,963,207 as to divisibility by 7, 11, and 13, we form

$$207-963+847=91.$$

Since 91 is divisible by 7 and 13 but not by 11, it follows that 847,963,207 is divisible by 7 and by 13 but not by 11.

On examining the proofs above it appears that when the given divisor is not a factor of the number, the residue of the division will be furnished by the same test. Divisibility is simply the case in which the residue is zero.

Thus, the residue when a number is divided by 9 is the same as the residue when the sum of its digits is divided by 9.

Likewise, the number 847,963,207 has the residue 3, when divided by 11, since 91 (found as above) has the residue 3 on division by 11.

31. Roots of congruences.

The congruence

$$a_0x^n+a_1x^{n-1}+a_2x^{n-2}+\ldots+a_{n-2}x^2+a_{n-1}x+a_n\equiv 0 \pmod{m}$$

where the a's are any numbers except that a_0 is not a multiple of m, is said to be of degree n in the unknown x.

Any number x_1, which, when substituted for x, makes the left member congruent to the right (mod. m) is said to **satisfy** the congruence and to be a **root** of the congruence.

If any number, x, is a root, all numbers congruent to x_1 (mod. m) also satisfy the congruence (sec. 26). But these are not regarded as different roots. Taken modulo m, the totality of all numbers that are congruent to x_1 are regarded as a single value, and any number whatever of the totality may be selected to represent it; the least positive residue (mod. m), for example, may be so chosen. The numbers 0, 1, 2, 3, . . . $m-1$, thus represent all the different values that exist (mod. m); if we test a congruence for these, no other possibilities remain.

It is easy to show by special examples that the properties of equations as to existence and number of roots do not hold unmodified for congruences.

Thus, the equation $ax=b$, always has one, and only one, root.

But we readily show by particular instances that the congruence

$$ax\equiv b \pmod{m}$$

may have:

(1) *No root at all.*

Example: $3x\equiv 5$ (mod. 9).

By trying the nine possible values for x,

$$x\equiv 0,\ 1,\ 2,\ 3,\ 4,\ 5,\ 6,\ 7,\ 8 \pmod{9},$$

it appears that none satisfies the congruence. This could also be seen without trial by writing the congruence in the form:

$$3x-5\equiv 0 \pmod{9}.$$

This means that x must be so chosen that $3x-5$ is a multiple of 9. But whatever the value of x, $3x-5$ is not even a multiple of 3, much less of 9.

(2) *One root.*

Example: $5x \equiv 3 \pmod{9}$.

By trying the nine possible values, it appears that the value 6, and no other, satisfies the congruence.

(3) *More than one root.*

Example: $6x \equiv 3 \pmod{9}$.

By trial it appears that the values 2, 5, 8, and no others satisfy the congruence.

The roots of such congruences will be discussed in more detail in the next section.

It is not difficult to prove the following theorem, which is somewhat analogous to the fundamental theorem of algebra that every equation of degree n has precisely n roots.*

Theorem. *A congruence of degree n, and with a prime modulus cannot have more than n roots.*

We omit the proof. The reader may supply it, following a line of argument analogous to that used for equations.†

32. Theoretic solution of the linear congruence in one unknown.

Given $ax \equiv b$ (mod. m).

It may be assumed that b is positive and less than m. If not given so it may readily be made so by addition or subtraction of a multiple of m.

Case I. a prime to m.

In ax substitute for x in turn the values $0, 1, 3 \ldots m-1$, obtaining

$$ax = 0,\ a,\ 2a,\ 3a,\ \ldots\ (m-1)a,$$

or taking least positive residues (mod. m)

$$ax \equiv c_0 (=0),\ c_1,\ c_2,\ c_3\ \ldots\ c_{m-1} \pmod{m}.$$

* See Monograph V, secs. 7, 10, and Monograph IV, Appendix II.

† See Monograph V, sec. 10.

Can any of the c's be equal? Suppose

$$c_k = c_h \qquad k > h$$

By definition $$ka = c_k + rm$$

and $$ha = c_h + sm.$$

If $c_k = c_h$, we obtain

$$(k-h)a = (r-s)m.$$

But a is prime to m, hence $k-h$ is a multiple of m. But $k-h$ is positive, and k is less than m, being some one of the numbers 1, 2 . . . $m-1$.

Hence $k-h$ is less than m. Since $k-h$ is positive and less than m, it cannot be a multiple of m. Therefore the supposition $c_k = c_h$ is incorrect, and the c's are all different. Since there are m of them, and each one is some one of the m numbers 0, 1, 2 . . . $m-1$, the fact that they are all different has as consequence that the whole set of the c's must be the numbers 0, 1, 2, 3 . . . $m-1$ in some order.

In the last set of numbers, the number b occurs once and only once. There is therefore exactly one c that is equal to b, or exactly one value of x such that $ax \equiv b$ (mod. m).

We have thus shown that: *a linear congruence in which the coefficient of the unknown is prime to the modulus has one and only one solution.*

Case II. Let a and m have the highest common factor d; $d > 1$.

The congruence $$ax \equiv b \text{ (mod. } m)$$

means $$ax = b + km.$$

Since a and m have the factor d, this equation cannot be true if b does not also have the factor d. That is, if $b \not\equiv 0$ (mod. d), our congruence has no solution.

Let $$b \equiv 0 \text{ (mod. } d),$$

and let
$$a = a_1 d$$
$$b = b_1 d$$
$$m = m_1 d$$

(a_1 is prime to m_1, since d is the highest common factor of a and m).

Then we may divide the given congruence, including the modulus, by d, obtaining

$$a_1x \equiv b_1 \text{ (mod. } m_1).$$

By Property III, sec. 28, every root of this congruence is a root of the given congruence.

This congruence falls under the previous case, and has one and only one root. Let this root be r. Then all numbers of the form $r+km_1$ are equivalent so far as the modulus m_1 is concerned. All these numbers satisfy the given congruence. But are they equivalent to a single solution with respect to its modulus, m?

Let $r+k_1m_1$ and $r+k_2m_1$ ($k_1>k_2$) be equivalent according to the modulus m. That is:

$$r+k_1m_1 \equiv r+k_2m_1 \text{ (mod. } m)$$

or

$$(k_1-k_2)m_1 \equiv 0 \text{ (mod. } m).$$

Hence, dividing the members of the congruence and the modulus by m_1, we obtain

$$k_1-k_2 \equiv 0 \text{ (mod. } d)$$

or

$$k_1 \equiv k_2 \text{ (mod. } d).$$

That is, two numbers of the form $r+km_1$ are congruent, (mod. m) if, and only if, the values of k are congruent (mod. d).

Accordingly the given congruence has d solutions, obtained from the expression $r+km_1$ by giving k in turn the values $0, 1, 2, 3 \ldots d-1$.

EXAMPLES:

(1) $$12x \equiv 6 \quad \text{(mod. 15)}.$$

Here $$d=3, \quad m_1=5.$$

Dividing through by d,

$$4x \equiv 2 \quad \text{(mod. 5)}.$$

By trial, it is seen that this congruence is satisfied by $x \equiv 3 \pmod{5}$. Here $r=3$, and $r+km_1$ becomes $3+5k$. By giving k the values 0, 1, 2, we obtain the three roots (mod. 15), 3, 8, 13.

(2) $$8x \equiv 12 \quad (\text{mod. } 28).$$

Here $$d=4, \quad m_1=7.$$

Dividing through by 4,

$$2x \equiv 3 \quad (\text{mod. } 7).$$

By trial, this is seen to be satisfied by $x \equiv 5 \pmod{7}$. Here $r=5$, and $r+km_1$ becomes $5+7k$. Giving k the values 0, 1, 2, 3, we obtain the four roots of the given congruence: 5, 12, 19, 26 (mod. 28).

33. Numerical solution of the congruence ax ≡ b (mod. m). The preceding considerations merely proved the existence of one or more roots in certain cases, but provided no method other than trial for finding their numerical value. It will be sufficient to find such a method for the case, a prime to m, for we have seen above that the solution of a congruence in which a is not prime to m, may be accomplished by the solution of a congruence in which a is prime to m.

We assert further that the solution of $ax \equiv b$ (mod. m) can readily be found by means of the solution of $ax \equiv 1$ (mod. m). For let r be a root of the latter congruence; then

$$ar \equiv 1 \ (\text{mod. } m),$$

and, multiplying both members by b,

$$a(br) \equiv b \ (\text{mod. } m).$$

That is, br is the solution of the original congruence. The problem is then reduced to solving the congruence:

$$ax \equiv 1 \ (\text{mod. } m).$$

In this congruence there are really two unknowns, x and the multiple of the modulus, call it y. That is, we seek values of x and y to satisfy the equation:

$$ax = 1 + my$$

or $$ax - my = 1.$$

But the last equation is familiar from the theory of continued fractions.* If the fraction $\frac{a}{m}$ is developed into a continued fraction, and if $\frac{Y}{X}$ is the last convergent before the value $\frac{a}{m}$ is reached, it is known that the relation $aX-mY=\pm 1$ holds.

Hence either X or $-X$ is a root of $ax\equiv 1$ (mod. m)

We have thus established the following rule for the computation of the root of $ax\equiv b$ (mod. m).

Develop $\frac{a}{m}$ into a continued fraction. The denominator of the last convergent before $\frac{a}{m}$ is reached will be the absolute value of the root of $ax\equiv 1$ (mod. m). Determine by trial which sign is to be taken; the value thus obtained multiplied by b is the root of $ax\equiv b$ (mod. m).

*** It will be recalled that expressions of the form**

$$a+\cfrac{1}{b+\cfrac{1}{c+\cfrac{1}{d+\dots}}}$$

, a an integer, $b, c, d, \dots$, integers>0, are called continued fractions.

Every rational fraction can be expressed as a terminated continued fraction. Thus,

$$-\frac{29}{11}=-3+\frac{4}{11}=-3+\cfrac{1}{\frac{11}{4}}=-3+\cfrac{1}{2+\frac{3}{4}}=-3+\cfrac{1}{2+\cfrac{1}{\frac{4}{3}}}=-3+\cfrac{1}{2+\cfrac{1}{1+\frac{1}{3}}}.$$

The fractions, $\frac{a}{1}$, $a+\frac{1}{b}$, $a+\cfrac{1}{b+\frac{1}{c}}$, etc., are called the first, second, third . . . , convergents of the continued fraction. Thus the convergents of the fraction used as example above, are -3, $-3+\frac{1}{2}$, $-3+\cfrac{1}{2+\frac{1}{1}}$, $-3+\cfrac{1}{2+\cfrac{1}{1+\frac{1}{3}}}$, or in reduced form, -3, $-\frac{5}{2}$, $-\frac{8}{3}$, $-\frac{29}{11}$.

For proof of the property used in the main text, see works on college algebra.

For example:

$$49x \equiv 23 \pmod{125}.$$

$$\frac{49}{125}=\cfrac{1}{2+\cfrac{1}{1+\cfrac{1}{1+\cfrac{1}{4+\cfrac{1}{2+\cfrac{1}{2}}}}}}$$

The last convergent is $\frac{20}{51}$.

Hence $X=51$. By trial we find,

$$49 \cdot 51 \equiv -1 \pmod{125},$$

that is -51 is a solution of $49x \equiv 1 \pmod{125}$. Multiplying -51 by 23 we obtain a solution of the original congruence

$$23(-51) \equiv 77 \pmod{125}.$$

$\therefore$ 77 is the solution of the original congruence, as may be verified by substitution.

The reader may solve and verify similarly other congruences taken at random, such as:

$$83x \equiv 7 \pmod{96}; \quad 11x \equiv 81 \pmod{85};$$

$$72x \equiv 27 \pmod{75}; \quad 75x \equiv 73 \pmod{85};$$

and the like.

34. Fermat's Theorem. *If p is a prime, and a is prime to p then $a^{p-1} \equiv 1 \pmod{p}$.**

Proof. We have already proved (sec. 32) that the numbers

$$a, 2a, 3a \ldots (p-1)a$$

are congruent (mod. p) to the residues

$$1, 2, 3 \ldots p-1$$

---

* Announced without proof by *Fermat* in 1679; first proved by *Euler* in 1736. The Chinese are thought to have known this theorem for the case $a=2$, as early as 500 B.C.

in some order.* Multiplying these congruences together we have

$$a\cdot 2a\cdot 3a\ \ldots\ (p-1)a\equiv 1\cdot 2\cdot 3\ \ldots\ p\cdot a^{p-1}\ (\text{mod. } p).$$

Dividing both members by 1, 2, 3 . . . $p-1$, which is prime to the modulus, we obtain the desired result,

$$a^{p-1}\equiv 1\ (\text{mod. } p).$$

35. Applications. (1) Find a congruence equivalent to the following, but of degree lower than 13:

$$x^{27}+3x^{25}+4x^{18}-3x^{17}+6x^{13}-2x^{7}+11x-5\equiv 0\quad (\text{mod. } 13).$$

By inspection it is evident that $x\equiv 0$ (mod. 13) does not satisfy this congruence; we accordingly know that any root x is prime to 13, and hence that $x^{13-1}\equiv 1$(mod. 13). Further,

$$\begin{aligned} x^{27} &= (x^{12})^2\cdot x^3\equiv (1)^2x^3\equiv x^3 && (\text{mod. } 13),\\ 3x^{25} &= 3(x^{12})^2\cdot x\equiv 3x && (\text{mod. } 13),\\ 4x^{18} &= 4x^{12}\cdot x^6\equiv 4x^6 && (\text{mod. } 13),\\ 3x^{17} &\equiv 3x^5 && (\text{mod. } 13),\\ 6x^{13} &\equiv 6x. && (\text{mod. } 13). \end{aligned}$$

Substituting these results in the original congruence, we obtain,

$$-2x^7+4x^6-3x^5+x^3+20x-5\equiv 0\quad (\text{mod. } 13).$$

(2) To find the remainder when 47^{7385} is divided by 17.

Dividing 7385 by $17-1$ or 16, we have,

$$7385=461\cdot 16+9.$$

$$\therefore\quad 47^{7385}=(47^{16})^{461}\cdot 47^9$$

$$\equiv (1)^{461}\cdot 47^9\quad (\text{mod. } 17).$$

$$47=2\cdot 17+13\quad \text{or}\quad 47\equiv 13\quad (\text{mod. } 17).$$

Hence, by sec. 28, IV, Cor. 2,

$$(47)^9\equiv 13^9\quad (\text{mod. } 17),$$

or,

$$47^{7385}\equiv 13^9\quad (\text{mod. } 17).$$

---

* This statement follows at once from the result in sec. 32, if we remember that $0\equiv 0$ (mod. p).

We proceed to work out 13^9:

$$13^2 = 169$$
$$\equiv -1 \quad (\text{mod. } 17).$$

Squaring $\quad 13^4 \equiv 1 \quad (\text{mod. } 17).$

Squaring again, $\quad 13^8 \equiv 1 \quad (\text{mod. } 17).$

Multiplying both members by 13,

$$13^9 \equiv 13 \quad (\text{mod. } 17).$$

$\therefore \quad 47^{7385} \equiv 13 \quad (\text{mod. } 17).$

The remainder is 13.

The reader may solve similarly other problems of this sort taken at random. For example, to find the remainder when 123^{7841} is divided by 29; when 300^{67489} is divided by 41, and the like.

(3) If n is any integer greater than 1, show that $n^{13}-n$ has the factor 2730.

Since $2730 = 2 \cdot 3 \cdot 5 \cdot 7 \cdot 13$, it is sufficient to show that $n^{13}-n$ has each of these primes as factor.

The factor 2. $\quad n^{13}-n = n(n^{12}-1)$.

If n is even the factor 2 is present. If n is odd we must show that $n^{12}-1$ is even. This is evident at once, since any power of an odd number is odd; hence n^{12} is odd and $n^{12}-1$ is even.

It also appears by Fermat's theorem thus:

Since n is prime to 2,

$$n^{2-1} \equiv 1 \quad (\text{mod. } 2).$$

$\therefore \quad n^{12} = (n^{2-1})^{12} \equiv 1 \quad (\text{mod. } 2),$

or, $\quad n^{12}-1 \equiv 0 \quad (\text{mod. } 2).$

The factor 3. As above, unless n is a multiple of 3, we must show that $n^{12}-1$ is a multiple of 3.

But by Fermat's theorem,

$$n^{3-1} \equiv 1 \quad (\text{mod. } 3).$$

$\therefore \quad n^{12} = (n^{3-1})^6 \equiv 1 \quad (\text{mod. } 3),$

and $\quad n^{12}-1 \equiv 0 \quad (\text{mod. } 3).$

Similarly by writing our given expression in the forms,

$$n[(n^{5-1})^3-1], \quad n[(n^{7-1})^2-1], \quad n[n^{13-1}-1],$$

we show that it must have the factors 5, 7, and 13, and the proof is completed.

(4) Show that every prime number (except 2 and 5) is a factor of a boundless number of numbers all of whose digits are 9's.

Let p be a prime other than 2 or 5. Then 10^n is prime to p. Hence, by Fermat's theorem,

$$(10^n)^{p-1}-1\equiv 0 \pmod{p}.$$

This is true for every n.

The number $(10^n)^{p-1}-1$ always consists of 9's exclusively, and hence the theorem is proved.

(5) The congruence $ax\equiv b \pmod{p}$, where a is prime to p, can be solved by multiplying both members by a^{p-2} and applying Fermat's theorem, with the result, $x\equiv ba^{p-2} \pmod{p}$.

36. Wilson's Theorem. *If p is a prime,* $(p-1)!\equiv -1 \pmod{p}$.*

For $p=2$, the theorem is obviously true.

We accordingly suppose $p>2$, and to prove the theorem for this case, first prove the following lemma:

Lemma. *The root of the congruence $ax\equiv 1 \pmod{p}$ is congruent to a, if, and only if, $a\equiv 1$ or $a\equiv p-1 \pmod{p}$.*

Proof. By sec. 32 the congruence

$$ax\equiv 1 \pmod{p}$$

has one root. Suppose it to be a. Then

$$a^2\equiv 1 \pmod{p}$$

or

$$(a-1)(a+1)\equiv 0 \pmod{p}.$$

But a product is a multiple of a prime p, if and only if one of its factors is a multiple of p. Hence, either $a-1\equiv 0$ or $a+1\equiv 0$, (mod. p). That is the root of the congruence $ax\equiv 1 \pmod{p}$ can be congruent to a only if $a\equiv 1$, or $p-1 \pmod{p}$. It can readily be verified that the root is congruent to a in these cases, and the lemma is thus proved.

---

* First published, without proof, by *Waring* in his Meditationes Algebraicæ, Cambridge, 1770, and ascribed by him to *J. Wilson*. It was proved by *Euler* in 1773, and by *Gauss* in his Disquisitiones Arithmeticæ, 1801.

If now a_1 is one of the numbers 2, 3, 4 . . . $p-2$, the root of the congruence $a_1x \equiv 1$ (mod. p) will, by the lemma, be different from a_1; calling the root a_2, we have $a_1a_2 \equiv 1$ (mod. p).

Consider next a_3, a third number of the set above. Denote the root of the congruence, $a_3x \equiv 1$ (mod. p) by a_4. Then we have $a_3a_4 \equiv 1$ (mod. p), and by the lemma, a_4 is not congruent to a_3. We show further that it is not congruent to a_2. For, if $a_2 \equiv a_4$ (mod. p), then multiplying both members by a_3,

$$a_3a_2 \equiv a_3a_4 \text{ (mod. } p)$$

or $$a_3a_2 \equiv 1 \text{ (mod. } p).$$

But we know $$a_1a_2 \equiv 1 \text{ (mod. } p).$$

$$\therefore \quad a_3a_2 \equiv a_1a_2 \text{ (mod. } p).$$

Dividing both numbers by a_2

$$a_3 \equiv a_1 \text{ (mod. } p).$$

This is contrary to the choice of a_3 as different from a_1. Hence the hypothesis $a_2 \equiv ax$ (mod. p) is incorrect. Similarly, it appears that $a_4 \not\equiv a_1$ (mod. p).

If now a_5 is a fifth number of the set different from the form already considered, and if a_6 denote the root of the congruence $a_5x \equiv 1$ (mod. p), then by the same reasoning as above it appears that a_6 is not congruent to any one of the numbers a_1 . . . a_5. Continuing in the same way, the entire set of numbers 2, 3, . . . $p-2$ can be grouped in pairs such that the product of the numbers in each pair is congruent 1 (mod. p).

That is
$$\left.\begin{array}{r} a_1a_2 \equiv 1 \\ a_3a_4 \equiv 1 \\ \cdot\ \cdot\ \cdot\ \cdot \\ a_{p-4}a_{p-3} \equiv 1 \\ p-1 \equiv -1 \end{array}\right\} \text{(mod. } p).$$

We know further that $p-1 \equiv -1$

Multiplying all these congruences member by member and remembering that the a's are the numbers 2, 3, . . . $p-2$ in some order, we obtain

$$2\cdot 3\cdot \ldots \cdot(p-2)(p-1)\equiv -1 \pmod{p}$$

or

$$(p-1)!\equiv -1 \pmod{p}.$$

37. Wilson's theorem does not hold for composite moduli. For if m is a composite number, and k is one of its factors, $(1<k<m)$, then $(m-1)!$ will have k as a factor, and consequently $(m-1)!+1$ will not be a multiple of k and, therefore, not of m.

Accordingly, Wilson's theorem furnishes a theoretically complete criterion for determining whether or not a given number n is prime. Namely, form $(n-1)!$; divide it by n; if the residue -1 can be obtained, n is a prime; otherwise, n is composite. But with large numbers, this method is of no practical use, on account of the enormous calculations that would be required.

38. Applications. (1) If p is a prime number, the residue when $1\cdot 2\cdot 3\ldots p-1$ is divided by $1+2+3+\ldots+(p-1)$ is $p-1$. In symbols:

$$(p-1)!\equiv p-1 \quad (\text{mod. } \overline{1+2+3+\ldots+p-1}).$$

By Wilson's theorem,

$$1\cdot 2\cdot 3\ldots p-1=-1+kp$$
$$=(k-1)p+(p-1).$$

As the left member has the factor $p-1$, and the second term on the right is $p-1$, it follows that $(k-1)p$ must have the factor $p-1$, and since $p-1$ is prime to p, that $k-1$ has the factor $p-1$.

Let

$$k-1=h(p-1).$$

Substituting, we obtain,

$$1\cdot 2\cdot 3\ldots p-1=h(p-1)p+p-1$$
$$=2h\frac{(p-1)p}{2}+p-1.$$

But $\dfrac{(p-1)p}{2}=1+2+\ldots+(p-1)$.

Hence the assertion is proved.

(2) If a prime of the form $4n+1$, then $(1\cdot2\cdot3\ldots2n)^2+1$ is a multiple of p.

By Wilson's theorem,

$$1\cdot2\cdot3\ldots(p-1)+1\equiv0 \pmod{p}.$$

Or $$1\cdot2\cdot3\ldots2n(2n+1)\ldots(4n-2)(4n-1)(4n)+1\equiv0 \pmod{p}. \quad (1)$$

But, since $p=4n+1$,

$$4n\equiv-1 \pmod{p},$$

$$4n-1\equiv-2 \pmod{p},$$

$$\cdot\quad\cdot\quad\cdot\quad\cdot\quad\cdot\quad\cdot\quad\cdot$$

$$2n+2\equiv-(2n-1) \pmod{p},$$

$$2n+1\equiv-2n \pmod{p}.$$

$$\therefore (2n+1)(2n+2)\ldots(4n-1)(4n)\equiv(-1)^{2n}1\cdot2\cdot3\ldots2n \pmod{p}. \quad (2)$$

From (2) and (1),

$$[1\cdot2\cdot3\ldots2n]^2+1\equiv0 \pmod{p}.$$

V. BINOMIAL CONGRUENCES

39. Definition. Congruences of the form $x^n-A\equiv0 \pmod{m}$ are called **binomial congruences.**

We shall consider only $x^n-1\equiv0 \pmod{p}$ where p is a prime. By Fermat's theorem (sec. 34) we can always make $n<p$. If $p=2$, the congruence is linear (since $n<p$), and has already been solved. We accordingly suppose throughout the subject of binomial congruences that p is a prime greater than 2.

40. The solutions of $x^m\equiv1 \pmod{p}$ where m is any positive integer, must be prime to p, and are therefore, by Fermat's theorem, also solutions of:

$$x^{p-1}\equiv1 \pmod{p}.$$

Further, by sec. 28, IV., Cor. 2, every solution of

$$x^m\equiv1 \pmod{p}$$

will also be a solution of

$$x^{km}\equiv1 \pmod{p}, \qquad \text{for every } k.$$

41. Theorem. *If α is a root of* $x^n \equiv 1$ (mod. p) *and also of* $x^q \equiv 1$ (mod. p) *and if d is the highest common factor of n and q, then α is a root of* $x^d \equiv 1$(mod. p).

Proof. Let $n = n'd$, $q = q'd$. Then n' and q' are relatively prime, and the congruence:

$$n'z \equiv 1 \text{ (mod. } q')$$

admits one solution (sec. 32). That is, there exist numbers z and y satisfying the equation

$$n'z = 1 + yq'$$

or

$$n'z - yq' = 1;$$

or, multiplying through by d,

$$nz - yq = d.$$

By hypothesis: $\alpha^n \equiv 1$ (mod. p); hence $\alpha^{nz} \equiv 1$ (mod. p) and $\alpha q \equiv 1$ (mod p); hence $\alpha^{qy} \equiv 1$ (mod. p).

Subtracting:

$$\alpha^{nz} - \alpha^{qy} \equiv 0 \text{ (mod. } p)$$

or

$$\alpha^{qy}(\alpha^{nz-qy} - 1) \equiv 0 \text{ (mod. } p).$$

Since α must be prime to p,

$$\alpha^{nz-qy} - 1 \equiv 0 \text{ (mod. } p)$$

or

$$\alpha^d - 1 \equiv 0 \text{ (mod. } p).$$

That is:

$$\alpha \text{ is a root of } x^d \equiv 1 \text{ (mod. } p).$$

Corollary. If d is the highest common factor of n and $p-1$, the solutions of $x^n \equiv 1$ (mod. p) satisfy also $x^d \equiv 1$ (mod. p).

It is accordingly sufficient to consider only congruences of the type:

$$x^d \equiv 1 \text{ (mod. } p), \qquad d, \text{ a divisor of } p-1.$$

42. Definition. The number a is said to **belong** to the exponent d (mod. p), if $a^d \equiv 1$ (mod. p) and if $a^y \not\equiv 1$ (mod. p), whenever $y < d$.

43. Theorem. *If a belongs to the exponent d* (mod. p), *then* $a^t \equiv 1$ (mod. p) *if and only if t is a multiple of d.*

Proof. Let $a^t \equiv 1$ (mod. p) and let D be the highest common factor of t and d. Hence by sec. 41, $a^D \equiv 1$ (mod. p). If t is not a multiple of d, $D < d$, and in this case a would satisfy a congruence of degree D, less than d, the exponent to which a belongs. Hence t must be a multiple of d.

44. Theorem. *If a belongs to the exponent r, and b belongs to the exponent s* (mod. p) *and if r and s are relatively prime, then ab belongs to the exponent rs* (mod. p).

Proof. The hypotheses mean that:

$$a^r \equiv 1 \pmod{p}$$

$$b^s \equiv 1 \pmod{p},$$

and that a and b satisfy no congruences of this type of lower degree. We have to prove (i) that $(ab)^{rs} \equiv 1$ (mod. p), and (ii) that no lower power of ab is congruent to 1 (mod. p).

(i)
$$(ab)^{rs} = a^{rs}b^{rs} = (a^r)^s \cdot (b^s)^r$$
$$\equiv 1^s \cdot 1^r \pmod{p}$$
$$\equiv 1 \pmod{p}.$$

(ii) Let k be any exponent such that

$$(ab)^k \equiv 1 \pmod{p}.$$

Then
$$a^k \cdot b^k \equiv 1 \pmod{p}.$$

Raising both members to the power r,

$$a^{rk}b^{rk} \equiv 1 \pmod{p}.$$

or, since
$$a^r \equiv 1 \pmod{p}$$

$$b^{rk} \equiv 1 \pmod{p}.$$

Hence, since b belongs to s, rk is a multiple of s, by sec. 43, and therefore since r is prime to s, k is a multiple of s. Quite similarly, it may be shown that k is a multiple of r. Hence, since r and s are relatively prime, k is a multiple of rs.

Hence the lowest value of k is rs itself, and the proof that ab belongs to rs is completed.

45. If r and s are not relatively prime, and if m denote their least common multiple, it can be proved in an analogous manner that a number belonging to m can be determined by means of a and b.

46. Theorem. *To every divisor, d, of p−1, there belongs (mod. p) at least one number a.*

Proof. (1) We take up first the case: $d = q^\alpha$, where q is a prime.

Then the congruence:

$$x^{p-1} - 1 \equiv 0 \text{ (mod. } p), \quad . \quad . \quad . \quad . \quad . \quad (1)$$

may be written

$$x^{fq^\alpha} - 1 \equiv 0 \text{ (mod. } p); \quad . \quad . \quad . \quad . \quad . \quad (2)$$

or

$$(x^{q^\alpha} - 1)(x^{(f-1)q^\alpha} + x^{(f-2)q^\alpha} + \ldots + x^{q^\alpha} + 1) \equiv 0 \text{ (mod. } p). \quad . \quad (3)$$

But by Fermat's theorem the congruence (1) is satisfied for every value of x except those $\equiv 0$ (mod. p). Accordingly the congruence (3) has the maximum number of roots. But since neither factor of the left member of (3) can be congruent zero for more roots than there are units in its degree, it follows that each factor is congruent zero for as many roots as there are units in its degree. In particular:

$$x^{q^\alpha} - 1 \equiv 0 \text{ (mod. } p) \quad . \quad . \quad . \quad . \quad . \quad . \quad (4)$$

has q^α roots. Some of these will also satisfy congruences of this type and of lower degree. By secs. 41, 40, all such roots will satisfy $x^{q^{\alpha-1}} - 1 \equiv 0$ (mod. p). But by what has just been proved this congruence has precisely $q^{\alpha-1}$ roots. Hence (sec. 40), there are precisely $q^\alpha - q^{\alpha-1}$ or $q^{\alpha-1}(q-1)$ roots of the congruence (4) that satisfy no congruence of lower degree. That is, there exist precisely $q^{\alpha-1}(q-1)$ incongruent numbers belonging to the exponent q^α (mod. p).

(2) Case, d any divisor of $p-1$.

Let $d=q^{\alpha}r^{\beta}s^{\gamma}$ . . ., where q, r, s are different primes. Then by (1), there exists a number, call it a, belonging to q^{α}; and there exists a number, call it b, belonging to r^{β}. Hence, by the theorem of sec. 44, ab belongs to $q^{\alpha}r^{\beta}$.

By (1) there exists a number, call it c, belonging to s^{γ}. Since $q^{\alpha}r^{\beta}$ and s^{γ} are relatively prime, $(ab)c$ belongs to $q^{\alpha}r^{\beta}s^{\gamma}$. Continuing in this way, all the factors of d are used, and the existence of a number belonging to d is established.

Corollary. There exists at least one number, call it g, belonging to $p-1$.

47. Definition. If g belongs to the exponent $p-1$, then g is called a **primitive root** of the congruence

$$x^{p-1}\equiv 1 \pmod{p},$$

or briefly, a primitive root of p.

48. Theorem. *If g is a primitive root of p, the numbers g, g^2, g^3 . . . g^{p-1} are distinct* (mod. p) *and have the residues* 1, 2, 3 . . . $p-1$ *in some order.*

Proof. Suppose $g^h\equiv g^k \qquad \pmod{p}\ p-1 \geqq h > k \geqq 1.$

Then $\qquad g^{h-k}\equiv 1 \pmod{p}.$

But $p-1>h-k\geqq 1$. Hence this result contradicts the hypothesis that g is a primitive root of p. Consequently, the $p-1$ powers, g, g^2, . . . g^{p-1}, all have different residues (mod. p), and therefore have the residues 1, 2, 3 . . . $p-1$ in some order.

49. Theorem. *If g is a primitive root of p, and if k is prime to $p-1$, g^k is a primitive root of p.*

Proof. Let $\qquad (g^k)^h\equiv 1 \pmod{p}.$

Then, since g belongs to exponent $p-1$,

$$kh\equiv 0 \pmod{p-1}.$$

Hence, since k is relatively prime to $p-1$,

$$h\equiv 0 \pmod{p-1}.$$

The lowest admissible value of h is therefore $p-1$; that is, g^k belongs to the exponent $p-1$, and is hence a primitive root of p.

Corollary. There are $\phi(p-1)$ primitive roots of p.

50. The actual value of a primitive root may be found by trial, if the modulus is small.

Thus, for $p=17$, we try 2,

$$\begin{array}{llll} 2=2 & & 2^5\equiv-2 & (\text{mod. } 17) \\ 2^2=4 & & 2^6\equiv-4 & (\text{mod. } 17) \\ 2^3=8 & & 2^7\equiv-8 & (\text{mod. } 17) \\ 2^4=16 & & 2^8\equiv-16 & (\text{mod. } 17) \\ \quad\equiv-1 & (\text{mod. } 17) & \quad\equiv 1 & (\text{mod. } 17) \end{array}$$

That is, 2 belongs to the exponent 8, and is not a primitive root of 17. Nor can any of the residues obtained, 2, 4, 8, 16, 15 ($\equiv-2$), 13, 9, 1, be primitive roots. For they are all of the form 2^k and $(2^k)^8$ or 2^{8k} is $\equiv 1$ (mod. p) since 2^8 is so. Hence all of these residues belong either to 8 or to a divisor of 8.

The smallest number not in the above list is 3. Trying 3 it is found to belong to the exponent 16; that is, 3 is a primitive root of 17.

It can also be proved without trial that 3 must be a primitive root. For, since $\phi(16)=8$, 17 has 8 primitive roots. But there are 8 residues of 2^k, none of which is a primitive root, consequently, each one of the 8 other non-zero residues must be a primitive root. In particular, 3 is a primitive root.

If the second trial likewise does not lead to a primitive root, the theorems above (secs. 44, 45) enable us to determine a number belonging to the least common multiple of the two exponents. If this least common multiple is $p-1$ itself, we have found a primitive root. If not, we have at least a number belonging to a much larger exponent, and all its powers are thus excluded from further consideration. In this way, systematic trial enables us to find a primitive root.

For large primes, the calculations may become laborious. Some general theorems are known as to primitive roots. For example: *If a prime is of the form* $2^{2n}+1$, *it has the primitive root* 3.

If a prime p *is of the form* $8n+3$, *and if* $4n+1$ *is also prime,* p *has the primitive root* 2.*

* *Tschebyscheff*, Theorie der Congruenzen, Berlin, 1889, p. 306, et seq., where others are given and proved.

VI. QUADRATIC CONGRUENCES

51. The most general congruence of the second degree in one unknown is:

$$ax^2+bx+c\equiv 0 \text{ (mod. } m).$$

We simplify the form of this as follows: Multiply both members and the modulus by $4a$,

$$4a^2x^2+4abx+4ac\equiv 0 \text{ (mod. } 4am).$$

(The modulus is multiplied also, so that the inverse operation may always be possible);

or: $$(2ax+b)^2-b^2+4ac\equiv 0 \text{ (mod. } 4am).$$

Putting $$y\equiv 2ax+b \text{ (mod. } 4am)$$

$$d\equiv b^2-4ac \text{ (mod. } 4am)$$

the congruence becomes:

$$y^2\equiv d \text{ (mod. } 4am).$$

From the values of y, we find the values of x, by solution of the linear congruence:

$$y\equiv 2ax+b\text{(mod. } 4am).$$

52. If $4am=p_1^{k_1}\cdot p_2^{k_2}\cdot \ldots p_l^{k_l}$, where p_1, $p_2 \ldots p_2$ are different primes, any number that satisfies the congruence:

$$y^2-d\equiv 0 \text{ (mod. } 4am) \quad \ldots\ldots \quad (1)$$

will also satisfy each of the congruences:

$$\left.\begin{array}{c} y^2-d\equiv 0 \text{ (mod. } p_1^{k_1}) \\ \ldots\ldots \\ y^2-d\equiv 0 \text{ (mod. } p_l^{k_l}) \end{array}\right\} \ldots\ldots (2)$$

Conversely, the definition of a congruence shows that any number that satisfies each of the congruences (2), satisfies also congruence (1).

53. The solution of the general quadratic congruence is thus reduced to that of the type:

$$x^2 - a \equiv 0 \text{ (mod. } p^k\text{)}, \quad \text{where } p \text{ is a prime.}$$

Any solution of this congruence is also a solution of:

$$x^2 - a \equiv 0 \text{ (mod. } p^h\text{)}, \quad \text{where } h < k,$$

and, in particular, of:

$$x^2 - a \equiv 0 \text{ (mod. } p \text{ . . . . (3)}$$

We shall restrict further consideration to congruences of this type, and as preliminary example take the modulus 7. Forming the squares of the seven least positive residues (mod. 7) we have:

$$0^2 \equiv 0 \quad 2^2 \equiv 4 \quad 4^2 \equiv 2 \quad 6^2 \equiv 1 \quad \text{(mod. 7)}$$
$$1^2 \equiv 1 \quad 3^2 \equiv 2 \quad 5^2 \equiv 4$$

We see from this that the congruence

$$x^2 \equiv a \text{ (mod. 7)}$$

has a solution if $a \equiv 0, 1, 2, 4$, but has no solution if $a \equiv 3, 5, 6$.

The former numbers are residues of squares according to the modulus 7, or briefly quadratic residues of 7; the latter numbers are not such residues.

54. Definition. If the congruence $x^2 \equiv a$ (mod. p) admits a solution, the number a is called a **quadratic residue of p**: otherwise it is called a **quadratic non-residue of p.** When there is no danger of misinterpretation, the word "quadratic" is often omitted for brevity.

55. It can be proved without much difficulty that the product of two residues of p is also a residue; that the product of two non-residues is a residue; and that the product of a residue and a non-residue is a non-residue.

56. These results can be stated in the form of a single equation by the use of the symbol $\left(\frac{a}{p}\right)$* which is defined as

* Introduced by *Legendre*, and known as "Legendre's symbol."

having the value $+1$, if a is a residue of p, and -1, if a is a non-residue of p. Then we have always:

$$\left(\frac{a}{p}\right)\left(\frac{b}{p}\right)=\left(\frac{ab}{p}\right).$$

It follows that if

$$m=(-1)^a 2^b p_1{}^c p_2{}^d \ldots$$

then:
$$\left(\frac{m}{p}\right)=\left(\frac{-1}{p}\right)^a\left(\frac{2}{p}\right)^b\left(\frac{p_1}{p}\right)^c\left(\frac{p_2}{p}\right)^d \cdots.$$

57. To determine whether or not any number m is a residue of p, it is sufficient to determine whether or not -1, 2, and the odd prime factors of m are residues of p.

The following results may be proved:

I. $$\left(\frac{-1}{p}\right)=(-1)^{\frac{p-1}{2}}.$$

II. $$\left(\frac{2}{p}\right)=(-1)^{\frac{p^2-1}{8}}.$$

III. $$\left(\frac{p}{q}\right)\left(\frac{q}{p}\right)=(-1)^{\frac{p-1}{2}\cdot\frac{q-1}{2}}. \qquad (p,\ q \text{ odd primes}).$$

58. The last is an important theorem, known as **Legendre's Law of Reciprocity,** and may be stated as follows: *If p and q are two odd primes and if at least one of them is of the form* $4n+1$, *then q is a residue of p, if and only if p is a residue of q, while if both p and q are of the form* $4n+3$, *then q is a residue of p when p is a non-residue of q, and vice versa.*

This theorem was discovered empirically by *Euler* (1783), announced in its general form by *Legendre* (1785), and partly proved by him. The first complete proof was, however, due to *Gauss*, who gave eight distinct proofs. Many others have been given down to the present time.* For further information and for a full presentation of some of the proofs, the reader is referred to the works mentioned in the Bibliography.

* A chronological list of 49 proofs, extending from the first proof, published by *Gauss* in 1801, to three proofs by *Lange* in 1896–97, is given in *Bachmann*, Niedere Zahlentheorie, I, pp. 203–4.

VII. BIBLIOGRAPHY

59. The classic work in our subject is the Disquisitiones Arithmeticæ of *C. F. Gauss*, published in 1801, when *Gauss* was only twenty-four years of age, and really completed a few years earlier. In this work *Gauss* gave a masterly presentation of the subject which has remained unequalled; unlike many masterpieces, it is written so clearly and simply that much of it is intelligible to the beginner. A German translation by *Maser* (Berlin, 1889), and a French translation by *Poullet-Delisle* (Paris, 1807), make the work more widely accessible.

The following texts also take up the subject from the beginning, reaching varying degrees of advancement:

Dirichlet-Dedekind, Zahlentheorie, Braunschweig, 4th ed., 1894.

Bachmann, Niedere Zahlentheorie, I, Leipzig, 1902.

Cahen, Théorie des Nombres, Paris, 1900.

Mathews, Theory of Numbers, I, Cambridge, 1892.

These works contain numerous references, both to the older and the contemporary literature. An excellent sketch of the principal results and present state of our subject is given in the Encyclopädie der Mathematischen Wissenschaften, Band I, 2ter Teil, appearing with additions in the French translation, Encyclopédie des Sciences Mathématiques, Tome I, Vol. III.

The theory of numbers figures largely in the field of "Mathematical recreations." An introduction to this field may be obtained through some or all of the following:

Ball, Mathematical Recreations and Problems, 3d ed., London, 1890.

Bachet de Méziriac, Problèmes plaisants et délectables qui se font par les nombres. First published in 1612, and reprinted at Paris in 1884.

Lucas, Récréations Mathématiques, 4 vols., Paris, 1891–96.

Ahrens, Mathematische Unterhaltungen und Spiele, Leipzig, 1900.

In this connection mention may also be made of a paper by *Bouton* on "Nim, A Game with a Complete Mathematical Theory" (Annals of Math., ser. 2, Vol. III, pp. 35–39, 1901), recently generalized by *Moore* (*ibid.*, Vol. XI, pp. 90–94, 1910).

VIII

CONSTRUCTIONS WITH RULER AND COMPASSES; REGULAR POLYGONS

By L. E. Dickson

CONTENTS

VIII

CONSTRUCTIONS WITH RULER AND COMPASSES; REGULAR POLYGONS

By L. E. Dickson

1. Introduction. The Greek geometricians discovered constructions by ruler and compasses for various elementary problems. There arose, however, certain famous problems, such as the duplication of a cube, the trisection of an angle, and the quadrature of a circle, for which the ancients vainly sought constructions by ruler and compasses. The impossibility of these constructions was proved only in recent times. As such proofs are beyond the scope of elementary geometry, recourse must be had to analytic methods, in particular to the general processes and theorems of algebra. To these analytic methods is due likewise the discovery of the possibility of certain constructions. This is the case, for instance, with the regular polygon of seventeen sides, the possibility of whose construction by ruler and compasses was not suspected during the twenty centuries from *Euclid* to *Gauss*.

2. Analytic criterion for constructibility. The first step in our consideration of a proposed construction consists in formulating the problem analytically. In some instances elementary algebra suffices for this formulation. For example, in the ancient problem of the duplication of the cube, we are given the length s of a side and seek a number x such that $x^3=2s^3$. But usually it is convenient to employ analytic geometry; a point is determined by its coordinates x and y with reference to fixed axes, a straight line or circle by an equation of the first or second degree between the coordinates of the general point on it. Hence we are concerned with certain numbers, some being the coordinates of points, others being the ratios of the coefficients in equations, and others expressing lengths, areas, or volumes. We shall establish the following

Criterion. *A proposed construction is possible by ruler and compasses if, and only if, the numbers which define analytically the desired geometric elements can be derived from those defining the given elements by a finite number of rational operations and extractions of real square roots.*

Suppose, first, that the construction is possible. The straight lines and circles drawn in making the construction are located by means of points either initially given or obtained as the intersections of two straight lines, a straight line and a circle, or two circles. The coordinates of the intersection of two straight lines are rational functions of the coefficients of the equations of the lines. To determine the coordinates of the intersections of the straight line $y=mx+b$ with the circle

$$(x-c)^2+(y-d)^2=r^2,$$

we eliminate y between the equations and obtain a quadratic equation for x. Thus x (and hence $mx+b$ or y) involves no irrationality (in addition to those in m, b, c, d, r) other than the square root of a certain known expression. Finally, the intersections of the preceding circle with a second circle,

$$(x-e)^2+(y-f)^2=s^2,$$

are given by the intersections of one of the circles with their common chord, whose equation is obtained by subtracting the members of the equation of one circle from those of the other. This third case has therefore been reduced to the second. The property stated in the criterion is thus proved.

Conversely, let there be no irrationalities other than real square roots. Then the construction is possible by ruler and compasses. First, a rational function of given quantities is obtained by the operations, addition, subtraction, multiplication, and division. The construction of the sum or differ-

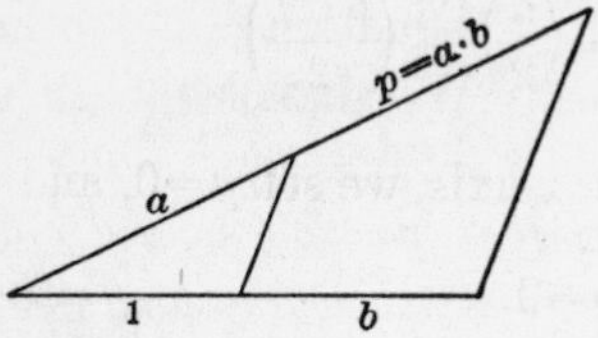

FIG. 1.

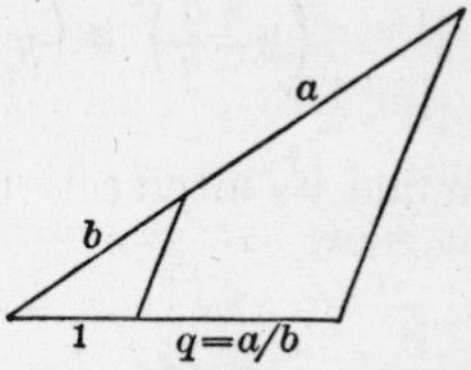

FIG. 2.

ence of two segments is obvious. The construction, by means of parallel lines, of a segment whose length p is the product $a \cdot b$ of the lengths of two given segments is shown in Fig. 1; that for the quotient $q = a/b$ in Fig. 2.

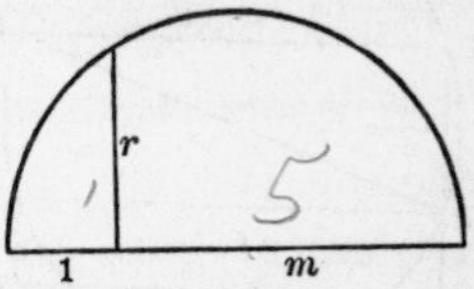

FIG. 3.

Next, a segment of length $r = \sqrt{m}$ may be constructed, as in Fig. 3, by drawing a semicircle on a diameter composed of two segments of lengths 1 and m, then a perpendicular to the diameter.

3. Graphical solution of a quadratic equation. The roots of

$$x^2 - ax + b = 0$$

are $\frac{1}{2}(a \pm \sqrt{a^2 - 4b})$. When the roots are real, the only irrationality is a real square root. The criterion for constructibility in sec. 2 is therefore satisfied. Of various methods of making the construction, the following * is especially simple:

Draw a circle having as diameter the line BQ joining the points $B = (0, 1)$ *and* $Q = (a, b)$. *The abscissas ON and OM of the points of intersection of this circle with the x-axis are the roots of the quadratic* $x^2 - ax + b = 0$.

First Proof. In Fig. 4, $OB = 1$, $OT = a$, $TQ = b$. The centre of circle is thus $\left(\frac{a}{2}, \frac{b+1}{2}\right)$, its diameter is the hypote-

* Acredited to *Lill* by *D'Ocagne*, Le Calcul Simplifié, Paris, 1905, p. 139.

nuse of a right triangle with legs a and $b-1$. Hence the equation of the circle is

$$\left(x-\frac{a}{2}\right)^2+\left(y-\frac{b+1}{2}\right)^2=\left(\frac{a}{2}\right)^2+\left(\frac{b-1}{2}\right)^2.$$

To find its intersection with the x-axis, we set $y=0$, and get

$$x^2-ax+b=0.$$

Second Proof. To give a proof by elementary geometry, let OB meet the circle again at C, and let TQ meet it at D. Join CQ and BD. Since BQ is a diameter, angles C and D are right angles. Hence $OC=b$, $DT=OB$. Since parallel lines intercept equal arcs, chords BN and DM are equal. Thus triangles BON and DTM are congruent, whence $ON=MT$. Thus,

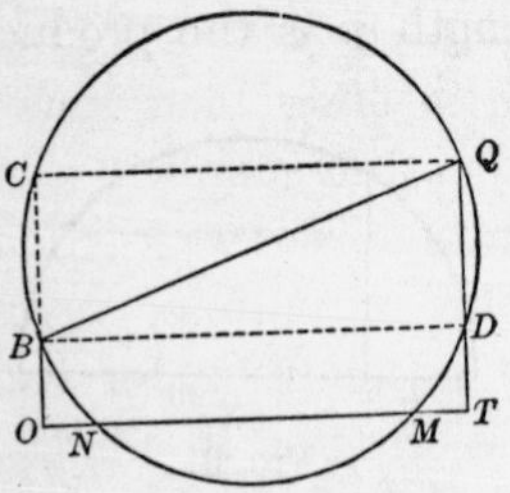

FIG. 4.

$$OM+ON=OM+MT=OT=a.$$

The product of the segments on one secant equals the product of those on another from the same point. Hence

$$OM\cdot ON=OC\cdot OB=b\cdot 1=b.$$

Since OM and ON have the sum a and the product b, they are the roots of $x^2-ax+b=0$.

4. Domain of rationality. If a set of numbers has the property that, when each of the rational operations, addition, subtraction, multiplication, and division (the divisor not being zero), is performed on any two numbers of the set, the result is one of the numbers of the given set, the set of numbers is said to form a **domain of rationality.**

For example, the set of all real numbers forms a domain of rationality since the sum, difference, product, or quotient of any two real numbers is a real number. Again, the set of all rational numbers (that is, all positive and negative integers and fractions) forms a domain of rationality. But the set of all positive integers is not a domain of rationality, since the difference of two positive integers is not always a positive integer. Nor is the set of all positive and negative integers a domain of rationality, since the quotient of two integers is not always an integer.

The set of all rational functions, with integral coefficients, of assigned numbers $a, b, c, \ldots$, forms a domain of rationality; it is said to be **defined** by $a, b, c, \ldots$.*

If, in a proposed construction, the given geometric elements are determined analytically by the numbers $a, b, c, \ldots$, the domain of rationality defined by $a, b, c, \ldots$ will be called the **domain of the geometric data** and designated by D.

5. Functions involving no irrationalities other than square roots. Let x be a function derived from the numbers $a, b, c, \ldots$ of the domain D by rational operations and extractions of square roots, finite in number. The purpose of investigating such functions x is to deduce a condition for constructibility more easily applied than the criterion in sec. 2.

The number of superimposed radical signs in a term of x is called the **order** of the term; the maximum order of the various terms of x is denoted by m. For example, in

$$x=\sqrt{\sqrt{a}+\sqrt{b}}+\sqrt{c+\sqrt{d}}+\sqrt{\sqrt{e}+\sqrt{f}}+g,$$

the first three terms are of order 2, the fourth is of order 1, the last term g is of order zero; consequently, $m=2$.

Frequently a function x can be given a modified form involving fewer radicals. Thus, $\sqrt{9}$ can be replaced by 3, and $\sqrt{10-2\sqrt{3}}$ by $\sqrt{3}-1$. If $r=\sqrt{3+\sqrt{5}}$ and $r'=\sqrt{3-\sqrt{5}}$, then $rr'=2$, so that $2r-7r'$, which involves two radicals of order 2, can be replaced by $2r-\frac{14}{r}$, which involves only one radical of order 2. Again, if x involves $\sqrt{3}$, $\sqrt{5}$, and $\sqrt{15}$, we would replace $\sqrt{15}$ by the product $\sqrt{3}\cdot\sqrt{5}$. In general, if any of the various radicals of order n is a rational function

* See also Monograph V, sec. 9.

of the remaining radicals of order n and the radicals of lower order, we assume that it is so expressed in terms of the other radicals. Hence, after all such simplifications are made, *no one of the various radicals of order m is a rational function of the remaining radicals of order m, and the radicals of lower order occurring separately or underneath other radical signs; likewise, no radical of order $m-1$ is a rational function of the remaining radicals of order $m-1$ and the radicals of lower order, etc.* The distinct radicals which occur in this simplified form of x will therefore be said to be **independent.**

In case the resulting function x is a sum of several fractions, we bring them to a common denominator and express x as the quotient of two integral functions of the radicals. For example, if $x=\sqrt{5}+2r-14/r$, where $r=\sqrt{3+\sqrt{5}}$, we give x the form $\frac{A}{r}$, where $A=r\sqrt{5}+2(3+\sqrt{5})-14$.

Next, we rationalize the denominator by the following process: If the denominator contains a radical $\sqrt{k}$ of the maximum order m, it can be given the form $a+b\sqrt{k}$, where a and b do not involve $\sqrt{k}$. We then multiply the numerator and denominator by $a-b\sqrt{k}$. Similarly, we rid the denominator of each radical of order m, then rid it of each radical of order $m-1$, etc. Thus, in the preceding example, $x=\frac{A}{r}$, where $r=\sqrt{3+\sqrt{5}}$, the first step gives

$$x=\frac{A(-r)}{r(-r)}=\frac{-Ar}{-3-\sqrt{5}}.$$

The next step gives

$$x=\frac{-Ar(-3+\sqrt{5})}{(-3-\sqrt{5})(-3+\sqrt{5})}=\frac{3Ar-Ar\sqrt{5}}{4}.$$

We have now proved that *x can be given a normal form composed of a sum of terms each a product of radicals, having as coefficient a number of the domain D, and such that the distinct radicals are independent.*

For example, $5+\frac{2}{3}\sqrt{5}-\frac{1}{2}\sqrt{7}+4\sqrt{5}\sqrt{7}$ is in normal form.

6. Let n be the number of distinct radicals (including radicals occurring beneath radical signs) found in the normal form of x. By changing the sign of one or more of these n radicals everywhere that it occurs in x, we obtain 2^n **conjugate** functions $x_1=x$, $x_2, \ldots, x_{2^n}$.

For example,

$$x_1=\sqrt{3+2\sqrt{5}}+\sqrt{3-2\sqrt{5}}$$

is one of $2^3=8$ conjugates, of which only 4 are distinct, namely,

$$x_1,\quad x_2=\sqrt{3+2\sqrt{5}}-\sqrt{3-2\sqrt{5}},\quad x_3=-\sqrt{3+2\sqrt{5}}+\sqrt{3-2\sqrt{5}},$$
$$x_4=-\sqrt{3+2\sqrt{5}}-\sqrt{3-2\sqrt{5}}.$$

The 2^n conjugate quantities $x_1, x_2, \ldots$, are the roots of the equation

$$F(x)=(x-x_1)(x-x_2)\ldots(x-x_{2^n})=0.$$

The expanded form of this product is

$$F(x)=x^{2^n}+k_1x^{2^n-1}+\ldots+k_{2^n},$$

where, as shown in the theory of equations,*

$$k_1=-(x_1+x_2+\ldots+x_{2^n}),\qquad k_2=x_1x_2+x_2x_3+x_1x_3+\ldots$$

For example, $x=3a+2\sqrt{b}$ and its conjugate $3a-2\sqrt{b}$ are the roots of the equation $x^2-6ax+9a^2-4b=0$ with coefficients in the domain defined by a and b.

Although the roots $x_1, x_2, \ldots$ involve radicals, the symmetrical combinations k_i of the roots will be shown to equal expressions free of these radicals, and hence rational functions with integral coefficients of the given numbers $a, b, c, \ldots,$ defining the domain D. Indeed, suppose that k_i involves one of the radicals, say $\sqrt{r}$. Then it can be put into the form

$$k_i=p+q\sqrt{r},$$

where neither p nor q involves $\sqrt{r}$. When any one of the n distinct radicals is changed in sign, the roots $x_1, x_2, \ldots$ are

* See Monograph No. V, sec. 10.

interchanged in pairs and the product $F(x)$ is unaltered. Since k_i must therefore remain unaltered when $\sqrt{r}$ is changed into $-\sqrt{r}$, we have

$$p+q\sqrt{r}=p-q\sqrt{r}, \quad q=0,$$

so that $k_i=p$ is free of $\sqrt{r}$. Since k_i involves no one of the n radicals, it equals a number of the domain D. Hence, *the function x satisfies an equation $F(x)=0$ of degree 2^n with coefficients in the domain D.*

7. The quantity x_1 satisfies various equations with coefficients in the domain D; for example, $M(x)\cdot F(x)=0$, where $M(x)$ is any integral function with coefficients in D. We next prove an important property of all such equations.

Theorem. *If one of the conjugate quantities $x_1, x_2, \ldots, x_{2^n}$ satisfies any equation $f(x)=0$ with coefficients in the domain D, then all the quantities x_i satisfy this equation.*

Let $x_1=p+q\sqrt{r}$, where $\sqrt{r}$ is a radical of the maximum order m, while p and q do not involve $\sqrt{r}$ but may contain some of the remaining radicals of order m and radicals of lower order. By changing the sign of $\sqrt{r}$, we obtain another x_i, say

$$x_2=p-q\sqrt{r}.$$

Now $f(x_1)$ may be given the form $A+B\sqrt{r}$, where A and B do not involve $\sqrt{r}$. By hypothesis, $f(x_1)=0$; that is. $A+B\sqrt{r}=0$. If $B\neq 0$, we would have $\sqrt{r}=-A/B$, contrary to the assumption (sec. 5) on the independence of the radicals. Hence $B=0$ and therefore also $A=0$. Since

$$f(x_2)=A-B\sqrt{r},$$

we have $f(x_2)=0$. Thus x_2 is a root of $f(x)=0$.

The proof that any x_i is a root of $f(x)=0$ is based upon the same principles. To simplify the formulas, let x_1 contain just two radicals $\sqrt{r}$ and $\sqrt{r'}$ of the maximum order m. Then (end of sec. 5),

$$f(x_1)=A+B\sqrt{r}+C\sqrt{r'}+E\sqrt{r}\sqrt{r'},$$

where A, B, C, E involve only radicals of orders $< m$. In view of the independence of the radicals (sec. 5), we see as above that A, B, C, E must each be zero. Let A contain just three radicals $\sqrt{s}$, $\sqrt{s'}$, $\sqrt{s''}$ of order $m-1$. Then

$$A = g + h\sqrt{s} + i\sqrt{s'} + j\sqrt{s''} + k\sqrt{s}\sqrt{s'} + \ldots + q\sqrt{s}\sqrt{s'}\sqrt{s''}.$$

As before, $A=0$ requires that $g, h, \ldots q$ shall be zero. Likewise, the coefficients of $\sqrt{s}$, $\sqrt{s'}$, $\ldots$, in B, C, E must be zero. We may proceed similarly with the radicals of orders $m-2$, $\ldots$, 1. Hence in the expression (end of sec. 5)

$$f(x_1) = d + e\sqrt{r} + f\sqrt{r'} + g\sqrt{s} + \ldots + p\sqrt{r}\sqrt{r'} + q\sqrt{r}\sqrt{s} + \ldots + t\sqrt{r}\sqrt{r'}\sqrt{s} + \ldots$$

of $f(x_1)$ as a sum of terms each a product of radicals with coefficients in the domain D, each coefficient $d, e, f, \ldots$ is zero. Now x_i can be derived from x_1 by changing the signs of certain of the radicals $\sqrt{r}$, $\sqrt{r'}$, $\sqrt{s}, \ldots$ Thus $f(x_i)$ is derived from the preceding expression for $f(x_1)$ by the same changes. Since $d, e, f, \ldots$ are zero, it follows that $f(x_i)$ is zero. Hence x_i is a root of $f(x)=0$.

8. It was shown in sec. 6 that x_1 satisfies an equation $F(x)=0$ of degree 2^n with coefficients in the domain D. Of all the equations, with coefficients in D, which are satisfied by x_1, let $\phi(x)=0$ be one of the lowest degree l. The coefficient of x^l may be assumed to be unity. There cannot be two such equations of degree l, since by subtraction we would obtain an equation of degree $<l$, with its coefficients in D and having the root x_1.

We shall prove that the function $F(x)$ is an exact power of this unique function $\phi(x)$. Divide $F(x)$ by $\phi(x)$ and let the quotient be $F_1(x)$ and the remainder be $r(x)$ of degree $<l$, where $F_1(x)$ and $r(x)$ are integral functions with coefficients in D. Then

$$F(x) = \phi(x) \cdot F_1(x) + r(x).$$

Let $x = x_1$; since $F(x_1)=0$ and $\phi(x_1)=0$, we have $r(x_1)=0$. If $r(x)$ is not identically zero, $r(x)=0$ is an equation, with coefficients in D, having the root x_1 and of degree $<l$, contrary to the hypothesis that l is the lowest degree of such equations. Hence $r(x)$ is identically zero, so that

$$F(x)=\phi(x)\cdot F_1(x).$$

If $F_1(x)$ reduces to a constant, necessarily unity, $F(x)$ is the first power of $\phi(x)$ and our theorem is proved. In the contrary case, $F_1(x)$ is a factor of degree $\geqq 1$ of $F(x)$ and $F_1(x)=0$ has as a root at least one of the roots x_i of $F(x)=0$, and hence (sec. 7) has every one of the x_i as roots. In particular, $F_1(x)=0$ has the root x_1, so that by the above argument,

$$F_1(x)=\phi(x)\cdot F_2(x),$$

where $F_2(x)$ is an integral function with coefficients in D. If $F_2(x)$ reduces to a constant, necessarily unity, $F(x)$ is the square of $\phi(x)$ and the theorem is proved. On the contrary case, the same argument shows that

$$F_2(x)=\phi(x)\cdot F_3(x).$$

Proceeding in this way, we find ultimately that

$$F(x)=[\phi(x)]^k.$$

The degree of the second member is lk and the degree of $F(x)$ is 2^n. Thus l is a divisor of 2^n. Hence the degree of $\phi(x)$ is a power of 2. We have therefore proved the following theorem:

The unique equation of lowest degree with coefficients in the domain D which is satisfied by a function x_1 derived from numbers of D by a finite number of rational operations and extractions of square roots is of degree a power of 2.

9. Reducible and irreducible functions. An integral function $f(x)$ with coefficients in a given domain D is called reducible, or irreducible in the domain, according as it can or cannot be factored into two integral functions, each of degree $\geqq 1$, with coefficients in D.

For example, x^2-4 is reducible in any domain; x^2-3 is

irreducible in the domain of all rational numbers, but is reducible in the domain of all real numbers; x^2+4 is irreducible in the latter domain, but is reducible in the domain of all real and complex numbers, since

$$x^2+4=(x+2i)(x-2i), \quad i=\sqrt{-1}.$$

10. The function $\phi(x)$, defined in sec. 8, is irreducible in the domain D. For, if $\phi(x)$ be the product of two integral functions, each of degree $\geqq 1$, with coefficients in D, one of the factors equated to zero would give an equation, with coefficients in D, which is satisfied by x_1 and is of lower degree than $\phi(x)$. But this would contradict the hypothesis concerning $\phi(x)$.

An equation $G(x)=0$ is said to be irreducible in D, if the function $G(x)$ is irreducible in D. The equation $\phi(x)=0$ is the only equation irreducible in D, which has the root x_1. For, if $G(x)=0$ is irreducible in D and has the root x_1, the argument used in sec. 8 shows that $G(x)$ has the factor $\phi(x)$, so that $G(x)$ must be the product of $\phi(x)$ and a constant. The theorem in sec. 8 is therefore equivalent to the following:

The unique equation, irreducible in the domain D, which is satisfied by a function x_1 derived from numbers of D by a finite number of rational operations and extractions of square roots is of degree a power of 2.

11. From the last theorem and the criterion in sec. 2 we deduce the

Fundamental theorem. *A proposed construction is not possible by ruler and compasses if any one of the numbers which define analytically the required geometric elements satisfies an equation irreducible in the domain of the geometric data whose degree is not a power of* 2.

12. The preceding result enables us to treat the three famous problems mentioned in the Introduction.

Duplication of the cube. The problem is to construct a cube whose volume is twice the volume of a given cube. Taking as the unit of length an edge of the given cube, we see that an edge x of the required cube is a root of $x^3=2$. The equation

$x^3 - 2 = 0$ is irreducible in the domain of all rational numbers. For, if reducible, it would have a linear factor and hence a rational root. But if a/b is a root, where a and b are integers with no common divisor except unity, then $a^3 = 2b^3$. Hence a^3, and therefore a, is even, $a = 2c$. Then $4c^3 = b^3$, so that b is even. Thus a and b are both even and hence have the common factor 2, contrary to hypothesis. Since the degree of the irreducible equation $x^3 = 2$ is not a power of 2, it follows from sec. 11 that the duplication of a cube is not possible by ruler and compasses.

Trisection of an angle. To prove the impossibility of the trisection of an arbitrary* angle by ruler and compasses, it is sufficient to prove it for a particular angle, for example, for 120°. The construction of the angle $\frac{1}{3}$ (120°) = 40° is equivalent to the construction of a right-angled triangle whose hypotenuse is unity and base is cos 40°. In the trigonometric identity $\cos 3x = 4 \cos^3 x - 3 \cos x$, take $x = 40°$. Since $\cos 120° = -\frac{1}{2}$, we get

$$4 \cos^3 40° - 3 \cos 40° + \tfrac{1}{2} = 0.$$

Multiply by 2 and write $y = 2 \cos 40°$. Then

$$y^3 - 3y + 1 = 0.$$

This equation is irreducible in the domain of rational numbers. For, if reducible, it would have a linear factor and hence a root a/b, where a and b are integers with no common factor except unity and b is positive. In the cubic equation, set $y = a/b$ and multiply by b^2. We get

$$\frac{a^3}{b} - 3ab + b^2 = 0,$$

so that a^3/b is an integer. If $b > 1$, a and b would have a common factor > 1. Hence $b = 1$. The integral root $y = a$ makes $a^3 - 3a$ an integral multiple of a, so that the constant term 1 must be a multiple of a. Hence $a = \pm 1$. By trial

---

*** Certain special angles like 360°, 180°, 90° can be trisected, since angles 120°, 60°, 30° can be constructed by ruler and compasses.**

neither $+1$ nor -1 is a root of the cubic. It now follows from sec. 11 that the trisection of 120° is not possible by ruler and compasses.

Another proof follows from the fact (sec. 27) that a regular polygon of 9 sides cannot be inscribed in a circle by ruler and compasses.

Quadrature of the circle. The problem is to construct by ruler and compasses a square whose area shall equal the area πR^2 of a circle of given radius R. The construction is impossible. For, if it were possible, and R is taken as the unit of length, the number π of the units of area would satisfy an algebraic equation with rational coefficients (sec. 2, sec. 6). But this is not the case.*

13. Connection between regular polygons and roots of unity. Consider a regular polygon of n sides (an n-gon) inscribed in a circle of unit radius. We employ a rectangular system of coordinates with the origin at the centre of the circle and the x-axis passing through a vertex of the polygon. This vertex is therefore (1, 0). For $n=4$, the remaining vertices of the square have their coordinates marked in Fig. 5. For

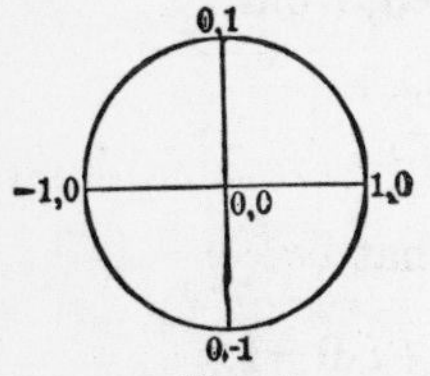

FIG. 5.

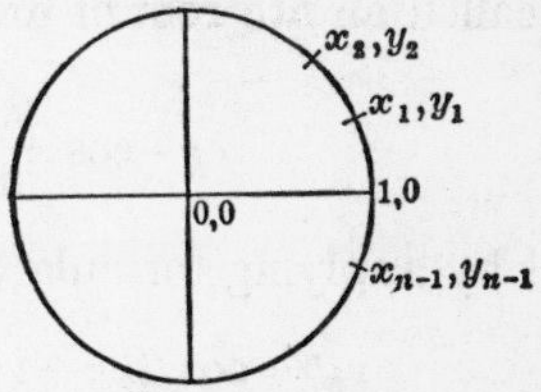

FIG. 6.

any n, the remaining vertices, taken in counter-clockwise order, will be designated (x_1, y_1), (x_2, y_2), . . . , (x_{n-1}, y_{n-1}), as in Fig. 6. Since a side of the n-gon subtends at the centre an angle whose magnitude is $360/n$ degrees, or $2\pi/n$ radians,

$$x_1 = \cos\frac{2\pi}{n},\quad y_1 = \sin\frac{2\pi}{n},\quad x_2 = \cos\frac{4\pi}{n},\quad y_2 = \sin\frac{4\pi}{n},\ \ldots$$

* See Monograph No. IX.

Each point (x, y) of the plane uniquely determines a complex number $x+iy$, where $i=\sqrt{-1}$. Conversely, a complex number $x+iy$ uniquely determines a point (x, y). With the vertices of our square are thus associated the four distinct complex numbers

$$1, \quad i, \quad -1, \quad -i. \qquad (1)$$

With the vertices of the n-gon are associated the distinct complex numbers

$$\left.\begin{aligned} &1,\ r_1=\cos\frac{2\pi}{n}+i\sin\frac{2\pi}{n},\ r_2=\cos\frac{4\pi}{n}+i\sin\frac{4\pi}{n},\ldots,\\ &r_{n-1}=\cos\frac{2(n-1)\pi}{n}+i\sin\frac{2(n-1)\pi}{n}.\end{aligned}\right\} \qquad (2)$$

Since $i^2=-1$, the four numbers (1) are roots of

$$x^4=1, \qquad (3)$$

and hence are called **fourth roots of unity.**

Any one of the numbers (2) is a root of the equation

$$x^n=1, \qquad (4)$$

and is called an **nth root of unity.** Indeed, from

$$r_k=\cos\frac{2k\pi}{n}+i\sin\frac{2k\pi}{n}, \qquad (2')$$

we find by applying formula (5) below that

$$r_k{}^n=\cos 2k\pi+i\sin 2k\pi=1+i\cdot 0=1.$$

14. De Moivre's theorem. *For any positive integer n, we have*

$$(\cos A+i\sin A)^n=\cos nA+i\sin nA. \qquad (5)$$

We first prove the formula

$$(\cos A+i\sin A)(\cos B+i\sin B)=\cos(A+B)+i\sin(A+B). \qquad (6)$$

The product of the two numbers is $a+ib$, where

$$a=\cos A\cos B-\sin A\sin B=\cos(A+B),$$

$$b=\cos A\sin B+\sin A\cos B=\sin(A+B).$$

If we take $B=A$ in (6), we obtain formula (5) for the case $n=2$; (5) is evidently true for the case $n=1$. In general, the proof of (5) for any exponent n is made by mathematical induction. Assume that it is true for the case $n=m$, that is,

$$(\cos A+i \sin A)^m=\cos mA+i \sin mA.$$

Multiply each member by $\cos A+i \sin A$. For the product on the right we employ (6) with $B=mA$. Hence we get

$$(\cos A+i \sin A)^{m+1}=\cos (m+1)A+i \sin (m+1)A,$$

so that (5) holds also for $n=m+1$. The induction is thus complete.

15. It follows from De Moivre's theorem that (2′) is the kth power of

$$r=\cos \frac{2\pi}{n}+i \sin \frac{2\pi}{n}. \quad . \quad . \quad . \quad . \quad . \quad . \quad (7)$$

Hence the numbers (2) may be expressed in the form

$$1=r^n, \quad r_1=r, \quad r_2=r^2, \quad \ldots, \quad r_k=r^k, \quad \ldots, \quad r_{n-1}=r^{n-1}.$$

Since these n numbers were seen to be distinct and to be roots of (4), they give all the roots of (4). Indeed, an algebraic equation of degree n cannot have more than n distinct roots.* *With the successive vertices of the regular n-gon inscribed as in Fig. 6 in a circle of unit radius are associated the n distinct numbers*

$$1, \quad r, \quad r^2, \ldots, r^k, \ldots, r^{n-1}, \quad . \quad . \quad . \quad (8)$$

which give all the nth roots of unity. Here r is defined by (7).

For $n=4$, these numbers are 1, i, $i^2=-1$, $i^3=-i$.

16. The complex number $C=\cos A+i \sin A$ has the reciprocal $C^{-1}=\cos A-i \sin A$, since the product of the two is $\cos^2 A+\sin^2 A=1$. Hence their sum $C+C^{-1}$ is the real number $2 \cos A$.

The inscription of a regular n-gon by ruler and compasses is equivalent to the construction of the angle $2\pi/n$, and hence

* See Monograph No. V, sec. 10.

is equivalent to the construction of a right-angled triangle with hypotenuse unity and base $\cos 2\pi/n$. Instead of determining the complex root of unity r, defined by (7), it is therefore sufficient to determine

$$r+r^{-1}=2\cos 2\pi/n.$$

Since $r^n=1$, we have $r^{-1}=r^{n-1}$. We shall therefore seek certain real-valued combinations, such as $r+r^{n-1}$, of the roots (8).

17. Regular pentagon and decagon. For $n=5$, we wish to determine

$$\eta_0=r+r^4=2\cos\frac{2\pi}{5},$$

where $$r=\cos\frac{2\pi}{5}+i\sin\frac{2\pi}{5}.$$

Since $r^5=1$ and $r\neq 1$, we have

$$\frac{r^5-1}{r-1}=r^4+r^3+r^2+r+1=0.$$

Hence if $r+r^4$ is found, so is also $\eta_1=r^2+r^3$, since

$$\eta_0+\eta_1=-1.$$

Two numbers can be determined when their sum and product are known. We therefore evaluate $\eta_0\cdot\eta_1$. By actual multiplication,

$$(r+r^4)(r^2+r^3)=r^3+r^4+r^6+r^7=r^3+r^4+r+r^2=-1,$$

since $r^5=1$. Hence η_0 and η_1 are the roots $\frac{1}{2}(-1\pm\sqrt{5})$ of

$$x^2-(\eta_0+\eta_1)x+\eta_0\eta_1\equiv x^2+x-1=0.$$

Since the cosine of an acute angle is positive, we have

$$\eta_0=2\cos\frac{2\pi}{5}=\tfrac{1}{2}(-1+\sqrt{5}),\qquad \eta_1=\tfrac{1}{2}(-1-\sqrt{5}).$$

From the value of η_0, we may construct the angle $2\pi/5$. Let AOA' and BOB' be perpendicular diameters in a circle of radius R, and M the middle point of OA' (Fig. 7). Then

$$BM^2=R^2+(\tfrac{1}{2}R)^2,\qquad BM=\tfrac{1}{2}R\sqrt{5}.$$

Let the circle with centre M and radius BM cut OA at C. Let N be the middle point of OC. Then

$$OC = \tfrac{1}{2}R(\sqrt{5} - 1) = R\eta_0, \qquad ON = R\cos\frac{2\pi}{5}.$$

Draw DN parallel to OB. Then angle DON equals $2\pi/5$. Hence AD is the side s_5 of regular inscribed pentagon.

We may omit the construction of DN, DO, DA, and prove that $CB = s_5$, $CO = s_{10}$, the side of a regular decagon. The latter follows from

$$s_{10} = 2R\sin 18° = 2R\cos 72° = 2R\cos\frac{2\pi}{5} = R\eta_0 = OC.$$

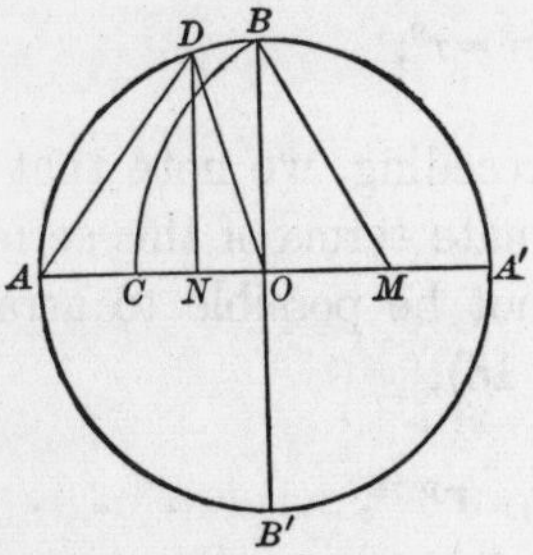

FIG. 7.

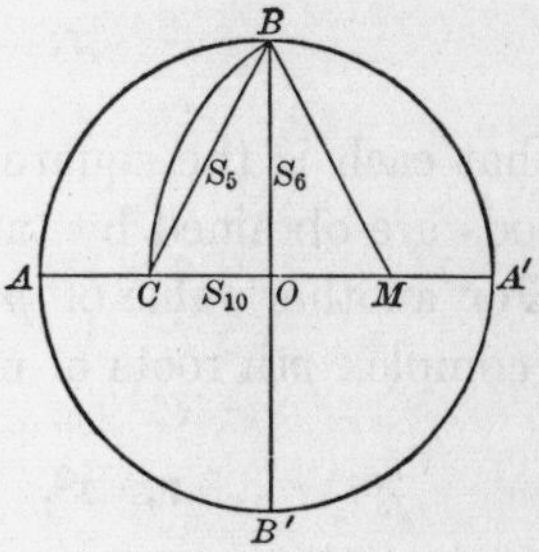

FIG. 8.

Next, $\sin 18° = \cos 72° = 1 - 2\sin^2 36°$. Multiplying by $2R^2$ and replacing $2R\sin 36°$ by its value s_5, and $2R\sin 18°$ by s_{10}, we get

$$Rs_{10} = 2R^2 - s_5^2.$$

But η_0 is a root of $x^2 + x - 1 = 0$, and $R\eta_0 = s_{10}$. Hence

$$s_{10}^2 + Rs_{10} - R^2 = 0.$$

It follows that

$$s_{10}^2 + R^2 = s_5^2.$$

Since $OC = s_{10}$, $OB = R$, the hypotenuse BC must equal s_5. We have now established the following elegant construction of the regular pentagon and decagon:

If AOA' and BOB' are perpendicular diameters, and M is the middle point of the radius OA', a circle with centre M and radius MB will cut OA at a point C such that OC and BC are the sides s_{10} and s_5 of the inscribed regular decagon and pentagon.

In particular, Fig. 8 exhibits the above relation $s_{10}^2+s_6^2=s_5^2$ between the sides of the inscribed regular decagon, hexagon, and pentagon.

18. If p is a prime number, a regular polygon of p sides can be inscribed by ruler and compasses not merely in the well-known cases $p=3$ and $p=5$, but also when $p=17$ and when p has certain larger values. This important discovery was made by *Gauss*. For the general theorem see sec. 27.

In the treatment of the case $p=5$ (sec. 17), we made use of the combinations $r+r^4$ and r^2+r^3, called *periods*, of the complex fifth roots of unity. If the latter be written in the order

$$r, \quad r^2, \quad r^4, \quad r^3=r^8,$$

so that each is the square of the preceding, we note that the periods are obtained by taking alternate terms of this series.

For another value of p it may not be possible to arrange the complex pth roots of unity (sec. 15),

$$r, \quad r^2, \quad r^3, \ldots, \quad r^{p-1}, \quad . \quad . \quad . \quad . \quad . \quad . \qquad (9)$$

in such an order that each term is the square of the preceding. In fact, this is not possible when $p=7$, since the fourth term r^8 is now identical with the first term r. But when $p=7$ the roots can be arranged so that each is the cube of the preceding, namely,

$$r, r^3, r^2, r^6, r^4, r^5.$$

It is shown in Monograph No. VII, sec. 46, that for any prime p there exists an integer g (called a primitive root of p), such that the remainders obtained upon dividing

$$1, g, g^2, \ldots, g^{p-2},$$

by p are in some order $1, 2, \ldots, p-1$. Hence the roots

$$r, r^g, r^{g^2}, \ldots, r^{g^{p-2}} \quad . \quad . \quad . \quad . \quad . \qquad (10)$$

are identical in some order with the roots (9).

19. Regular polygon of 17 sides. For $p=17$, we may take $g=3$, since the remainders obtained upon dividing the successive powers $1, 3, 3^2, \ldots, 3^{16}$ of 3 by 17 are

$$1, 3, 9, 10, 13, 5, 15, 11, 16, 14, 8, 7, 4, 12, 2, 6,$$

which form a permutation of $1, 2, \ldots, 16$. Taking alternate terms, we form the periods

$$\eta_0 = r + r^9 + r^{13} + r^{15} + r^{16} + r^8 + r^4 + r^2,$$
$$\eta_1 = r^3 + r^{10} + r^5 + r^{11} + r^{14} + r^7 + r^{12} + r^6.$$

Since $r^{17}=1$ and $r \neq 1$, we have

$$\frac{r^{17}-1}{r-1} = r^{16} + r^{15} + \ldots + r + 1 = 0.$$

Hence $\eta_0 + \eta_1 = -1$. In the 64 terms of the product $\eta_0\eta_1$ we reduce exponents by means of $r^{17}=1$ and find that each root $r, r^2, \ldots, r^{16}$ occurs exactly four times. Hence

$$\eta_0\eta_1 = 4(r + r^2 + \ldots + r^{16}) = -4.$$

But η_0, η_1 are the roots of $x^2 - (\eta_0 + \eta_1)x + \eta_0\eta_1 = 0$. Hence

$$\eta_0, \eta_1 \quad \text{satisfy} \quad x^2 + x - 4 = 0. \quad . \quad . \quad . \quad (11)$$

By taking alternate terms in η_0 we form two periods η_0' and η_2'; likewise, two periods from η_1.

$$\eta_0' = r + r^{13} + r^{16} + r^4, \qquad \eta_1' = r^3 + r^5 + r^{14} + r^{12},$$
$$\eta_2' = r^9 + r^{15} + r^8 + r^2, \qquad \eta_3' = r^{10} + r^{11} + r^7 + r^6,$$
$$\eta_0 = \eta_0' + \eta_2', \qquad \eta_1 = \eta_1' + \eta_3'.$$

We readily verify that $\eta_0'\eta_2' = -1 = \eta_1'\eta_3'$. Hence

$$\eta_0', \eta_2' \quad \text{satisfy} \quad x^2 - \eta_0 x - 1 = 0, \quad . \quad . \quad . \quad (12)$$
$$\eta_1', \eta_3' \quad \text{satisfy} \quad x^2 - \eta_1 x - 1 = 0. \quad . \quad . \quad . \quad (13)$$

In view of sec. 16, it suffices to determine $r + r^{16}$. The periods

$$\eta_0'' = r + r^{16}, \qquad \eta_4'' = r^{13} + r^4,$$

have the sum η_0' and the product η_1'. Hence

$$\eta_0'', \eta_4'' \quad \text{satisfy} \quad x^2 - \eta_0' x + \eta_1' = 0. \quad . \quad . \quad (14)$$

To decide which root of (11) is η_0 and which is η_1, and the similar question in (12)–(14), we employ the formulas

$$r = \cos\frac{2\pi}{17} + i\sin\frac{2\pi}{17}, \qquad r^k = \cos\frac{2k\pi}{17} + i\sin\frac{2k\pi}{17}.$$

Hence, as in sec. 16,

$$\eta_0'' = 2\cos\frac{2\pi}{17}, \quad \eta_4'' = 2\cos\frac{8\pi}{17}, \quad \eta_0'' > \eta_4''.$$

Similarly, employing $\cos\frac{10\pi}{17} = -\cos\frac{7\pi}{17}$, we get

$$\eta_0' = 2\cos\frac{2\pi}{17} + 2\cos\frac{8\pi}{17}, \quad \eta_1' = 2\cos\frac{6\pi}{17} - 2\cos\frac{7\pi}{17}.$$

Hence η_0' and η_1' are positive. Further,

$$\eta_1 = 2\cos\frac{6\pi}{17} - 2\cos\frac{5\pi}{17} - 2\cos\frac{7\pi}{17} - 2\cos\frac{3\pi}{17}$$

is negative, since the first cosine is less than the second. But we had $\eta_0\eta_1 = -4$. Hence η_0 is positive. Hence (11)–(14) give

$$\eta_0 = \tfrac{1}{2}(\sqrt{17} - 1), \qquad \eta_1 = \tfrac{1}{2}(-\sqrt{17} - 1),$$

$$\eta_0' = \tfrac{1}{2}\eta_0 + \sqrt{1 + \tfrac{1}{4}\eta_0^2}, \quad \eta_1' = \tfrac{1}{2}\eta_1 + \sqrt{1 + \tfrac{1}{4}\eta_1^2}.$$

20. Construction of the regular polygon of 17 sides. In a circle of radius unity construct two perpendicular diameters AB, CD, and at A, D draw tangents which intersect at S.

Determine the point E so that $AE = \tfrac{1}{4}AS$ (for example, by two bisections). Then

$$AE = \tfrac{1}{4}, \quad OE = \sqrt{\overline{AO}^2 + \overline{AE}^2} = \tfrac{1}{4}\sqrt{17}.$$

Let the circle with centre E and radius OE cut AS at F and F'. Then

$$AF = EF - EA = OE - \tfrac{1}{4} = \tfrac{1}{2}\eta_0,$$

$$AF' = EF' + EA = OE + \tfrac{1}{4} = -\tfrac{1}{2}\eta_1,$$

$$OF = \sqrt{\overline{AO}^2 + \overline{AF}^2} = \sqrt{1 + \tfrac{1}{4}\eta_0^2}, \quad OF' = \sqrt{1 + \tfrac{1}{4}\eta_1^2}.$$

Let the circle with centre F and radius FO cut AS at H; that with centre F' and radius $F'O$ cut AS at H'. Then

$$AH = AF + FH = AF + OF = \tfrac{1}{2}\eta_0 + \sqrt{1 + \tfrac{1}{4}\eta_0^2} = \eta_0',$$
$$AH' = F'H' - F'A = OF' - AF' = \eta_1'.$$

It remains to construct the roots of (14). This may be done by sec. 3. Draw HTQ parallel to AO and intersecting OC produced at T. Make $TQ = AH'$. Draw a circle having as diameter the line BQ joining $B = (0, 1)$ with $Q = (\eta_0', \eta_1')$. The abscissas ON and OM of the intersections of this circle

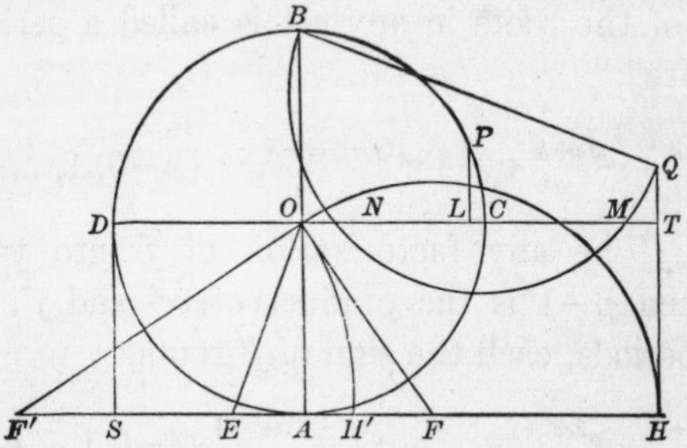

FIG. 9.

with the x-axis OT are the roots of (14). Hence the larger root η_0'' is

$$OM = 2 \cos \frac{2\pi}{17}.$$

The perpendicular bisector LP of OM cuts the unit circle at P. Then $\cos LOP = OL = \cos \frac{2\pi}{17}$, $LOP = \frac{2\pi}{17}$. Hence the chord CP is a side of the inscribed regular 17-gon.

For an elegant construction by *von Staudt* which employs only straight lines and the given circle, see *Bachmann*, Kreistheilung, pp. 69–75. The figure cannot, however, be conveniently drawn on a single page of the size of the present book.

21. Having treated in detail the special cases $p = 5$ and $p = 17$, we proceed to develop *Gauss's* theory for any prime p.

Let $p - 1 = e \cdot f$ be any factorization of $p - 1$ into two positive integers. We separate the $p - 1$ roots (10) into e sets each of f roots. For the first set, we take the first root r, the eth root r^{g^e} following it, then the eth root following the latter, etc. For the second set, we take the second root r^g, the eth root following it, etc. The exponents in the various sets are therefore

$$\left.\begin{array}{l} 1, \quad g^e, \quad g^{2e}, \ \ldots, g^{(f-1)e}, \\ g, \quad g^{e+1}, \quad g^{2e+1}, \ldots, g^{(f-1)e+1} \\ \cdot \quad \cdot \quad \cdot \quad \cdot \quad \cdot \quad \cdot \quad \cdot \quad \cdot \quad \cdot \quad \cdot \\ g^{e-1}, \ g^{2e-1}, \ g^{3e-1}, \ldots, g^{fe-1}. \end{array}\right\} \quad . \quad . \quad (15)$$

The sum of the roots in any set is called a **period.** Hence the periods are

$$\eta_k = r^{g^k} + r^{g^{e+k}} + r^{g^{2e+k}} + \ldots + r^{g^{(f-1)e+k}}, \quad (k=0, 1,\ldots, e-1). \quad (16)$$

Let $f=e'\cdot f'$ be any factorization of f into two positive integers. Then $p-1$ is the product of ee' and f'. As above we have ee' periods, each the sum of f' roots,

$$\eta'_j = r^{g^j} + r^{g^{ee'+j}} + r^{g^{2ee'+j}} + \ldots + r^{g^{(f'-1)ee'+j}} \ (j=0,1,\ldots,ee'-1). \quad (17)$$

Each period (16) is the sum of certain e' periods (17),

$$\eta_k = \eta'_k + \eta'_{e+k} + \eta'_{2e+k} + \ldots + \eta'_{(e'-1)e+k}, \quad (k=0, 1,\ldots, e-1). \quad (18)$$

Indeed, the second member is seen to contain each root

$$r^{g^{se+k}} \qquad (s=0, 1, \ldots, f'e'-1),$$

once and but once, while this is also true of η_k.

Let $f'=e''f''$ be any factorization of f' into two positive integers. Then $p-1$ is the product of $ee'e''$ and f''. Hence there are $ee'e''$ periods, each of f'' roots,

$$\eta_t'' = r^{g^t} + r^{g^{ee'e''+t}} + r^{g^{2ee'e''+t}} + \ldots + r^{g^{(f''-1)ee'e''+t}}$$
$$(t=0, 1, \ldots, ee'e''-1). \quad (19)$$

Each period (17) is the sum of certain e'' periods (19),

$$\eta_j' = \eta_j'' + \eta''_{ee'+j} + \eta''_{2ee'+j} + \ldots + \eta''_{(e''-1)ee'+j}$$
$$(j=0, 1, \ldots, ee'-1). \quad (20)$$

Similarly, we may take any factorization $f''=e'''f'''$ of f'', then any factorization of f''', etc., until we reach $f^{(l)}=1$. Thus, each period separates into periods of fewer terms, the final periods having a single term.

For example, if $p=17$ we may take $e=2, f=8, e'=2, f'=4, e''=2, f''=2, e'''=2, f'''=1$, and obtain the periods given in sec. 19.

The following theorems will be proved in sec. 38:

Theorem I. *The periods $\eta_0, \eta_1, \ldots, \eta_{e-1}$ are the roots of an equation $F(x)=0$ of degree e with integral coefficients.*

Theorem II. *The e' periods, each of f' terms,*

$$\eta'_k, \quad \eta'_{e+k}, \quad \eta'_{2e+k}, \quad \ldots, \quad \eta'_{(e'-1)e+k}, \quad . \quad . \quad . \qquad (21)$$

whose sum is η_k, are the roots of an equation $\phi'_k(x)=0$ of degree e' whose coefficients are linear functions of $\eta_0, \eta_1, \ldots, \eta_{e-1}$ with integral coefficients.

Since Theorem II relates to any factorization $p-1=ee'f'$ of $p-1$, we may, by a suitable change of notation, apply it to any other factorization of $p-1$. Taking the factors ee', e'', f'', we conclude that the e'' periods, each of f'' terms,

$$\eta''_k, \quad \eta''_{ee'+k}, \quad \eta''_{2ee'+k}, \quad \ldots, \quad \eta''_{(e''-1)ee'+k}, \quad . \qquad (22)$$

whose sum is η'_k, are the roots of an equation $\phi''_k(x)=0$ of degree e'' whose coefficients are linear functions of $\eta_0', \eta_1', \ldots \eta'_{ee'-1}$ with integral coefficients. Next, taking the factors $ee'e''$, e''', f''', we conclude that the e''' periods, each of f''' terms,

$$\eta'''_k, \quad \eta'''_{ee'e''+k}, \quad \eta'''_{2ee'e''+k}, \quad \ldots, \quad \eta'''_{(e'''-1)ee'e''+k}, \qquad (23)$$

whose sum is η''_k, are the roots of an equation $\phi'''_k(x)=0$ of degree e''' whose coefficients are linear functions of η_0'', $\eta''_1, \ldots, \eta''_{ee'e''-1}$ with integral coefficients. Finally, we obtain equations of degree $e^{(l)}$ satisfied by periods composed of a single term, namely, one of the roots (10). We have now shown that if $e, e', \ldots, e^{(l)}$ are any integers whose product is $p-1$, there can be determined a series of equations,

$$F(x)=0, \quad \phi_k'(x)=0, \quad \phi_k''(x)=0, \quad . \ . \ . \ . \ \phi_k^{(l)}(x)=0. \qquad (24)$$

of degrees $e, e', e'', \ldots, e^{(l)}$, of which the first has integral coefficients, while the coefficients of $\phi_k^{(t)}(x)=0$ are linear functions, with integral coefficients, of the roots of $\phi_k^{(t-1)}(x)=0$, and such that the roots of the final equations $\phi_k^{(l)}(x)=0$ are the complex pth roots of unity (10).

22. If $p-1$ is a power of 2, the numbers $e, e' \ldots$, may each be taken to be 2, so that the auxiliary equations (24) are quadratics. For the application to regular polygons we may omit the final equations whose roots are the complex pth roots of unity, since (sec. 16) we require only the combination $r+r^{-1}$, and since $r+r^{-1}$ is a root of one of the equations (24) just preceding the final type. To prove the last statement, we note that by Monograph No. VII, sec. 47, a primitive root g of p satisfies the congruence $g^e \equiv -1$ (mod. p), where $e=\frac{1}{2}(p-1)$, so that $r^{g^e}=r^{-1}$. But to obtain the periods η_k composed of only two terms we must set $f=2$, $e=\frac{1}{2}(p-1)$ in (16). Then,

$$\eta_k=r^{g^k}+r^{g^{e+k}}=r^{g^k}+r^{-g^k}.$$

By the first remark in sec. 16, η_k is a real number. Since each period containing more than two terms is a sum of periods containing just two terms, it follows that every period is a real number, excepting only the periods containing a single term. Hence all the quadratic equations which are required to evaluate $r+r^{-1}=2\cos 2\pi/p$ have real roots. Hence if $p-1$ is of the form 2^h, the value of $2\cos 2\pi/p$ can be found by the solution of a series of quadratic equations with real roots, so that by sec. 3, the angle $2\pi/p$ can be constructed by ruler and compasses. Hence we may state the

Theorem. *If p is a prime number of the form 2^h+1, a regular polygon of p sides can be inscribed by ruler and compasses.*

23. We next investigate the regular polygon of n sides, when n has two or more distinct prime factors $p, q, \ldots$, namely,

$$n=p^s q^t \ldots$$

If we have a regular polygon of n sides, we may join certain vertices and obtain a regular polygon of p^s sides, or one of

q^t sides, ... Conversely, if the latter polygons are given, we can construct one of n sides. In general, if a and b are any relatively prime numbers, we can derive a regular ab-gon from a regular a-gon and a regular b-gon. Indeed, by Monograph No. VII, sec. 32, there exist integers c and d, such that $ca+db=1$. Since we have the angles $2\pi/a$ and $2\pi/b$, we can construct multiples of them, add these multiples, and obtain the angle

$$d\cdot\frac{2\pi}{a}+c\cdot\frac{2\pi}{b}=\frac{2\pi}{ab}(db+ca)=\frac{2\pi}{ab},$$

and therefore construct a regular ab-gon. We have thus proved the

Theorem. *If $n=p^sq^t\ldots$, where $p, q, \ldots$ are distinct primes, a regular polygon of n sides can be inscribed by ruler and compasses if, and only if, regular polygons of p^s sides, q^t sides, . . . can be inscribed.*

24. It therefore remains to consider a regular polygon the number of whose sides is a power of a prime, say p^s. The p^sth root of unity,

$$r=\cos 2\pi/p^s+i\sin 2\pi/p^s, \quad . \quad . \quad . \quad . \quad (25)$$

is a root of $x^{p^s}=1$, but not a root of $x^{p^{s-1}}=1$, as shown by De Moivre's theorem (sec. 5). Hence r is a root of

$$\frac{x^{p^s}-1}{x^{p^{s-1}}-1}=x^{p^{s-1}(p-1)}+x^{p^{s-1}(p-2)}+\ldots+x^{p^{s-1}}+1=0. \quad (26)$$

It will be shown in sec. 31 that this equation is irreducible in the domain of rational numbers. If a regular p^s-gon can be inscribed by ruler and compasses, the coordinates x_k, y_k of its vertices (sec. 13) involve no irrationalities other than real square roots (sec. 2). Hence, x_k+iy_k, where $i=\sqrt{-1}$, will involve no irrationalities other than real or imaginary square roots. In the algebraic discussion in secs. 5–10 the radicals were not restricted to real radicals. Hence, by sec. 10, the equation (26), which is irreducible in the domain of rational numbers and has the root $r=x_1+iy_1$, must be of degree a power of 2. If $s>1$, $p^{s-1}(p-1)$ is not a power of 2 except in the case $p=2$. Hence we may state the

Theorem. *When p is a prime number >2, a regular polygon of p^s sides cannot be inscribed by ruler and compasses if $s>1$, or if $s=1$ and $p-1$ is not of the form 2^h.*

25. In view of the theorems in secs. 22 and 24, a regular polygon of p sides, where p is a prime number >2, can be inscribed by ruler and compasses if, and only if, p is of the form 2^h+1. We note that 2^h+1 is composite if h has an odd factor $2k+1$, so that $h=(2k+1)q$, since in that case 2^h+1 has the factor 2^q+1. If a number h has no odd factor it must be a power 2^t of 2. We therefore have the result:

A regular polygon of p sides, where p is a prime >2, can be inscribed by ruler and compasses if, and only if, p is of the form

$$2^{2^t}+1. \quad . \quad . \quad . \quad . \quad . \quad . \quad . \quad . \quad . \qquad (27)$$

26. We are thus led to ask for what values of t the number (27) is a prime. For $t=0, 1, 2, 3, 4$, the numbers are 3, 5, 17, 257, 65537, each being prime. The famous arithmetician *Fermat* expressed his belief that the number (27) was a prime for every t, but admitted that he had no proof of his conjecture. But *Euler* proved in 1732 that when $t=5$ the number is not prime,

$$2^{32}+1=641\cdot 6700417.$$

Further, the number (27) is known * to be not prime for

$$t=6, 7, 8, 9, 11, 12, 18, 23, 36, 38, 73.$$

The regular 257-gon has been discussed at length by *Richelot* in Crelle's Journal für Mathematik, 1832, pp. 1–26, 146–161, 209–230, 337–356; and geometrically by *Affolter* and *Pascal* in Rendiconti della R. Accademia di Napoli, 1887.

The regular polygon of $2^{16}+1=65,537$ sides has been discussed by *Hermes*, Göttingen Nachrichten, 1894.

---

*Proceedings of the London Mathematical Society, 1903, p. 175, 1905, p. xxi; Bulletin of the American Mathematical Society, 1906, p. 449; Vol. XI, p. 543; 1909, p. 1.

27. Since any angle can be bisected, a regular $2k$-gon is inscriptible if a regular k-gon is. Hence the results in secs. 23–25 lead to the

Theorem. *A regular polygon of* n *sides can be inscribed by ruler and compasses if, and only if,* $n=2^l p_1 p_2 \ldots$, *where* $p_1, p_2, \ldots$ *are distinct primes of the form* $2^{2^t}+1$.

The lowest primes p_i are 3, 5, 17, 257, 65537. For the succeeding values 5, 6, 7, 8, 9 of t, the number is not prime. For the next case $t=10$, the number has 155 digits; whether or not it is prime has not yet been determined.

The regular polygons of n sides, where n lies between 2 and 26, fall into the following two classes:

Inscriptible:	3, 4, 5, 6, 8, 10, 12, 15, 16, 17, 20, 24;
Not inscriptible:	7, 9, 11, 13, 14, 18, 19, 21, 22, 23, 25.

28. Primitive roots of unity. A root r of $x^n=1$ is called a primitive nth root of unity if it is not the root of a similar equation of lower degree, namely, $x^l=1$, with $0<l<n$.

For example, $i=\sqrt{-1}$ is a primitive fourth root of unity, since $i^4=1$, while i, i^2, and i^3 are distinct from 1.

There exist primitive nth roots of unity, for instance,

$$r_1=\cos\frac{2\pi}{n}+i\sin\frac{2\pi}{n};$$

by De Moivre's theorem, r_1^n is the least positive power of r_1 equal to 1.

If r is any primitive nth root of unity, the powers

$$r,\ r^2,\ \ldots,\ r^n \qquad (28)$$

give all the nth roots of unity. In fact, these powers are roots of $x^n=1$ and are all distinct; furthermore, there cannot be more than n distinct roots of an equation of degree n.

It is easy to determine which of the roots (28) are primitive nth roots of unity. Consider r^k and let g be the greatest common divisor of k and n. Then

$$(r^k)^{n/g}=(r^n)^{k/g}=1.$$

Hence, if $g>1$, so that $n/g<n$, r^k is not a primitive nth root of unity. But if $g=1$, there exist (Monograph No. VII, sec. 32) integers a and b for which

$$ak+bn=1.$$

Then if $(r^k)^l=1$, for $0<l<n$, we would have

$$r^l=r^{(ak+bn)l}=(r^{kl})^a(r^n)^{bl}=1,$$

whereas $r^l\neq 1$. Hence, if $g=1$, r^k is a primitive root. We have thus proved that *when r is any primitive nth root of unity, r^k is also a primitive root if, and only if, k is relatively prime to n.*

For example, $i=\sqrt{-1}$ is a primitive fourth root of unity and hence also $i^3=-i$ is, whereas $i^2=-1$ is not a primitive root.

Another statement of the preceding theorem is the following: *If r is any primitive nth root of unity and if $1, a, b, \ldots, l$ are the integers less than n and relatively prime to n, then*

$$r,\ r^a,\ r^b,\ \ldots,\ r^l \quad \ldots\ldots \quad (29)$$

give the all distinct primitive nth roots of unity.

29. Let $n=p^s$, where p is a prime, and let r be a primitive p^sth root of unity. Of the $n=p^s$ roots (28) of $x^{p^s}=1$, r^p, $r^{2p}, \ldots, r^{p^s}$ give the p^{s-1} distinct roots of $x^{p^{s-1}}=1$. The remaining p^s-p^{s-1} roots are primitive p^sth roots of unity (sec. 28). Hence *the roots of equation* (26) *give all the primitive p^sth roots of unity.*

To complete the discussion in sec. 24, we must prove that this equation is irreducible in the domain of all rational numbers. This proof will be based upon a lemma of great importance. For the case of the special function y^3-3y+1, this lemma states that the function is the product of two factors with rational coefficients only when these coefficients are integers. For this case a proof has been given in sec. 12.

30. Gauss's lemma. *If an integral function $f(x)$ with integral coefficients, that of the highest power being unity, is the product of two integral functions*

$$\phi(x)=x^m+b_1x^{m-1}+\ldots+b_m, \quad \psi(x)=x^{m'}+c_1x^{m'-1}+\ldots+c_{m'}$$

with rational coefficients, these coefficients are integers.

Let the fractions $b_1, \ldots, b_m$ be brought to their least positive common denominator β_0 and set $b_i = \beta_i/\beta_0$. Hence $\beta_0, \ldots, \beta_m$ have no common divisor except unity. Similarly, let $c_i = \gamma_i/\gamma_0$, where $\gamma_0, \ldots, \gamma_{m'}$ are integers with no common divisor >1. Multiplying $f = \phi \cdot \psi$ by $\beta_0\gamma_0$, we get

$$\beta_0\gamma_0 f(x) = \phi_1(x) \cdot \psi_1(x), \quad . \quad . \quad . \quad . \quad . \quad (30)$$

where

$$\phi_1 = \beta_0 x^m + \beta_1 x^{m-1} + \ldots + \beta_m, \qquad \psi_1 = \gamma_0 x^{m'} + \gamma_1 x^{m'-1} + \ldots + \gamma_{m'}.$$

The lemma is proved if $\beta_0 = \gamma_0 = 1$. Suppose, however, that $\beta_0\gamma_0 > 1$. Then every term of the left member of (30) is a multiple of any prime divisor p of $\beta_0\gamma_0$. Not all the β's have a common divisor p. Let β_i be the first coefficient in $\phi_1(x)$ which is not divisble by p. At least one of the γ's is not divisible by p; let γ_k be the first one. The total coefficient o $x^{m+m'-i-k}$ in the product $\phi_1(x) \cdot \psi_1(x)$ is

$$\beta_i\gamma_k + \beta_{i-1}\gamma_{k+1} + \beta_{i-2}\gamma_{k+2} + \ldots$$
$$+ \beta_{i+1}\gamma_{k-1} + \beta_{i+2}\gamma_{k-2} + \ldots$$

and this sum must be divisible by p, since every term on the left of (30) is divisible by p. By hypothesis, $\beta_{i-1}, \beta_{i-2}, \ldots$ and $\gamma_{k-1}, \gamma_{k-2}, \ldots$ are divisible by p. Hence $\beta_i\gamma_k$ must be divisible by p, contrary to hypothesis.

31. Of various proofs of the irreducibility of equation (26), we shall reproduce *Kronecker's* first proof. To prove that the function $f(x)$, defined by (26), is irreducible in the domain of rational numbers, it suffices, in view of the preceding lemma, to show that $f(x)$ is not the product of two polynomials $\phi(x)$, $\psi(x)$, with *integral* coefficients. Suppose that such a factorization

$$f(x) = \phi(x) \cdot \psi(x)$$

is possible. For $x = 1$, we get

$$p = \phi(1) \cdot \psi(1).$$

Since p is a prime, one of these integers, say $\phi(1)$, must equal ± 1. Let r be any primitive p^sth root of unity. Now all the primitive roots are given by (29), where $1, a, b, \ldots, l$

denote the $t=p^s-p^{s-1}$ integers less than p^s and relatively prime to p^s. Further, by sec. 29, these numbers (29) give all the roots of (26). Hence the factor $\phi(x)$ must vanish when one of these numbers is substituted for x, so that

$$\phi(r)\cdot\phi(r^a)\cdot\phi(r^b)\ldots\phi(r^l)=0.$$

In other words, the function

$$P(x)=\phi(x)\cdot\phi(x^a)\cdot\phi(x^b)\ldots\phi(x^l)$$

vanishes when x is replaced by any primitive p^sth root r of unity. Since $P(x)$ thus vanishes for each root of $f(x)$, and since the roots of $f(x)$ are all distinct, it follows that $P(x)$ is divisible by $f(x)$. Thus

$$P(x)=f(x)\cdot q(x),$$

where $q(x)$ is a polynomial with integral coefficients. The number of factors ϕ in $P(x)$ is t. Hence, for $x=1$,

$$[\phi(1)]^t=p\cdot q(1).$$

Since $\phi(1)=\pm1$, p cannot divide $[\phi(1)]^t$. The assumption that $f(x)$ is reducible has therefore led to a contradiction.

32. The proof of the theorems stated in sec. 21 rests upon four lemmas which will now be established.

While, in sec. 21, r denoted the particular pth root of unity,

$$\cos\frac{2\pi}{p}+i\sin\frac{2\pi}{p},$$

we shall henceforth denote by r any primitive pth root of unity. In view of sec. 28, the powers (9) continue to give all the complex pth roots of unity. The same is true of the powers (10). Hence when r is any primitive pth root of unity, the various roots (10) can be separated into periods exactly as in sec. 21.

33. It is shown in elementary algebra that if an equation $F(x)=0$ with real coefficients has a complex root $a+bi$, where $i=\sqrt{-1}$ and $b\neq0$, it has also the root $a-bi$, so that $F(x)$ has the factor

$$\phi(x)=(x-a-bi)(x-a+bi)=x^2-2ax+a^2+b^2.$$

Since $\phi(x)$ has no factor $x-d$, where d is real, it is irreducible in the domain of real numbers (sec. 9). This result is merely a special case of the following:

Lemma I. *If $F(x)$ and $\phi(x)$ are integral functions with coefficients in the domain D, and $\phi(x)$ is irreducible in D, and if $F(x)$ vanishes for one root x_1 of $\phi(x)=0$, then $F(x)$ is the product of $\phi(x)$ by an integral function with coefficients in D.*

The ordinary process for finding the greatest common divisor $g(x)$ of $F(x)$ and $\phi(x)$ involves only rational operations. Hence $g(x)$ is an integral function with coefficients in the domain D. Moreover, $g(x)$ is not a constant, since $F(x)$ and $\phi(x)$ have the common factor $x-x_1$. Since $\phi(x)$ is irreducible in D, its factor $g(x)$ must equal $c\phi(x)$, where c is a constant. Hence $\phi(x)$, as well as $g(x)$, is a factor of $F(x)$.

Corollary. If the degree of $F(x)$ is less than that of $\phi(x)$, then $F(x)$ has all its coefficients zero.

34. Lemma II. *Any integral function $f(r)$ of a primitive pth root r of unity can be given the normal form*

$$c_0 r + c_1 r^g + c_2 r^{g^2} + \ldots + c_{p-2} r^{g^{p-2}}, \quad . \quad . \quad . \quad (31)$$

in which each c_i is an integral function, with integral coefficients, of the coefficients of $f(x)$. If $f(r)$ has rational coefficients, it has a single normal form.

Since $r^p=1$ and $r\neq 1$, r is a root of

$$\frac{x^p-1}{x-1}=x^{p-1}+x^{p-2}+\ldots+x+1=0. \quad . \quad . \quad . \quad (32)$$

Hence

$$r^{p-1}+\ldots+r^2+r+1=0. \quad . \quad . \quad . \quad . \quad (33)$$

By employing $r^p=1$, we may give $f(r)$ the form

$$f(r)=a_0+a_1r+a_2r^2+\ldots+a_{p-1}r^{p-1}.$$

From this we subtract a_0 times (33) and obtain

$$f(r)=A_1r+A_2r^2+\ldots+A_{p-1}r^{p-1}, \quad . \quad . \quad . \quad (34)$$

where $A_i=a_i-a_0$. Since the quantities (9) are identical in some order with the quantities (10), we may give (34) the normal form (31). The first part of the lemma is therefore proved.

We now make the assumption that the coefficients of the initial function $f(r)$ are rational numbers. Then the a_i, and hence also the A_i, are rational numbers. In this case $f(r)$ can be expressed in the form (34) in only one way. For, if also

$$f(r)=B_1r+B_2r^2+\ldots+B_{p-1}r^{p-1},$$

in which the B_i are rational numbers, we obtain by subtraction and removal of the factor r an equation,

$$o=A_1-B_1+(A_2-B_2)r+\ldots+(A_{p-1}-B_{p-1})r^{p-2},$$

with rational coefficients. But equation (32) is irreducible in the domain of rational numbers (sec. 31 with $s=1$). Hence by the Corollary in sec. 33, each coefficient A_i-B_i is zero.

35. The periods $\eta_0, \eta_1, \ldots, \eta_{e-1}$, defined by (16), have the important property that *each is unaltered when r is replaced by r^{g^e}*. In fact, r^{g^s} is then replaced by

$$(r^{g^e})^{g^s}=r^{g^{e+s}},$$

so that any term, except the last, of a period η_k is replaced by the next succeeding term, and the last term by the first The last statement follows from

$$g^{fe}=g^{p-1}\equiv 1 \pmod{p}.$$

36. Lemma III. *Any integral function $f(r)$ of a primitive pth root of unity, with integral coefficients a_i, and having the property that it remains unaltered when r is replaced by r^{g^e}, equals a linear function of the periods,*

$$k_0\eta_0+k_1\eta_1+\ldots+k_{e-1}\eta_{e-1}, \quad \ldots \quad (35)$$

where each k_i is an integral function of the a_i with integral coefficients. If the a_i are all integers, then the k_i are integers.

Let $f(r)$ be given the normal form (31), but with the powers of r arranged in tabular form as in (15). Thus,

$$f(r) = c_{00}r + c_{10}r^{g^e} + c_{20}r^{g^{2e}} + \ldots + c_{f-1\,0}r^{g^{(f-1)e}}$$
$$\cdots\cdots\cdots\cdots\cdots$$
$$+ c_{0k}r^{g^k} + c_{1k}r^{g^{e+k}} + c_{2k}r^{g^{2e+k}} + \ldots + c_{f-1\,k}r^{g^{(f-1)e+k}}$$
$$\cdots\cdots\cdots\cdots\cdots$$

When r is replaced by r^{g^e}, the powers in any row are permuted cyclically (end of sec. 35). The coefficients of the resulting function must equal those of $f(r)$, by Lemma II. Hence

$$c_{0k} = c_{1k},\ c_{1k} = c_{2k},\ \ldots,\ c_{f-1\,k} = c_{0k} \qquad (k = 0, 1, \ldots, e-1).$$

Thus the c's in each row are all equal. Removing the common factor, we obtain a sum of powers of r which defines a period η_k. Hence

$$f(r) = c_{00}\eta_0 + c_{01}\eta_1 + \ldots + c_{0k}\eta_k + \ldots + c_{0\,e-1}\eta_{e-1}.$$

37. Lemma IV. *An integral function $f(r)$ of a primitive pth root of unity with integral coefficients, which remains unaltered when r is replaced by r^g, equals an integer.*

We apply Lemma III for the case $e = 1$. Then

$$\eta_0 = r + r^g + r^{g^2} + \ldots + r^{g^{p-2}}$$

is the only period of $f = p - 1$ terms. By (33), $\eta_0 = -1$. Hence, by (35), $f(r)$ equals the integer $-k_0$.

38. We are now in a position to prove Theorems I and II of sec. 21. First, $\eta_0, \ldots, \eta_{e-1}$ are the roots of

$$F(x) = (x - \eta_0)(x - \eta_1) \ldots (x - \eta_{e-1}) = 0.$$

Its coefficients are symmetric functions, with integral coefficients, of the periods η_i. When r is replaced by r^g, these periods are permuted cyclically, that is, η_0 is replaced by η_1, η_1 by $\eta_2, \ldots$, and η_{e-1} by η_0. Hence a symmetric function of these periods remains unaltered and, by Lemma IV, equals an integer. Theorem I is therefore true.

Next, the e' periods (21) are the roots of

$$\phi_k'(x) = (x - \eta_k')(x - \eta'_{e+k}) \dots (x - \eta'_{(e'-1)e+k}) = 0,$$

whose coefficients are symmetric functions, with integral coefficients, of these periods (21). But the latter are permuted cyclically when r is replaced by r^{g^e}. Hence Theorem II follows from Lemma III.

39. References. The proof that regular polygon of p sides, where p is a prime of the form 2^h+1, is geometrically inscriptible was first made by *Gauss*, Disquisitiones Arithmeticæ, translated into German by *Maser*. On p. 447 of the latter, *Gauss* states that a regular n-gon is not inscriptible if n contains an odd prime factor not of the form 2^h+1, or the square of a prime 2^h+1 (i.e., states the theorems of secs. 23 and 24 above); but no proof appears to have been published by *Gauss*. References to the proof (secs. 5–11) of this impossibility may be made to

Petersen, Theorie der Algebraischen Gleichungen, Kopenhagen, 1878, p. 156.

Klein, Vorträge über ausgewählte Fragen der Elementargeometrie, Leipzig, 1895; English translation by *Beman* and *Smith*, Boston, 1897.

Enriques, Questioni Riguardanti la Geometria Elementare, Bologna, 1900, Articles 10 and 11; German edition.

The theorems may be readily proved by means of *Galois's* theory of algebraic equations. For the domain of rational numbers, the Galois group of equation (26), whose roots are the primitive p^sth roots of unity, is cyclic, so that its factors of composition are the prime factors of $p^{s-1}(p-1)$. If, and only if, these factors are all 2 will the equation be equivalent to a chain of quadratic equations.

IX

THE HISTORY AND TRANSCENDENCE OF π

By David Eugene Smith

CONTENTS

IX

THE HISTORY AND TRANSCENDENCE OF π

By David Eugene Smith

1. Nature of the problem. The first areas that the world measured accurately were doubtless rectangles, and, in particular, squares. If the sides of the rectangles were commensurable with common units of linear measure, and for practical purposes they were, at least with some convenient submultiples of those units, then the problem was easily solved. The next step was probably the mensuration of the parallelogram or triangle, to be followed by that of the trapezoid, thus completing the most common rectilinear forms. In theory the measurement of these polygons offered no serious difficulties, and by means of these figures the areas of other polygons could easily be found. When it came to finding the area of curvilinear figures, however, the problem assumed new difficulties, and in connection with the most common of these figures the effort was early made to find a square that should have an area equal to that of a given circle, the subsequent problem of measurement of the square being then a simple one. In other words, the problem was one of "squaring the circle." Since, however, it was early seen that $a = \frac{1}{2}rc$, it was evident that the problem could be solved if a straight line could be found that should equal the circumference. For if this line could be found, then the formula $a = \frac{1}{2}rc$ would give a rectangle with the same area as the circle, and it is a simple matter to construct a square with area equal to that of a given rectangle. The problem thus reduces to "rectifying the circumference," or "rectifying the circle," as we would now say. Furthermore, since $c=2\pi r$, if we could find the value of π, as an integer or a common fraction (or finite decimal), we could easily rectify the circle. Since we can construct $\sqrt{ab}$ by the use of the compasses and straightedge, it would also be possible to rectify the circle if we could express π by means of a finite number of square roots. In other words, the circle would be rectified if π could be expressed by rational operations and by irrational operations involving a finite number of square roots. On the other hand, every particular geometric construction effected by the straightedge and compasses reduces to the determination of the intersection of two straight lines, of one straight line and a circle, or of two circles, and is equivalent to a rational operation or the extracting of a square root. A geometric construction is therefore impossible unless it can be effected by rational operations or by the aid of a finite number of square roots.* The problem therefore finally reduces to the determining of the nature of π, whether or not it is the root of an algebraic equation that can be solved by these methods.

2. History of the problem. The history of the problem of "squaring the circle," or more specifically of investigating the nature of π, may be found in any of the standard histories of mathematics, and in particular in *Cantor's* Vorlesungen über die Geschichte der Mathematik (4 vols.). The subject has been specially treated, however, by *Rudio* in his work entitled Archimedes, Huygens, Lambert, Legendre, vier Abhandlungen über die Kreismessung, and in a more condensed manner in the German edition of *Enriques's* Fragen der Elementargeometrie, both of which works have been freely used in preparing this article.

There have been three well-defined epochs in the consideration of this problem. The first extended from the earliest times to about 1650 A.D. It is characterized by innumerable and ingenious attempts at finding a square equal in

---

* See Monograph No. VIII, secs. 2, 11.

area to a given circle, or at finding the approximate value of π by purely geometric methods, and especially by the methods now used in our elementary text-books.

The second period was about a century in length, extending from the invention of the differential and integral calculus to the year 1766, when *Lambert* published his work on the subject. In this period the methods of analysis replace the geometric methods of the ancients, and the names of *Newton, Leibnitz,* the *Bernoullis,* and *Euler* are prominently connected with the investigation. Instead of the Greek method of exhaustions, used to such advantage by *Archimedes,* we now find infinite series and products used to approximate the value of π, and *Euler's* remarkable formula, to be referred to later, is introduced into the discussion.

The third period extends from the middle of the eighteenth century to the present time, and is characterized by the efforts to discover not the approximate value of π, but the nature of this number, whether or not it is rational, or whether it is algebraic or transcendent. Since the two latter terms will enter into this discussion it should be understood that an algebraic number is a number that is the root of an equation, $C_0+C_1x+C_2x^2+\ldots+C_nx^n=0$, where the coefficients C_0, $C_1, \ldots, C_n$ are rational numbers. A number which is not algebraic, that is, which satisfies no such equation, is called **transcendent.*** It should further be mentioned that if a number is the root of an algebraic equation with rational coefficients it is also the root of an algebraic equation with integral coefficients. For this reason we may restrict our equations to those in which $C_0, C_1, \ldots, C_n$ are integers.

The first period begins in prehistoric times, the earliest approximation for π probably being 3, as in the Bible (I Kings vii 23, and II Chronicles iv 2). On the Babylonian cylinders there has not yet been found any definite statement as to this value, and the Hindu and Chinese records are untrustworthy for these remote times. We have, however, a valuable papyrus

*** See also Monograph No. VI, sec. 13.**

in the British Museum, probably copied about 1700 B.C. from a work of some centuries before, in which an approximation for π is given. This papyrus was copied by one *Ahmes*, a scribe, and states that the area of the circle is, in our symbolism, $\left(\frac{8}{9}\right)^2 d^2$, or $\frac{64}{81}d^2$. Now since $a=\frac{1}{4}\pi d^2$, it follows that the *Ahmes* value of π is $\frac{256}{81}$, or 3.1604 . . .

Among the Greeks, numerous philosophers attempted to solve the problem. One of the earliest to make any progress was *Hippias* of Elis (*c.* 420 B.C.) who invented a curve known as the τετραγωνίζουσα or quadratrix, which usually bears the name of *Dinostratos* (*c.* 350 B.C.) who studied it carefully.

The curve may be described as follows: If a circle of unit radius has its centre at the origin of rectangular coordinates, and if two points Q and R move with uniform velocity, one upon the quadrant AB and the other upon the radius OB, so that they start from A and O, respectively, at the same time, and reach B simultaneously, then the point of intersection, P, of OQ and of a perpendicular to OB from R, describes a quadratrix. It therefore follows that the ordinate y is proportional to the angle ϕ, and specifically that as we double y (within the quadrant) we double ϕ. Furthermore, since if $y=1$,

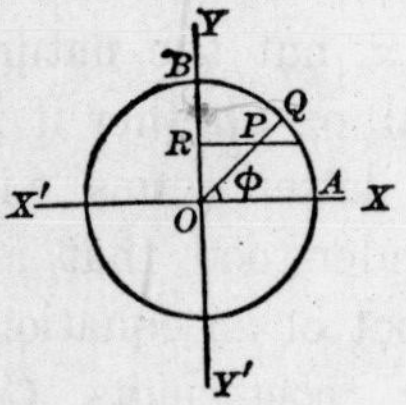

$$\phi=\frac{\pi}{2},$$

$$\therefore \quad \phi=\frac{\pi}{2}\cdot y.$$

Also $$\because \quad \phi=\tan^{-1}\frac{y}{x}, \text{ or arc } \tan\frac{y}{x},$$

$$\therefore \quad \frac{y}{x}=\tan\frac{\pi}{2}y,$$

and $$x=\frac{y}{\tan\frac{\pi}{2}y}.$$

Therefore the curve meets the x-axis at

$$x = \lim_{y \doteq 0} \frac{y}{\tan \frac{\pi}{2} y} = \frac{2}{\pi}.$$

That is, if we can construct the quadratrix we shall have an abscissa exactly equal to $\frac{2}{\pi}$, from which π can easily be constructed. The difficulty was at once seen, however, namely, that the construction of a quadratrix itself was as difficult as to find π, and that indeed it was practically the same problem.

Contemporary with *Hippias* were *Antiphon* and *Bryson*, to whom we are largely indebted for our present methods of attacking the problem in elementary geometry. *Antiphon* inscribed a square (or possibly an equilateral triangle) in a circle, and by continually doubling the number of sides he approximately exhausted the difference between the polygon and the circle, thus approximating the area. *Bryson*, of Heraclea, a follower of the Pythagoreans, not only inscribed a regular polygon, but also circumscribed one similar to it, and then assumed that the area of the circle was the arithmetic mean between the two areas, a false assumption that led only to a fair approximation. To *Antiphon*, therefore, we trace one of the earliest steps in the invention of the modern calculus.

The first one to actually square a curvilinear figure, in his efforts to square the circle, was *Hippocrates*, of Chios (*c.* 450 B.C.). He proved that if semicircles be described upon the sides of an isosceles right triangle, as shown in the figure, the lune A will equal the triangle A'. The proposition is easily generalized for scalene right triangles, but it contributed nothing to the general problem of the circle.

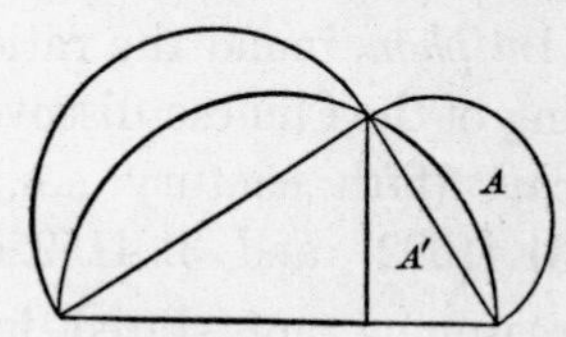

The greatest step among the Greeks was taken by *Archimedes* in his three propositions on the measurement of the circle (κύκλου μέτρησις). Substantially his method of finding the value of π is by inscribing and circumscribing regular polygons and doubling the number of sides, quite as in elementary geometry to-day. By this means, using a polygon of 96 sides, he showed that $3\frac{1}{7} > \pi > 3\frac{10}{71}$, from which fact $3\frac{1}{7}$ has often been called the Archimedean value of π. Since $3\frac{1}{7}$ is less than 0.2 per cent larger than the real value, and is such a simple number for ordinary computations, it is still in common use.

Ptolemy improved upon the values assigned by *Archimedes*, expressing the result in the sexagesimal system as 3 8′ 30″, i.e., $3+\frac{8}{60}+\frac{30}{60^2}$, which reduces to $3\frac{17}{120}=3.14166\ldots$

A somewhat similar value of π appeared in India as early as *c.* 500 A.D., when *Aryabhatta* gave the value $\frac{62832}{20000}$, which equals 3.1416, a value, however, that may be due to a later writer by the same name. *Brahmagupta* (born 598 A.D.) gave $\sqrt{10}$ as the exact value, perhaps because of the common approximation formula, $\sqrt{a^2+r}=a+\frac{1}{2a+r}$, this leading to $\sqrt{10}=3+\frac{1}{7}$, or the common Archimedean value. This value $\sqrt{10}$, was extensively used in mediæval times.

The next noteworthy step in obtaining an approximate value for π was taken by the Chinese. *Chang Hêng* (78–139 A.D.) gave a rule that was equivalent to taking $\sqrt{10}$ for π. *Wang Fan* (229–267) gave $\pi=142:45$, or 3.1555 . . . , and a contemporary writer, *Lui Hui*, proceeding in the same way as *Antiphon*, found the ratio 157:50, or 3.14. The most interesting of the Chinese discoveries, however, is that of *Tsu Ch'ung-chih* (fifth century A.D.), who found for the limits of 10π, 31.415927 and 31.415926, from which he inferred by some reasoning not stated in his works that $\frac{22}{7}$ and $\frac{355}{113}$ were approximate values. The latter is the one usually attributed to *Adriaen Anthonisz,* as mentioned hereafter. Various other attempts were made by the Chinese, but no noteworthy results were obtained until after the European influence had permeated their civilization. In the Su-li Ching-yün, compiled by Imperial order in 1713, the value of π is found to 19 figures.*

The greatest mathematical genius of the Middle Ages, *Leonardo Pisano*, Fibonacci, brought the limits of π somewhat closer than *Archimedes*, namely to $\frac{1440}{458\frac{1}{5}}=3.1427\ldots$ and $\frac{1440}{458\frac{4}{9}}=3.1410\ldots$, taking as the mean $\frac{1440}{458\frac{1}{3}}=3.1418$. No material improvement in methods or results were thereafter made until about the beginning of the seventeenth century. It was then that the Chinese value $\frac{355}{113}=3.1415929\ldots$, was rediscovered by *Adriaen Anthonisz* (1527–1607), being published by his son, *Adriaen* (1571–1635), who, from the fact that his family was originally from Metz, took the name of Metius. This publication took place in 1625, and it appears that the father had first shown that $3\frac{15}{106}<\pi<3\frac{17}{120}$, and that he had reached this value by assuming that $\pi=3\frac{15+17}{106+120}=3\frac{16}{113}=\frac{355}{113}$. The value is correct through the sixth decimal place. About the same time *Viète* (1540–1603), following the Greek method, considered polygons of $6\cdot 2^{16}$ sides, and found the value of π correct to nine decimal places. *Adriaen van Rooman* (*Adrianus Romanus*, 1561–1615), a Lyonese by birth, carried the computation to seventeen decimal places, and a little later *Ludolph van Ceulen* (1540–1610), extended it to thirty-five decimal places, a fact that was thought to be so noteworthy as to lead to π being called the Ludolphian number, a name still used in Germany.

The last noteworthy attempt by Greek methods was the improvement suggested by *Christian Huygens* (1629–95), by which he was enabled to find the value to nine decimal places by using only the inscribed polygon of 60 sides. With his labors the ancient methods may be said to close.

The second period in the solution of the problem begins in the second half of the seventeenth century. It was now that the new analysis came to the aid of the investigators, and the genius of men like *Newton, Leibnitz, Fermat, Wallis, Brouncker,*

* See *Mikami*, in the Bibliotheca Mathematica, 1909–10, p. 1.

and the *Bernoullis* asserted itself. Instead of the geometric methods of *Archimedes* there appeared methods of a radically different nature, having for their object the expressing of π analytically, and developing it as an infinite series or product. The first noteworthy attempts in this line were made by *John Wallis* (1616–1703) who proved that

$$\frac{\pi}{2}=\frac{2}{1}\cdot\frac{2}{3}\cdot\frac{4}{3}\cdot\frac{4}{5}\cdot\frac{6}{5}\cdot\frac{6}{7}\cdot\frac{8}{7}\cdot\frac{8}{9}\cdots,$$

and that

$$\frac{4}{\pi}=1+\cfrac{1}{2+\cfrac{9}{2+\cfrac{25}{2+\cfrac{49}{2+\cfrac{81}{2+\cdots}}}}},$$

this second form, the continued fraction, having already been given to him without proof by *Lord Brouncker* (1620–84).

The most important infinite series developed at this time for the study of the circle was discovered by *James Gregory* (1638–75) in 1670, and independently by *Leibnitz* (1646–1716) in 1673. This is the series:

$$\tan^{-1}x=x-\frac{x^3}{3}+\frac{x^5}{5}-\frac{x^7}{7}+\cdots$$

Gregory, moreover, recognized the necessity of considering the question of the convergency of such a series, a subject elaborated by *Leibnitz* a little later. *Gregory* also stated that in general the ratio of a sector of a circle to the area of any inscribed or circumscribed polygon cannot be expressed by a finite number of algebraic terms. He therefore concluded that the circle could not be squared, although as Mr. *Ball* has pointed out in his history, "it is conceivable that some particular sector might be squared, and this particular sector might be the whole circle."

In the series for $\tan^{-1} x$, if $x=1$, we have the series

$$\frac{\pi}{4}=1-\frac{1}{3}+\frac{1}{5}-\frac{1}{7}+\cdots,$$

but it converges so slowly as not to be convenient in practice. This series bears the name of *Leibnitz,* having been communicated by him to certain of his friends in 1674, and published by him in 1682. It was known before his time, however.

If, instead of using $x=1$, we take $x=\sqrt{\frac{1}{3}}$, the series for $\tan^{-1} x$ becomes

$$\frac{\pi}{6}=\sqrt{\frac{1}{3}}\cdot\left(1-\frac{1}{3\cdot 3}+\frac{1}{3^2\cdot 5}-\frac{1}{3^3\cdot 7}+\frac{1}{3^4\cdot 9}-\frac{1}{3^5\cdot 11}+\dots\right),$$

which is more usable than that for $\frac{\pi}{4}$.

Still better than this formula is one derived from the series for $\tan^{-1} x$ by means of an addition theorem, viz.:

$$\tan^{-1} x+\tan^{-1} y=\tan^{-1}\frac{x+y}{1-xy},$$

which by repeated application leads to a formula for the sum of several antitangents or for multiples of a single antitangent. It was thus that the English mathematician *Machin* (1680–1752) established the relation

$$\begin{aligned}\frac{\pi}{4}&=4\tan^{-1}\frac{1}{5}-\tan^{-1}\frac{1}{239}\\ &=4\left(\frac{1}{5}-\frac{1}{3\cdot 5^3}+\frac{1}{5\cdot 5^5}-\frac{1}{7\cdot 5^7}+\dots\right)\\ &\quad-\left(\frac{1}{239}-\frac{1}{3\cdot 239^3}+\frac{1}{5\cdot 239^5}-\frac{1}{7\cdot 239^7}+\dots\right).\end{aligned}$$

By these means the value of π was computed to 100 decimal places after *Abraham Sharp* (1653–1742) had computed it to 72 decimal places by the help of the series for $\frac{\pi}{6}$.

The other attempts at computing the value of π by means of series may be summarized by mentioning the names of the French mathematician *Lagny* (1660–1734), who carried the computation to 127 decimal places; the Austrian *Georg Vega* (1756–1802), 140 places; the Hamburg computer *Zacharias*

Dase (1824–61), 200 places, using the formula $\frac{\pi}{4}=\tan^{-1}\frac{1}{2}+\tan^{-1}\frac{1}{5}+\tan^{-1}\frac{1}{8}$; *Richter*, who extended the value to 500 decimal places, and *Shanks*, who carried it to 700 decimal places. These efforts are of value chiefly in showing the superiority of the modern over the ancient methods. Practically, as the late Professor *Newcomb* remarked, "ten decimals are sufficient to give the circumference of the earth to the fraction of an inch, and thirty decimals would give the circumference of the whole visible universe to a quantity imperceptible with the most powerful microscope." The results of these extended computations revealed nothing concerning the real nature of π, nothing as to whether it is rational or irrational, and nothing as to its possible transcendental character.

The foundation for the solution of the problem as to the nature of π was furnished by *Euler* in connection with the formulas involving e, the base of the so-called Naperian logarithms, although first used as a base in the tables of *John Speidell*, published in London in 1619. Starting with Maclaurin's formula,

$$f(x)=f(0)+f'(0)\cdot x+f''(0)\cdot\frac{x^2}{1\cdot2}+f'''(0)\cdot\frac{x^3}{1\cdot2\cdot3}+\cdots,$$

it is evident that

$$e^x=1+\frac{x}{1}+\frac{x^2}{1\cdot2}+\frac{x^3}{1\cdot2\cdot3}+\cdots,$$

$$\cos x=1-\frac{x^2}{1\cdot2}+\frac{x^4}{1\cdot2\cdot3\cdot4}-\cdots,$$

and
$$\sin x=x-\frac{x^3}{1\cdot2\cdot3}+\frac{x^5}{1\cdot2\cdot3\cdot4\cdot5}-\cdots,$$

all being convergent series. It was by the help of these series that *Euler* (1707–83) showed that

$$e^{ix}=1+\frac{ix}{1}-\frac{x^2}{1\cdot2}-\frac{ix^3}{1\cdot2\cdot3}+\cdots$$

and $$i \sin x = ix - \frac{ix^3}{1\cdot 2\cdot 3} + \frac{ix^5}{1\cdot 2\cdot 3\cdot 4\cdot 5} - \ldots,$$

whence $$e^{ix} = \cos x + i \sin x.$$

If $x=\pi$, this reduces to the form

$$e^{i\pi} = -1,$$

whence $$1 + e^{i\pi} = 0,$$

an expression involving perhaps the five most interesting quantities in mathematics. It is by means of this equation that the transcendent nature of π was proved about a century and a half after *Euler's* discovery.

Euler also gave numerous other relations between e and π, and expressed in various ways the values of these numbers in infinite series and products, and as continued fractions. For example, he showed that the following relations exist:

$$\frac{\pi^2}{8} = 1 + \frac{1}{3^2} + \frac{1}{5^2} + \frac{1}{7^2} + \frac{1}{9^2} + \ldots$$

$$\frac{\pi^3}{32} = 1 - \frac{1}{3^3} + \frac{1}{5^3} - \frac{1}{7^3} + \frac{1}{9^3} - \ldots$$

$$\frac{\pi^2}{6} = \frac{2^2}{2^2-1}\cdot\frac{3^2}{3^2-1}\cdot\frac{5^2}{5^2-1}\cdot\frac{7^2}{7^2-1}\cdot\frac{11^2}{11^2-1}\cdots$$

$$e = 2 + \cfrac{1}{1 + \cfrac{1}{2 + \cfrac{1}{1 + \cfrac{1}{1 + \cfrac{1}{4 + \cfrac{1}{1 + \ldots}}}}}}$$

$$\frac{e-1}{2} = \cfrac{1}{1 + \cfrac{1}{6 + \cfrac{1}{10 + \cfrac{1}{14 + \cfrac{1}{18 + \ldots}}}}}$$

The third period in the history of the study of π begins with the work of the German mathematician *Johann Heinrich Lambert* (1728–77). In his treatise on the quadrature and rectification of the circle (1766) he set forth two fundamental propositions, viz.:

1. If x is a rational number, not 0, then e^x cannot be rational;
2. If e^x is a rational number, not 0, then x cannot be rational.

He reached these conclusions by starting with *Euler's* expression for $\frac{1}{2}(e-1)$, viz.:

$$\frac{e-1}{2}=\cfrac{1}{1+\cfrac{1}{6+\cfrac{1}{10+\cfrac{1}{14+\cfrac{1}{18+\cfrac{1}{22+\dotsb}}}}}}$$

He then showed that

$$\frac{e^x-1}{e^x+1}=\cfrac{1}{\cfrac{2}{x}+\cfrac{1}{\cfrac{6}{x}+\cfrac{1}{\cfrac{10}{x}+\cfrac{1}{\cfrac{14}{x}+\dotsb}}}}$$

and

$$\tan x=\cfrac{1}{\cfrac{1}{x}-\cfrac{1}{\cfrac{3}{x}-\cfrac{1}{\cfrac{5}{x}-\cfrac{1}{\cfrac{7}{x}-\cfrac{1}{\cfrac{9}{x}-\dotsb}}}}},$$

and from these continued fractions he drew the conclusions stated, the proof not being rigorous. For the special case of

$x=\frac{\pi}{4}$ we know that $\tan\frac{\pi}{4}=1$, whence he asserted that π cannot be rational. The failure of *Lambert* to prove that the continued fraction

$$\cfrac{m}{n+\cfrac{m'}{n'+\cfrac{m''}{n''+\ldots}}}$$

is irrational, the number of terms being infinite, m, m' ... and n, n' ... being integral, and $\frac{m}{n'}$, $\frac{m'}{n'}$, ..., being less than 1, was remedied by *Legendre* (1752–1833), who supplied the proof in his Eléments de géométrie (1794). With *Legendre's* work, therefore, the proof of the irrationality of π may be said to have been settled, and to this he added a proof of the irrationality of π^2.

The next noteworthy step was taken by *Liouville* (1809–82) in 1840, when he showed that e cannot be the root of a quadratic equation with rational coefficients, or, in other words, that if a, b, c are rational, $ae^2+be+c=0$ is impossible. This was the first successful attempt toward verifying what *Legendre* had stated to be probable,—that π is of such a nature that it cannot be classed among algebraic numbers, that is, that it is not the root of any algebraic equation with a finite number of terms with rational coefficients. The question then, as it stood after the contribution of *Liouville,* was twofold: Of what, if any, algebraic equations with a finite number of terms with rational coefficients can e and π be roots? Is it not possible to find numbers that are not roots of an algebraic equation of this kind? *Legendre* was the first to express the doubt contained in the second part of this question, and the doubt became a certainty when *Liouville* proved, in 1844, the existence of non-algebraic numbers and justified the division of numbers into algebraic and transcendental.

As the result of a careful investigation of the exponential function *Hermite* succeeded in proving, in 1873, that the number e is transcendental, and *Lindemann*, in 1882, succeeded in proving the same for π, basing his proof upon the labors of *Hermite*. *Lindemann* proved essentially that in an equation of the form $a_0+a_1e^p+a_2e^q+a_3e^r+\ldots=0$, the exponents and coefficients cannot all be algebraic numbers. It therefore follows that in the *Euler* equation, $1+e^{i\pi}=0$, where the coefficients are algebraic, the exponent $i\pi$ is not algebraic, and hence π is transcendental. While we shall not follow Lindemann's proof exactly, it is nevertheless necessary, as a preliminary to considering the nature of π, to prove that e is a transcendental number.

3. The transcendence of e. Since *Hermite* first proved that e is transcendental others have materially simplified his treatment of the problem. The contributions of *Hilbert*, *Hurwitz*, and *Gordan* were published in the Mathematische Annalen in 1893. The *Gordan* proof was still further simplified by *Weber* in his Algebra, and later in the Encyklopädie der Elementar-Mathematik (1903), and *Enriques*, in his Fragen der Elementargeometrie (German edition, 1907), presents it in its latest form. To the last-named work the basis of the following proof is due but the proof has been materially simplified, chiefly through the kind assistance of Professor *E. V. Huntington*, of Harvard University, who planned the treatment for e, and who made the suggestion of using the cubic instead of the general equation, and of distinctly setting forth the three lemmas.

To prove that e is a transcendental number means that it must be shown that e is not a root of any algebraic equation with rational coefficients. In other words, it must be shown that it is impossible to have a general equation of the form

$$C_0+C_1e+C_2e^2+\ldots+C_ne^n=0, \quad . \quad . \quad . \quad . \quad (1)$$

where n is any positive integer, and where the coefficients C_0, $C_1, \ldots,$ are any rational numbers, including 0, except that C_0 and C_n cannot be 0, since this would change the degree of the equation.

In order to simplify the proof it is proposed to take a cubic equation instead of this general equation of the nth degree, and to show that it is impossible to have

$$C_0+C_1e+C_2e^2+C_3e^3=0. \quad . \quad . \quad . \quad . \quad . \quad (2)$$

The proof, however, is essentially the same as that for the equation of the nth degree, the gain being in the simplicity of statement. The extension of the proof to the general equation is obvious.

The proof requires us to consider two important functions which, on account of their frequent use, we shall distinguish by the symbols $f(x)$ and $F(x)$. The first of these is a rational integral function of x of the nth degree, such that $f(0)=0$. It is therefore of the form

$$f(x)=a_1x+a_2x^2+a_3x^3+\ldots+a_nx^n,$$

where the a's are rational numbers, being the coefficients in the expansion of $f(x)$ in powers of x. The proof depends upon the ingenious selection of the following function:

$$f(x)=\frac{x^{p-1}[(x-1)(x-2)(x-3)]^p}{(p-1)!},$$

in which p is a prime number to be determined later in this discussion. If $f(x)$ is put into the form $a_1x+a_2x^2+\ldots+a_nx^n$, that is, if

$$f(x)=\frac{x^{p-1}[(x-1)(x-2)(x-3)]^p}{(p-1)!}$$
$$=a_1x+a_2x^2+a_3x^3+\ldots+a_nx^n, \quad . \quad . \quad . \quad (3)$$

it is evident that $n=3p+p-1$, and that a_{p-1} is the first coefficient that is not zero, since the lowest power of x is x^{p-1}. More generally, of course, the numerator of this fraction would be $x^{p-1}[(x-1)(x-2)\ldots(x-m)]^p$, but for our present purposes the one selected is sufficient.

The second function that enters into the discussion is

$$F(x)=f'(x)+f''(x)+f'''(x)+\ldots+f^{(n)}(x), \quad . \quad . \quad (4)$$

where $f'(x)$, $f''(x)$, $\ldots$, $f^{(n)}(x)$ are the successive derivatives of $f(x)$.

In order to bring clearly to view the principal steps of the proof, unencumbered by subordinate matters, it is now proposed to state three lemmas concerning these functions, $f(x)$ and $F(x)$, relegating the proofs of these lemmas to the end of this part of the discussion.

Lemma I. If $f(x)=a_1x+a_2x^2+a_3x^3+\ldots+a_nx^n$, and if S_n denotes the sum of the first n terms in the series e^x, so that

$$S_1=1,\ S_2=1+\frac{x}{1!},\ S_3=1+\frac{x}{1!}+\frac{x^2}{2!},\ \ldots,$$

$$S_n=1+\frac{x}{1!}+\frac{x^2}{2!}+\ldots+\frac{x^{n-1}}{(n-1)!},$$

then, from (4),

$$F(x)=1!\,S_1a_1+2!\,S_2a_2+3!\,S_3a_3+\ldots+n!\,S_na_n. \quad . \quad . \quad (5)$$

In particular,

$$F(0)=1!\,a_1+2!\,a_2+3!\,a_3+\ldots+n!\,a_n. \quad . \quad . \quad . \quad (6)$$

Lemma II. Again referring to

$$f(x)=\frac{x^{p-1}[(x-1)(x-2)(x-3)]^p}{(p-1)!},$$

and $F(x)=f'(x)+f''(x)+f'''(x)+\ldots+f^{(n)}(x)$, if p is any prime number and n is any positive integer, and C_0, C_1, C_2, C_3 are any integers, then

$$C_0F(0)+C_1F(1)+C_2F(2)+C_3F(3)=C_0(3!)^p+pQ, \quad . \quad . \quad (7)$$

where Q is some integer depending upon the values of the C's and p.

Lemma III. Again referring to $f(x)=a_1x+a_2x^2+a_3x^3+\ldots$ $+a_nx^n=\frac{x^{p-1}[(x-1)(x-2)(x-3)]^p}{(p-1)!}$, if we let $A_1=|a_1|$, $A_2=|a_2|$, $\ldots$ $A_n=|a_n|$, and $X=|x|$, then

$$A_1X+A_2X^2+A_3X^3+\ldots+A_nX^n$$
$$=\frac{X^{p-1}[(X+1)(X+2)(X+3)]^p}{(p-1)!}. \quad . \quad . \quad (8)$$

Assuming for the time being that these lemmas have been proved, or referring to the proofs at the close of this discussion, we now proceed to consider the transcendence of e.

As a point of departure we take the series defining e^x, already considered:

$$e^x = 1 + \frac{x}{1!} + \frac{x^2}{2!} + \frac{x^3}{3!} + \ldots + \frac{x^n}{n!} + \ldots, \quad . \quad . \quad . \quad (9)$$

which is convergent for all values of x. In this we let S_n stand for the sum of the first n terms as in Lemma I, so that

$$S_1 = 1, \quad S_2 = 1 + \frac{x}{1!}, \quad S_3 = 1 + \frac{x}{1!} + \frac{x^2}{2!}, \ldots$$

$$S_{n+1} = 1 + \frac{x}{1!} + \frac{x^2}{2!} + \ldots + \frac{x^n}{n!}.$$

If, now, we multiply (9) successively by $1!, 2!, 3!, \ldots n!$, and put

$$U_n = x^n + \frac{x^{n+1}}{n+1} + \frac{x^{n+2}}{(n+1)(n+2)} + \ldots, \quad . \quad . \quad (10)$$

so that we have

$$U_1 = x + \frac{x^2}{2} + \frac{x^3}{2 \cdot 3} + \ldots,$$

$$U_2 = x^2 + \frac{x^3}{3} + \frac{x^4}{3 \cdot 4} + \ldots, \text{ etc.,}$$

we shall have

$$\left.\begin{aligned}
1!\, e^x &= 1!\, S_1 + x + \frac{x^2}{2} + \frac{x^3}{2 \cdot 3} + \ldots &&= 1!\, S_1 + U_1, \\
2!\, e^x &= 2!\, S_2 + x^2 + \frac{x^3}{3} + \frac{x^4}{3 \cdot 4} + \ldots &&= 2!\, S_2 + U_2, \\
3!\, e^x &= 3!\, S_3 + x^3 + \frac{x^4}{4} + \frac{x^5}{4 \cdot 5} + \ldots &&= 3!\, S_3 + U_3, \\
&\text{etc.,} &&\text{etc.} \\
n!\, e^x &= n!\, S_n + x^n + \frac{x^{n+1}}{n+1} + \frac{x^{n+2}}{(n+1)(n+2)} + \ldots &&= n!\, S_n + U_n.
\end{aligned}\right\} \quad (11)$$

If we multiply both members of the successive equations of (11) by the successive coefficients $a_1, a_2, a_3, \ldots a_n$ of (3) and add, we shall have

$$(1!\,a_1+2!\,a_2+\ldots+n!\,a_n)e^x=(1!\,S_1a_1+2!\,S_2a_2+\ldots+n!\,S_na_n) \\ +(a_1U_1+a_2U_2+\ldots+a_nU_n).$$

But by (6) we know that

$$F(0)=1!\,a_1+2!\,a_2+\ldots+n!\,a_n,$$

and by (5) we know that

$$F(x)=1!\,S_1a_1+2!\,S_2a_2+\ldots+n!\,S_na_n.$$

It therefore follows, from the preceding equation, that

$$F(0)e^x=F(x)+a_1U_1+a_2U_2+\ldots+a_nU_n.$$

For brevity we let

$$\phi(x)=a_1U_1+a_2U_2+\ldots+a_nU_n, \quad \ldots \quad (12)$$

and we have

$$F(0)e^x=F(x)+\phi(x). \quad \ldots \quad (13)$$

We now have an expression for e^x which depends upon $F(x)$ of (4), and hence ultimately upon the choice of p in (3).

We now return to the essential point of the problem, and recall that we are to prove that it is impossible that $C_0+C_1e+C_2e^2+C_3e^3$ should equal zero. We shall evidently have this form as a factor if, in (13), we substitute 0, 1, 2, and 3, successively for x, multiply the results by C_0, C_1, C_2, and C_3, and then add, thus:

$$\left.\begin{aligned} F(0)C_0 &=C_0(F0)+C_0\phi(0),\\ F(0)C_1e &=C_1F(1)+C_1\phi(1),\\ F(0)C_2e^2&=C_2F(2)+C_2\phi(2),\\ F(0)C_3e^3&=C_3F(3)+C_3\phi(3). \end{aligned}\right\} \quad \ldots \quad (14)$$

Adding, $F(0)[C_0+C_1e+C_2e^2+C_3e^3]$

$$\left.\begin{aligned} &=C_0F(0)+C_1F(1)+C_2F(2)+C_3F(3)\\ &+C_0\phi(0)+C_1\phi(1)+C_2\phi(2)+C_3\phi(3). \end{aligned}\right\}. \quad (15)$$

We will now make the assumption of (2), that $C_0+C_1e+C_2e^2+C_3e^3=0$, and will show that (15) is impossible, and hence that the assumption is absurd. In making this substitution in (15) we also recall that

$$C_0F(0)+C_1F(1)+C_2F(2)+C_3F(3)=C_0(3!)^p+pQ,$$

by (7). We therefore have

$$0=[C_0(3!)^p+pQ]+[C_0\psi(0)+C_1\psi(1)+C_2\psi(2)+C_3\psi(3)], \quad (16)$$

where Q is some integer depending upon the values of C and p, and ψ is the function defined in (12).

The problem now reduces to showing that (16) is impossible, and hence that (15) is impossible, and hence that e cannot be a root of an equation like (3). We can show that (16) is impossible if we can prove that

(1) The absolute value of the first part, $C_0(3!)^p+pQ$, is greater than or equal to 1;

(2) The absolute value of the second part, $C_0\psi(0)+\ldots+C_3\psi(3)$, is less than 1.

For in case we can prove this, then in the most unfavorable case we shall have $\pm1\pm$ (a number less than 1) $=0$, which is manifestly impossible, whence (16) is impossible.

As to the first part, $C_0(3!)^p+pQ$, if we take p a prime number greater than 3, and not a factor of C_0, $C_0(3!)^p$ is not divisible by p, but pQ is divisible by p. Therefore, because C_0 is not zero, we have the absolute value of $C_0(3!)^p+pQ\geqq1$.

Consider now the second part of (16), $C_0\psi(0)+C_1\psi(1)+C_2\psi(2)+C_3\psi(3)$. In this we shall need to make use of the fact that the absolute value of a sum is less than, or at most equal to, the sum of the absolute values of the terms, as is seen in the simple case of $|2-2+2-2|=0$, while $|2|+|-2|+|2|+|-2|=8$. And since the ψ functions are defined (12) in terms of the U functions (10), we consider first U_n.

From (10), $$U_n=x^n\left[1+\frac{x}{n+1}+\frac{x^2}{(n+1)(n+2)}+\ldots\right].$$

Putting X for $|x|$, as in (8), we have

$$|U_n| \leqq X^n\left[1+\frac{X}{n+1}+\frac{X^2}{(n+1)(n+2)}+\ldots\right].$$

$$\therefore \quad |U_n| < X^n\left[1+\frac{X}{1!}+\frac{X^2}{2!}+\ldots\right],$$

since each denominator has here been replaced by a smaller one. Hence, from (9),

$$|U_n| < X^n e^X. \quad . \quad . \quad . \quad . \quad . \quad . \quad . \quad (17)$$

Having now considered the U function used in defining the ψ function (12), we consider the latter, i.e.,

$$\psi(x)=a_1U_1+a_2U_2+\ldots+a_nU_n.$$

In this we put A_1 for $|a_1|$, A_2 for $|a_2|$, . . . , and we have

$$|\psi(x)| < A_1|U_1|+A_2|U_2|+\ldots+A_n|U_n|,$$

as in the preliminary work of (17). Substituting the limiting value of $|U_n|$, from (17), and giving to n the successive values 1, 2, 3, . . . , we have

$$|\psi(x)| < e^X[A_1X+A_2X^2+\ldots+A_nX^n].$$

Whence, from (8)

$$|\psi(x)| < e^X\frac{X^{p-1}[(X+1)(X+2)(X+3)]^p}{(p-1)!},$$

whence

$$|\psi(x)| < e^X(X+1)(X+2)(X+3)\frac{[X(X+1)(X+2)(X+3)]^{p-1}}{(p-1)!}. \quad (18)$$

Now for any fixed value of X we can take for p a value so large that

$$\frac{[X(X+1)(X+2)(X+3)]^{p-1}}{(p-1)!}$$

shall be as small as we please, since this is of the form $\frac{y^n}{n!}$, and is therefore the pth term of the convergent exponential series and therefore approaches zero as p increases.

Hence, putting 0, 1, 2, and 3 successively for x, we see that $|\psi(0)|$, $|\psi(1)|$, $|\psi(2)|$, and $|\psi(3)|$ can all be made as small as we please by choosing p sufficiently large. Hence the absolute value of the second part of (16) which we are considering, viz.: $C_0\psi(0)+C_1\psi(1)+C_2\psi(2)+C_3\psi(3)$, can be made as small as we please, and hence less than 1, which was what we set out to show as the second part of the general proof.

It therefore appears that (16) cannot be true, and that therefore (15) cannot be true, and that therefore (3) cannot be true; in other words, that e is not the root of any cubic equation with integral coefficients. And what has been shown with respect to the cubic equation can evidently be shown with respect to an equation of the nth degree, since no essential use has been made of the restriction $n=3$. Hence e cannot be the root of any algebraic equation.

Proof of Lemma I. Lemma I asserts that if

$$f(x)=a_1x+a_2x^2+a_3x^3+\ldots+a_nx^n,$$

and if we let

$$S_1=1,\quad S_2=1+\frac{x}{1!},\quad S_3=1+\frac{x}{1!}+\frac{x}{2!},$$

$$\ldots S_n=1+\frac{x}{1!}+\ldots+\frac{x^{n-1}}{(n-1)!},$$

then

$$f'(x)+f''(x)+f'''(x)+\ldots+f^{(n)}(x)$$
$$=1!\,S_1a_1+2!\,S_2a_2+\ldots+n!\,S_na_n.$$

To prove this, first write $f(x)$ in this form:

$$f(x)=1!\,a_1\frac{x}{1!}+2!\,a_2\frac{x^2}{2!}+3!\,a_3\frac{x^3}{3!}+\ldots+n!\,a_n\frac{x^n}{n!}.$$

Taking the successive derivatives we have

$$f'(x)=1!\,a_1+2!\,a_2\frac{x}{1!}+3!\,a_3\frac{x^2}{2!}+\ldots+n!\,a_n\frac{x^{n-1}}{(n-1)!},$$

$$f''(x)=\qquad 2!\,a_2+3!\,a_3\frac{x}{1!}+\ldots+n!\,a_n\frac{x^{n-2}}{(n-2)!},$$

$$f'''(x)=\qquad 3!\,a_3+\ldots+n!\,a_n\frac{x^{n-3}}{(n-3)!},$$

$$f^{(n)}(x)=\qquad n!\,a_n.$$

By adding, and substituting $S_1, S_2, \ldots, S_n$ for their respective series, we have

$$f'(x)+f''(x)+\ldots+f^{(n)}(x)=1!S_1a_1+2!S_2a_2+\ldots+n!S_na_n.$$

Proof of Lemma II. Lemma II asserts that if

$$f(x)=\frac{x^{p-1}[(x-1)(x-2)(x-3)]^p}{(p-1)!},$$

and

$$F(x)=f'(x)+f''(x)+\ldots+f^{(n)}(x),$$

and p is any prime number, and n is any positive integer, and the C's are any integers, then

$$C_0F(0)+C_1F(1)+C_2F(2)+C_3F(3)=C_0(3!)^p+pQ,$$

where Q is some integer depending upon the values of the C's and p.

Arranging $f(x)$ according to ascending powers of x we have

$$f(x)=\frac{B_{p-1}x^{p-1}+B_px^p+B_{p+1}x^{p+1}+\ldots+B_{4p-1}x^{4p-1}}{(p-1)!},$$

since it is apparent from (3) that the lowest power of x is $p-1$, and the highest is $3p+p-1=4p-1$. It is evident that $B_{p-1}, B_p, \ldots B_{4p-1}$ are integral, since they are products of integers, and that

$$B_{p-1}=[(-1)(-2)(-3)]^p=\pm(3!)^p.$$

Taking the successive derivatives, so as to determine the values of $F(0)$, $F(1)$, $F(2)$, $F(3)$, we have, after putting 0 for x,

$$f'(0)=0,\quad f''(0)=0,\quad \ldots f^{(p-2)}(0)=0,$$

but

$$f^{(p-1)}(0)=B_{p-1},\quad f^{(p)}(0)=pB_p,\ldots,\quad f^{(n)}(0)=p(p+1)\ldots nB_n.$$

Hence

$$F(0)=B_{p-1}+pB_p+\ldots+[p(p+1)\ldots nB_n].$$

Substituting the value of B_{p-1} above, we have

$$C_0F(0)=C_0(3!)^p+\text{a set of integers in which } p \text{ is a factor.}$$

Similarly, taking the values of $f'(1)$, $f''(1)$, . . . , we shall ıd that $F(1)$ equals a series of integers in which p is a factor f each term, and so for $F(2)$ and $F(3)$. Hence

$$C_0F(0)+C_1F(1)+C_2F(2)+C_3F(3)=C_0(3!)^p+pQ.$$

Proof of Lemma III. Lemma III asserts that if

$$f(x)=a_1x+a_2x^2+a_3x^3+\ldots+a_nx^n=\frac{x^{p-1}[(x-1)(x-2)(x-3)]^p}{(p-1)!},$$

and if

$$A_1=|a_1|,\quad A=|a_2|,\ \ldots\ A_n=|a_n|,\ \text{ and }\ X=|x|,$$

then

$$A_1X+A_2X^2+A_3X^3+\ldots+A_nX^n=\frac{X^{p-1}[(X+1)(X+2)(X+3)]^p}{(p-1)!}.$$

Referring to the second form of $f(x)$ above, we see that $f(x)$ is a function of x with alternating signs. For if we take the general case of $x^k-a_1x^{k-1}+a_2x^{k-2}+\ldots$, and multiply this by $x-b$, the resulting function will have alternating signs, as in the case of $(x-c)(x-d)$. Furthermore, the result is the same, aside from the signs, as that obtained by multiplying $a^k+a_1x^{k-1}+a_2x^{k-2}+\ldots$ by $x+b$. Repeated application of this theorem shows that the expanded product of the general case,

$$f(x)=\frac{x^{p-1}[(x-1)(x-2)(x-3)\ldots(x-m)]^p}{(p-1)!},$$

has the same alternating signs, and reduces, when the absolute values A_n of all the coefficients a_n are taken, and when we take 3 for m, to

$$A_1X+A_2X^2+A_3X^3+\ldots+A_nX^n=\frac{X^{p-1}[(X+1)(X+2)(X+3)]^p}{(p-1)!}.$$

4. The transcendence of π. The proof of the transcendence of π is based upon three propositions already given, viz.:

$$F(0)e^x=F(x)+\psi(x);\quad .\ .\ .\ .\ .\ .\ .\ .\ \text{(13)}$$

$$|\psi(x)|<e^X\frac{X^{p-1}[(X+1)(X+2)(X+3)]^p}{(p-1)!};\quad .\ .\ \text{(18)}$$

$$1+e^{i\pi}=0,\quad \text{Euler's theorem.}\quad .\ .\ .\ .\ .\ \text{(19)}$$

If we assume π to be an algebraic number, then $i\pi$ is evidently an algebraic number, and therefore is the root of an algebraic equation with rational coefficients.

If this equation is taken, as before, to be of the third degree (the proof being essentially the same for the general case) we may indicate its roots by y_1, y_2, and y_3, and among these $i\pi$ must be found. But since $1+e^{i\pi}=0$, we should then have

$$(1+e^{y_1})(1+e^{y_2})(1+e^{y_3})=0,$$

whence

$$1+(e^{y_1}+e^{y_2}+e^{y_3})+(e^{y_1+y_2}+e^{y_2+y_3}+e^{y_3+y_1})+e^{y_1+y_2+y_3}=0. \qquad (20)$$

It is proposed to show that this equation is impossible.

The symmetric functions of the quantities y_1, y_2, y_3, are, by our hypothesis (1), rational numbers, and hence y_1, y_2, y_3 are roots of the rational algebraic equation

$$\phi(x)=0.$$

The symmetric functions of the quantities y_1+y_2, y_2+y_3, y_3+y_1 (for example, their power sum) are also symmetric functions of y_k, and are therefore rational numbers. The quantities y_1+y_2, y_2+y_3, y_3+y_1 are therefore roots of a second algebraic equation

$$\phi_1(x)=0.$$

Similarly, $y_1+y_2+y_3$ is the root of a third algebraic equation,

$$\phi_2(x)=0.$$

Therefore

$$\phi(x)\cdot\phi_1(x)\cdot\phi_2(x) \quad . \quad . \quad . \quad . \quad . \quad . \qquad (21)$$

is an integral function of x which becomes 0 as soon as x becomes equal to one of the numbers y_j, y_j+y_k, or $y_1+y_2+y_3$. Some of these numbers, say, N of them, may equal zero. If we place the product (21) equal to 0, and suppress the factor x^N, we have an equation $\theta(x)=0$, which we may consider as being reduced to a form having integral coefficients. Since the zero roots have just been suppressed, $\theta(0)$ cannot equal 0, and hence $\theta(x)$ may be written

$$\theta(x)=ax^m+a_1x^{m-1}+a_2x^{m-2}+\ldots+a_m=0,$$

where a, a_1, a_m are integral, and a and a_m are not 0, and a is positive.

This may easily be transformed, by multiplying by a^{m-1} and putting z for ax, into an equation with integral coefficients, of the form

$$\theta_1(z)=z^m+b_1z^{m-1}+b_2z^{m-2}+\ldots+b_m=0, \quad . \quad . \quad (22)$$

the coefficient of the highest power being unity. Let the roots of the equation $\theta(x)=0$ be x_1, x_2, x_3, . . . , these representing the numbers among the numbers y_j, y_j+y_k, $y_1+y_2+y_3$ that are not equal to 0. It is seen from (20) that they must satisfy the equation,

$$K+e^{x_1}+e^{x_2}+e^{x_3}+\ldots=0. \quad . \quad . \quad . \quad . \quad (23)$$

We now return to the fundamental equation (13)

$$F(0)e^x=F(x)+\psi(x).$$

If we put for x the numbers x_1, x_2, x_3, . . . , and add the results, we shall have, with attention to (23),

$$-K\cdot F(0)=F(x_1)+F(x_2)+F(x_3)+\ldots$$
$$+\psi(x_1)+\psi x_2)+\psi(x_3)+\ldots,$$

or

$$K\cdot F(0)+F(x_1)+F(x_2)+F(x_3)+\ldots$$
$$+\psi(x_1)+\psi(x_2)+\psi(x_3)+\ldots=0. \quad . \quad (24)$$

We now wish to prove that when we make a suitable choice of the integral function $f(x)$, which is entirely arbitrary except for the condition that $f(0)=0$, the equation (24) is impossible. It will then follow that our sole hypothesis, viz., that π is an algebraic number, is incorrect.

If we prove that

1. $K\cdot F(0)+F(x_1)+F(x_2)+F(x_3)+\ldots$ is integral and not 0;
2. The absolute value of $\psi(x_1)+\psi(x_2)+\psi(x_3)+\ldots<1$;

then we shall have proved the impossibility of (24), for the sum of an integer and a number whose absolute value is less than 1 cannot be 0.

We first let p represent a prime number, and we take for $f(x)$ the integral function

$$f(x)=\frac{z^{p-1}[\theta_1(z)]^p}{(p-1)!}=\frac{a^{mp-1}x^{p-1}[\theta(x)]^p}{(p-1)!}, \quad . \quad . \quad (25)$$

an equation that is evident from the fact that we took $z=ax$ and multiplied $\theta(x)$ by a^{m-1} when we formed $\theta_1(z)$.

We arrange $[\theta(z)]^p$ according to ascending powers of z, and we have

$$[\theta(z)]^p=A_0+A_1z+A_2z^2+\ldots=A_0+A_1ax+A_2a^2x^2+\ldots,$$

where the A's are integral, and, from (22), $A_0=b_m{}^p$, and therefore not 0. Now from (25),

$$f(x)=\frac{A_0a^{p-1}x^{p-1}+A_1a^px^p+A_2a^{p+1}x^{p+1}+\ldots}{(p-1)!}. \quad . \quad (26)$$

Taking the derivatives, and letting $x=0$, we have

$$f(0)=0,\quad f'(0)=0,\ \ldots,\quad f^{(p-2)}(0)=0,$$
$$f^{(p-1)}(0)=A_0a^{p-1}=b_m{}^pa^{p-1},$$
$$f^{(p)}(0)\quad=pA_1a^p,$$
$$f^{(p+1)}(0)=p(p+1)A_2a^{p+1},\ \ldots.$$

We now select a value for p greater than the greatest number a, b_m, K. Then $f^{(p-1)}(0)$ is not divisible by p, while all the other derived functions are either 0 or are divisible by p.

Therefore $F(0)$, which from (4) equals $f'(0)+f''(0)+\ldots$, is an integer not divisible by p, and thus $K\cdot F(0)$ is also an integer not divisible by p, which tells us the nature of part of the first function under consideration.

In deriving (22) we used z for ax, and we may therefore take $f(x)$ and arrange it according to ascending powers of $z-z_k$, where z_k is one of the roots of (22), and we have

$$f(x)=\frac{(z-z_k)^pB_1(z_k)+(z-z_k)^{p+1}B_2(z_k)+\ldots}{(p-1)!}$$
$$=\frac{a^p(x-x_k)^pB_1(z_k)+a^{p+1}(x-x_k)^{p+1}B_2(z_k)+\ldots}{(p-1)!}, \quad (27)$$

where $B_1(z_k)$, $B_2(z_k)$, . . . are integral functions of z_k with rational coefficients. Hence, as with equation (26), we have

$$f(x_k)=0,\quad f'(x_k)=0,\quad f''(x_k)=0,\ \ldots\ f^{(p-1)}(x_k)=0;$$
$$f^{(p)}(x_k)=pa^pB_1(z_k),\quad f^{(p+1)}(x_k)=p(p+1)a^{p+1}B_2(z_k),\ \ldots$$

If now we let

$$Q(z_k)=a^pB_1(z_k)+(p+1)a^{p+1}B_2(z_k)+\ldots,$$

we have from (4),

$$F(x_k)=pQ(z_k). \quad . \quad . \quad . \quad . \quad . \quad . \quad (28)$$

Therefore

$$F(x_1)+F(x_2)+F(x_3)+\ \ldots\ =p[Q(z_1)+Q(z_2)+Q(z_3)+\ldots]. \quad (29)$$

But the second member of (29) is an integral symmetric function of the m roots of equation (22), and hence is integral and contains the factor p. We have now proved that $K\cdot F(0)$ is an integer not divisible by p, and that the sum of the functions $F(x_k)$ is an integer that is divisible by p, so that $K\cdot F(0)+F(x_1)+F(x_2)+F(x_3)+\ldots$ is an integer and not divisible by p, and therefore is not 0, which was the first thing to be proved.

We now take up the second thing to be proved, that the absolute value of $\psi(x_1)+\psi(x_1)+\psi(x_2)+\ldots$ is less than 1. To do this we begin with

$$|\psi(x)|<e^X\cdot\frac{X^{p-1}[(X+1)(X+2)(X+3)]^p}{(p-1)!}. \quad . \quad . \quad (18)$$

Taking $\theta(x)=ax^m+a_1x^{m-1}+\ldots+a_m=0$, already considered, we write this

$$\theta(x)=a(x-x_1)(x-x_2)\ \ldots\ (x-x_m). \quad . \quad . \quad . \quad (30)$$

Then, from (25) and (30) we have

$$f(x)=\frac{a^{(m+1)p-1}x^{p-1}(x-x_1)^p(x-x_2)^p\ \ldots\ (x-x_m)^p}{(p-1)!}. \quad (31)$$

Letting X stand for $|x|$, and X_k for $|x_k|$, it is evident that the coefficients in (31) are not greater than those in

$$\frac{a^{(m+1)p-1}x^{p-1}(x+X_1)^p(x+X_2)^p \ldots (x+X_m)^p}{(p-1)!}.$$

If we now place

$$P(X)=a^{m+1}X(X+X_1)(X+X_2) \ldots (X+X_m),$$

then for every positive number X we have

$$\frac{X^{p-1}[(X+1)(X+2)(X+3)]^p}{(p-1)!} < \frac{[P(X)]^p}{aX(p-1)!},$$
$$< \frac{P(X)}{aX} \cdot \frac{[P(X)]^{p-1}}{(p-1)!}.$$

We now proceed as with (18). For any fixed value of X we can take a value of p so large that

$$\frac{X^{p-1}[(X+1)(X+2)(X+3)]^p}{(p-1)!}$$

shall be as small as we please.

We now recall that

$$\psi(x) < e^X \cdot \frac{X^{p+1}[(X+1)(X+2)(X+3)]^p}{(p-1)!}. \quad . \quad . \quad (18)$$

Hence $\psi(x)$ may be made as small as we please, and hence the absolute value of $\psi(x_1)+\psi(x_2)+\psi(x_3)+\ldots$ may be made less than 1 by taking a suitable value of p, which proves the second part of the proposition.

The two points necessary to show the transcendency of π have now been proved. In other words, π satisfies no algebraic equation with rational coefficients, and therefore cannot be found by means of the ordinary algebraic operations, and therefore cannot be constructed geometrically by the use of the instruments of elementary geometry, nor even by the aid of higher algebraic curves.